ARCHITECTS CONTRACTORS ENGINEERS

Guide To Construction COSTS

2008 Vol. XXXIX

Architects Contractors Engineers Guide to Construction Costs 2008, Volume 39.

ISBN 1-58855-076-1

ARCHITECTS CONTRACTORS & ENGINEERS
GUIDE TO CONSTRUCTION COSTS

EDITOR'S NOTE 2008

This annually published book is designed to give a uniform estimating and cost control system to the General Building Contractor. It contains a complete system to be used with or without computers. It also contains Quick Estimating sections for preliminary conceptual budget estimates by Architects, Engineers and Contractors. Square Foot Estimating is also included for preliminary estimates.

The Metropolitan Area concept is also used and gives the cost modifiers to use for the variations between Metropolitan Areas. This encompasses over 50% of the industry. This book is published annually to be historically accurate with the traditional May-July wage contract settlements and to be a true construction year estimating and cost guide.

The Rate of Inflation in the Construction Industry in 2007 was *3%*. Labor contributed a *4%* increase and materials rose *2%*.

The Wage Rate for Skilled Trades increased an average of *4%* in 2007. Wage rates will probably increase at a 4% average next year.

The Material Rate increased *2%* in 2007. The main increases were in asphalt, pipe, aluminum, steel and steel products, and copper products. Increases of double digits in some materials were offset by dramatic reductions in the price of lumber and wood products.

Construction Volume should stay level 2008. Housing will moderate yet again, and Industrial and Commercial Construction should rise. Highway and Heavy Construction should rise.

The Construction Industry has low to moderate inflation. Some materials should inflate at a slower pace, and some should be watched carefully in 2008.

We are recommending using an *4%* increase in your estimates for work beyond July 1, 2007.

Don Roth
Editor

State	Metropolitan Area	Multiplier	State	Metropolitan Area	Multiplier
AK	ANCHORAGE	137	CA	REDDING	111
AL	ANNISTON	90		RIVERSIDE-SAN BERNARDINO	112
	AUBURN-OPELIKA	90		SACRAMENTO	114
	BIRMINGHAM	88		SALINAS	116
	DOTHAN	86		SAN DIEGO	113
	GADSDEN	86		SAN FRANCISCO	125
	HUNTSVILLE	88		SAN JOSE	122
	MOBILE	90		SAN LUIS OBISPO	110
	MONTGOMERY	86		SANTA CRUZ-WATSONVILLE	116
	TUSCALOOSA	88		SANTA ROSA	117
AR	FAYETTEVILLE-SPRINGDALE-ROGERS	80		STOCKTON-LODI	113
	FORT SMITH	86		VALLEJO-FAIRFIELD-NAPA	116
	JONESBORO	85		VENTURA	112
	LITTLE ROCK-NORTH LITTLE ROCK	87		SANTA BARBARA	115
	PINE BLUFF	87	CO	BOULDER-LONGMONT	96
	TEXARKANA	86		COLORADO SPRINGS	101
AZ	FLAGSTAFF	98		DENVER	101
	PHOENIX-MESA	98		FORT COLLINS-LOVELAND	94
	TUCSON	97		GRAND JUNCTION	96
	YUMA	99		GREELEY	94
CA	BAKERSFIELD	112		PUEBLO	98
	FRESNO	114	CT	BRIDGEPORT	112
	LOS ANGELES-LONG BEACH	115		DANBURY	112
	MODESTO	111		HARTFORD	111
	OAKLAND	120		NEW HAVEN-MERIDEN	112
	ORANGE COUNTY	114		NEW LONDON-NORWICH	109

State	Metropolitan Area	Multiplier	State	Metropolitan Area	Multiplier
CT	STAMFORD-NORWALK	115	KS	TOPEKA	93
	WATERBURY	111		WICHITA	93
DC	WASHINGTON	104	KY	LEXINGTON	93
DE	DOVER	104		LOUISVILLE	96
	WILMINGTON-NEWARK	105		OWENSBORO	94
FL	DAYTONA BEACH	92	LA	ALEXANDRIA	88
	FORT LAUDERDALE	96		BATON ROUGE	92
	FORT MYERS-CAPE CORAL	88		HOUMA	92
	FORT PIERCE-PORT ST. LUCIE	95		LAFAYETTE	90
	FORT WALTON BEACH	97		LAKE CHARLES	92
	GAINESVILLE	90		MONROE	88
	JACKSONVILLE	94		NEW ORLEANS	95
	LAKELAND-WINTER HAVEN	90		SHREVEPORT-BOSSIER CITY	89
	MELBOURNE-TITUSVILLE-PALM BAY	98	MA	BARNSTABLE-YARMOUTH	115
	MIAMI	96		BOSTON	118
	NAPLES	98		BROCKTON	114
	OCALA	95		FITCHBURG-LEOMINSTER	111
	ORLANDO	95		LAWRENCE	114
	PANAMA CITY	83		LOWELL	109
	PENSACOLA	88		NEW BEDFORD	114
	SARASOTA-BRADENTON	89		PITTSFIELD	110
	TALLAHASSEE	85		SPRINGFIELD	110
	TAMPA-ST. PETERSBURG-CLEARWATER	93		WORCESTER	109
	WEST PALM BEACH-BOCA RATON	96	MD	BALTIMORE	98
GA	ALBANY	85		CUMBERLAND	96
	ATHENS	87		HAGERSTOWN	91
	ATLANTA	95	ME	BANGOR	95
	AUGUSTA	83		LEWISTON-AUBURN	96
	COLUMBUS	84		PORTLAND	97
	MACON	87	MI	ANN ARBOR	106
	SAVANNAH	89		DETROIT	111
HI	HONOLULU	135		FLINT	105
IA	CEDAR RAPIDS	97		GRAND RAPIDS-MUSKEGON-HOLLAND	100
	DAVENPORT	100		JACKSON	104
	DES MOINES	101		KALAMAZOO-BATTLE CREEK	96
	DUBUQUE	95		LANSING-EAST LANSING	104
	IOWA CITY	100		SAGINAW-BAY CITY-MIDLAND	102
	SIOUX CITY	95	MN	DULUTH	106
	WATERLOO-CEDAR FALLS	94		MINNEAPOLIS-ST. PAUL	111
ID	BOISE CITY	99		ROCHESTER	106
	POCATELLO	97		ST. CLOUD	108
IL	BLOOMINGTON-NORMAL	106	MO	COLUMBIA	99
	CHAMPAIGN-URBANA	105		JOPLIN	95
	CHICAGO	115		KANSAS CITY	102
	DECATUR	104		SPRINGFIELD	97
	KANKAKEE	107		ST. JOSEPH	99
	PEORIA-PEKIN	106		ST. LOUIS	99
	ROCKFORD	106	MS	BILOXI-GULFPORT-PASCAGOULA	87
	SPRINGFIELD	104		JACKSON	86
IN	BLOOMINGTON	101	MT	BILLINGS	98
	EVANSVILLE	100		GREAT FALLS	99
	FORT WAYNE	100		MISSOULA	97
	GARY	108	NC	ASHEVILLE	82
	INDIANAPOLIS	104		CHARLOTTE	83
	KOKOMO	100		FAYETTEVILLE	84
	LAFAYETTE	100		GREENSBORO-WINSTON-SALEM-H POINT	83
	MUNCIE	100		GREENVILLE	83
	SOUTH BEND	101		HICKORY-MORGANTON-LENOIR	79
	TERRE HAUTE	100		RALEIGH-DURHAM-CHAPEL HILL	83
KS	KANSAS CITY	99		ROCKY MOUNT	79
	LAWRENCE	94		WILMINGTON	84

State	Metropolitan Area	Multiplier
ND	BISMARCK	95
	FARGO	96
	GRAND FORKS	94
NE	LINCOLN	92
	OMAHA	96
NH	MANCHESTER	100
	NASHUA	98
	PORTSMOUTH	92
NJ	ATLANTIC-CAPE MAY	110
	BERGEN-PASSAIC	113
	JERSEY CITY	112
	MIDDLESEX-SOMERSET-HUNTERDON	108
	MONMOUTH-OCEAN	111
	NEWARK	114
	TRENTON	111
	VINELAND-MILLVILLE-BRIDGETON	109
NM	ALBUQUERQUE	96
	LAS CRUCES	92
	SANTA FE	98
NV	LAS VEGAS	108
	RENO	107
NY	ALBANY-SCHENECTADY-TROY	102
	BINGHAMTON	100
	BUFFALO-NIAGARA FALLS	108
	ELMIRA	95
	GLENS FALLS	94
	JAMESTOWN	102
	NASSAU-SUFFOLK	115
	NEW YORK	132
	ROCHESTER	106
	SYRACUSE	103
	UTICA-ROME	103
OH	AKRON	103
	CANTON-MASSILLON	101
	CINCINNATI	98
	CLEVELAND-LORAIN-ELYRIA	106
	COLUMBUS	101
	DAYTON-SPRINGFIELD	99
	LIMA	101
	MANSFIELD	97
	STEUBENVILLE	104
	TOLEDO	103
	YOUNGSTOWN-WARREN	100
OK	ENID	88
	LAWTON	89
	OKLAHOMA CITY	91
	TULSA	90
OR	EUGENE-SPRINGFIELD	106
	MEDFORD-ASHLAND	104
	PORTLAND	108
	SALEM	107
PA	ALLENTOWN-BETHLEHEM-EASTON	105
	ALTOONA	103
	ERIE	103
	HARRISBURG-LEBANON-CARLISLE	101
	JOHNSTOWN	104
	LANCASTER	101
	PHILADELPHIA	114
	PITTSBURGH	104
	READING	103
	SCRANTON-WILKES-BARRE-HAZLETON	102

State	Metropolitan Area	Multiplier
PA	STATE COLLEGE	98
	WILLIAMSPORT	100
	YORK	102
RI	PROVIDENCE	109
SC	AIKEN	91
	CHARLESTON-NORTH CHARLESTON	85
	COLUMBIA	85
	FLORENCE	82
	GREENVILLE-SPARTANBURG-ANDERSON	84
	MYRTLE BEACH	90
SD	RAPID CITY	89
	SIOUX FALLS	90
TN	CHATTANOOGA	88
	JACKSON	87
	JOHNSON CITY	84
	KNOXVILLE	88
	MEMPHIS	93
	NASHVILLE	92
TX	ABILENE	86
	AMARILLO	87
	AUSTIN-SAN MARCOS	88
	BEAUMONT-PORT ARTHUR	88
	BROWNSVILLE-HARLINGEN-SAN BENITO	89
	BRYAN-COLLEGE STATION	87
	CORPUS CHRISTI	85
	DALLAS	91
	EL PASO	85
	FORT WORTH-ARLINGTON	91
	GALVESTON-TEXAS CITY	90
	HOUSTON	92
	LAREDO	78
	LONGVIEW-MARSHALL	83
	LUBBOCK	88
	MCALLEN-EDINBURG-MISSION	84
	ODESSA-MIDLAND	85
	SAN ANGELO	83
	SAN ANTONIO	89
	TEXARKANA	86
	TYLER	86
	VICTORIA	86
	WACO	86
	WICHITA FALLS	86
UT	PROVO-OREM	94
	SALT LAKE CITY-OGDEN	93
VA	CHARLOTTESVILLE	88
	LYNCHBURG	87
	NORFOLK-VA BEACH-NEWPORT NEWS	91
	RICHMOND-PETERSBURG	91
	ROANOKE	85
VT	BURLINGTON	98
WA	BELLINGHAM	112
	BREMERTON	110
	OLYMPIA	108
	RICHLAND-KENNEWICK-PASCO	106
	SEATTLE-BELLEVUE-EVERETT	111
	SPOKANE	108
	TACOMA	111
	YAKIMA	106
WI	APPLETON-OSHKOSH-NEENAH	101
	EAU CLAIRE	100
	GREEN BAY	101

State	Metropolitan Area	Multiplier
WI	JANESVILLE-BELOIT	101
	KENOSHA	103
	LA CROSSE	99
	MADISON	100
	MILWAUKEE-WAUKESHA	107
	RACINE	103
	WAUSAU	100

State	Metropolitan Area	Multiplier
WV	CHARLESTON	99
	HUNTINGTON	100
	PARKERSBURG	98
	WHEELING	100
WY	CASPER	92
	CHEYENNE	93

HOW TO USE THIS BOOK

Labor Unit Columns
➢ Units *include* all taxable (vacation) and untaxable (welfare and pension) fringe benefits.
➢ Units *do not include* taxes and insurance on labor (approximately 35% added to labor cost). (Workers Compensation, Unemployment Compensation, and Employers FICA.)
➢ Units *do not include* general conditions and equipment (approx. 10%).
➢ Units *do not include* contractors' overhead and profit (approx. 10%).
➢ Units are Union or Government Minimum Area wages.

Material Unit Columns
➢ Units *do not include* general conditions and equipment (approx. 10%).
➢ Units *do not include* sales or use taxes (approx. 5%) of material cost.
➢ Units *do not include* contractors' overhead and profit (approx. 10%).
➢ Units are mean prices FOB job site.

Cost Unit Columns (Subcontractors)
➢ Cost is complete with labor, material, taxes, insurance and fees of a subcontractor. This also applies to Quick Estimating sections.
➢ Units *do not include* general contractors' overhead or profit.

Quick Estimating Sections - For Preliminary and Conceptual Estimating
➢ Includes all labor, material, general conditions, equipment, taxes, insurance and fees of contractors combined for items not covered in Cost Unit columns.

Construction Modifiers - For Metro Area Cost Variation Adjustments
➢ Labor items are percentage increases or decreases from 100% for labor units used in the book's labor unit columns. (See first page of each Division.)
➢ Material and Labor combined are percentage increases and decreases from 100% for metro variations used in the book's Unit Cost columns, Quick Estimating sections and Sq.Ft. Cost Section - see Page 2.
➢ Recommend Unit Costs of 10% less than Book Units for Residential Construction.

EXAMPLE:	UNIT	LABOR	MATERIAL	COST
2" x 4" Wood Studs & Plates - 8' @ 16" O.C.	BdFt	.74	.45	1.19
Add 35% Taxes & Insurance on Labor		.26	-	.26
Add 5% Material Sales Tax		-	.03	.03
				1.48
Add 10% General Conditions & Equipment				.15
				1.63
Add 10% Overhead & Profit				.17
BdFt Cost - Bid Type Estimating			BdFt	1.80
or SqFt Wall Cost with 3 Plates - Quick Estimating (page 6A-14)			or SqFt	1.36

Purchasing Practice (usual) in the industry for each section of work is indicated immediately after section heading in parenthesis and defined as follows:

L&M - Labor and Material Subcontractor - Firm bid to G.C. according to plans and specifications for all labor and material in that section or subsection.

M - Material Subcontractor - Firm bid to G.C. according to plans and specifications for all material in that section or subsection.

L - Labor Subcontractor - Firm bid to G.C. to *install only* material furnished according to plans and specifications by others.

S - Material Supplier - Firm Price for materials delivered only.

E - Equipment Supplier - Firm Price for Equipment Rented or Purchased.

Installation Practice by particular trades are listed behind each section heading and are according to "Agreement and Decisions Rendered Affecting the Building Industry," by the A.F.L. Building and Construction Trades Department, A.F.L.-C.I.O. Area variations, jurisdictional problems and multiple jurisdictions are possible.

General Requirements amount to approximately 6% to 15% of total job costs for General Construction and 5% to 10% for Residential Construction. All items below are included in G.R. except 0101.32, .33, and .34 (taxes and insurance on labor). See Square Foot Costs (SF Section) for more accurate Dollar Value of Job Costs.

				UNIT	LABOR	COST
0101.0	**GENERAL CONDITIONS - Specified (AIA Doc A201)**					
.1	SUPERINTENDENT Job Size/Complexity			Week	$2,000	-
.2	PERMITS AND FEES					
	Concrete and Commercial	- Approx. Average		MCuFt	-	$3.90
	Residential (Finish Area)	- Approx. Average		SqFt	-	$1.20
	Remodeling	- Approx. Average		M$	-	$7.00
	Varies with Each Permit Division					
.3	TAXES (Art. 3.6)					
.31	Sales and Use Tax (Varies as to State)			%		Avg. 5.7%

		Payroll Max	Per $100 or % Gross Payroll	
.32	Unemployment Compensation	to $ 24,000	State Maximum	9.5%
	(Varies as to State)		State Minimum	2.0%
.33	Unemployment Compensation	to $ 7,000	Fed. Maximum	.8%
.34	FICA - Employer's Share	to $ 97,500		6.2%
	Medicare	No Limit		1.45%
.4	INSURANCE - CONTRACTOR'S LIABILITY			
	(Worker's Compensation, P.L. & P.D.)			
	Classification Avg - Contractors Experience		Gross Payroll	14.0%
	Clerical - Office	(#8810)	" "	1.0%
	Supervision	(#5606)	" "	2.5%
	Excavation	(#6217)	" "	12.0%
	Concrete - Structural - N.O.C.	(#5213)	" "	20.0%
	Slabs on Ground, Flat	(#5221)	" "	8.0%
	Masonry	(#5022)	" "	12.0%
	Iron and Steel - N.O.C.	(#5057)	" "	32.0%
	Carpentry - N.O.C. Commercial	(#5403)	" "	19.0%
	Interior & Dwellings	(#5437)	" "	12.0%
	Wallboard	(#5445)	" "	13.0%
	Plumbing			7.0%
	Electrical			6.0%
	Wrecking (Demolition)			40.0%
	PL. and PD.			1.5%
	Add for Assigned Risk			75%

				UNIT	LABOR	COST
.5	INSURANCE - HOLD HARMLESS			M$		$ .80
	(By Owner) (Art. 11.2) (Contract Amount)					
.6	INSURANCE - ALL RISK (Fire/Ext.Cov./Theft/etc.)					
	(By Owner) (Art. 11.2) ($1,000 Deductible)					
	Fire Proof - All Concrete	(Annual)				$2.20
	Fire Resistive - Covered Steel	(Insurable)				$2.75
	Ordinary - Masonry, Ext. Walls & Joists	(Value)				$3.80
	Frame, Wood	(per M$)				$6.50
	Deduct for $2,500 Deductible					10%
	Add for Light Protection Areas - Approx.					50%
.7	CLEANUP (Art. 3.15)					
.71	Progress		Bldg - SqFt		$.20	$ .06
.72	Glass, 2 Sides		Glass Area - SqFt		$.40	-
.8	PERFORMANCE & PAYMENT BOND		(If Specified) (Art. 11.4)			
	$ -0- to $ 99,999		Job Bureau Comp. Contr. Amount			2.50%
	$ 100,000 to $ 499,999					1.50%
	$ 500,000 to $2,499,999					1.00%
	$2,500,000 to $4,999,999					.75%
	$5,000,000 to $7,499,999					.70%
	$7,500,000 Up					.65%
.9	SAFETY OF PERSONS & PROPERTY - Job Condition					
.10	TESTS AND SAMPLES - See Appropriate Division					

0102.0   SPECIAL CONDITIONS (Changes to G.C. 0101 and Temporary Utilities & Facilities, usually Specified)

		UNIT	LABOR	MATERIAL
.1	TEMPORARY OFFICE			
	Fixed - 10' x 16" Wood	Each	1,500	2,800
	Mobile (Special Construction) 8' x 32'	Each	-	4,360
		Month	-	210
	Mobile (Special Construction) 10' x 50'	Each	1,200	7,500
		Month	-	310
	Mobile (Special Construction) 12' x 60'	Each	1,400	10,800
		Month	-	430
	Add for Delivery & Pickup	Each	-	430
.2	TEMPORARY STORAGE SHED -12' x 24'	Each	1,900	4,000
.3	TEMPORARY SANITARY FACILITIES - Chemical Toilet	Month	-	110
.4	TEMPORARY TELEPHONE (No Long Distance) - Per line	Month	-	100
	TEMPORARY TELEPHONE	Initial	-	320
	TEMPORARY TELEPHONE - Cellular	Month	-	100
	TEMPORARY FAX	Initial	-	1,200
.5	TEMPORARY POWER AND LIGHT			
	Initial Service 110V	Job	-	1,800
	220V	Job	-	2,500
	440V	Job	-	5,000
	Monthly Service and Material	Month	-	300
	Temporary Wiring and Lighting-Total Job	SqFt	-	.13
.6	TEMPORARY WATER -Initial Service	Initial	Job Condition	
	Monthly Service	Month	-	115.00
.7	TEMPORARY HEAT (after Enclosed)			
	See Divisions 3 & 4 for Temporary Heat, Concrete & Masonry			
	See Division 1A for Equipment Rental Rates			
	Heaters:			
	Steam & Unit - Heater Rent - SqFt Htd Area	Month	-	.15
	Piping - SqFt Htd Area	Month	-	.18
	Condensate - SqFt Htd Area	Month	-	.22
	Mobile Home Heater Rent - SqFt Htd Area	Month	-	.14
	Fuel SqFt Htd Area	Month	-	.38
	Tending 8 - Hour/Day	8 Hrs	-	270.00
.8	TEMPORARY ENCLOSURES AND COVERS			
	Per Door - Wood	Each	36.00	48.00
	Per Window - Polyethylene and Frame	Each	16.50	13.00
	Walls - Frame and Reinforced Poly - 1 use	SqFt	.25	.22
	2 uses	SqFt	.23	.18
	Frame and 1/2" Plywood - 1 use	SqFt	.68	1.05
	2 uses	SqFt	.57	.70
	Floors- 2" Fiberglass & 7 mil Poly- 1 use	SqFt	.15	.52
.9	TEMPORARY ROADS & RAMPS - No Surfacing	SqYd	Job Condition	
.10	TEMPORARY DEWATERING - No Tending			
	Pumping - 2" Pump	Day	-	105.00
	3" Pump	Day	-	115.00
	4" Pump	Day	-	145.00
	Add for Tending			
	Well Points - LnFt Header	Month	-	115.00
	Add Each Month	Month	-	87.00
.11	TEMPORARY SIGNS - 4' x 8'	Each	105.00	480.00
.12	TEMP. FENCING, BARRICADES & WARNING LIGHTS			
	6' Chain Link - Rented (Erected and Removed)	LnFt	1.35	6.50
	Add for Barbed Wire	LnFt	.42	1.10
	Add for Gates	LnFt	8.75	25.00
	Snow Fence - New	LnFt	.47	1.40
	Concrete Barriers (Rented - Month)	LnFt	-	4.50
	Flasher Warning Light (Rented - Month)	Each	-	22.00
	8' Barricade (Rented - Month)	Each	-	48.00
	12' Barricade (Rented - Month)	Each	-	58.00

0103.0	MISCELLANEOUS CONDITIONS (Non-Specified)	UNIT	LABOR*	MATERIAL
.1	FIELD ENGINEERING AND LAYOUT	Week		Job Cond.
.2	TIMEKEEPERS AND ACCOUNTANTS	Week		Job Cond.
.3	SECURITY	Week		Job Cond.
.4	OPERATING ENGINEERS FOR HOISTING	Week		Job Cond.
.5	TRAVEL AND SUBSISTENCE - Field Employees			Job Cond.
.6	TRAVEL AND SUBSISTENCE - Office Employees			Job Cond.
.7	OFFICE SUPPLIES AND EQUIPMENT	Week		25.00
.8	COMMUNICATIONS EQUIPMENT			
	Radio-Multi Channel Hand Unit with Charger & Battery	Each	-	1,350
	Base Unit - F.M. with Antenna and Mike	Each	-	1,500
.9	HOISTING EQUIPMENT (Towers, Cranes and Lifts)			
.91	Towers and Hoists - Portable Self-Erecting Style			
	Skip (Based on 100' Unit) -3000# to 5000# Capacity	Month	-	2,400
	2000# to 3000# Capacity	Month	-	2,200
	Add to Heights Above 100'	LnFtMo	-	22
	Towers - Fixed (based on 100') - 30' Override			
	Tubular Frame - Double Well - 5000# Capacity	Month	-	2,100
	Installation - Double Well - Subcont - Up	LnFt	65	-
	Double Well - Down	LnFt	50	-
	Add for Concrete Bucket and Hopper	Month	-	4400
	Add for Chicago Boom	Month	-	2430
	Add for Gates, Signals, etc (Safety)	Job	750	1,250
	Hoist Engine, Gas Powered - 2 Drum	Month	-	1,980
	Towers and Hoists - Personnel 6000# Capacity			
	Based on 100' Unit - 8 1/2' Override	Month	-	3,500
	Add Above 100'	LnFt	-	35
	Installation - Up	LnFt	-	40
	Down	LnFt	-	38
.92	Cranes - Climbing - 20' Override			
	Based on 125' Bldg-130' Boom, 4000#	Month	-	6,700
	to 200' Boom, 7000#	Month	-	9,200
	230' Boom, 7000#	Month	-	10,800
	Add for LnFt Tower above 125'	Month	-	42
	Installation			
	Foundation	Each	-	13,000
	440-Volt Transformer Install	Each	-	2,600
	Installation - Up & Down	LnFt	-	115
	Up	Each	-	16,000
	Down	Each	-	16,000
	Avg - Up, Down & Haul - 125' Tower	Each	-	32,000
	Add per Lift - Jacking	LnFt	-	60
	Add per Floor Pattern	Each	-	1,050

.93	Cranes - Mobile Lifting (no Operator)	HOUR	DAY	MONTH
	15-Ton Hydraulic	110	620	3,900
	20-Ton	120	670	4,100
	25-Ton	125	720	6,700
	30-Ton	140	770	7,100
	45-Ton	160	820	7,900
	75-Ton Cable	175	930	8,800
	90-Ton	200	1,150	9,600
	125-Ton	240	1,600	13,200

.94	Fork Lifts - Construction	UNIT	LABOR	MATERIAL
	Four-Wheel Drive - 28' 5000# Capacity	Month		2,400
	36' 6000# Capacity	Month		2,500
	37' 6000# Capacity	Month		2,600
	42' 6000# Capacity	Month		2,700
	42' 8000# Capacity	Month		2,800

Add for Local Travel & Setup Time - 4 Hours

*Subcontract

0103.0   MISCELLANEOUS CONDITIONS, Cont'd...

			UNIT	LABOR	MATERIAL
.95	Platform Lifts				
	Scissor Lifts – Electric	26'	Month		620
		32'	Month		810
	Telescoping Boom Lifts	46'	Month		4,900
		66'	Month		2,500
	Articulating Boom Lifts	86'	Month		5,200
		36'	Month		1,550
		51'	Month		1,950
		66'	Month		2,500
.10	TRUCKS AND OTHER JOB VEHICLES (Site Use)				
	$ 500,000 Job		JobAvg		1,800
	$1,000,000 Job		JobAvg		6,500
	$5,000,000 Job		JobAvg		15,000
	1-Ton Pickup		Month		650
	2-Ton Flatbed		Month		920
	2 1/2-Ton Dump		Month		1,550
.11	MAJOR EQUIPMENT (See Div. 2,3,4,5,& 6 if Subbed)				
	(See 1-6A & 7A: Rental Rates, Purchase Prices)				
	$ 100,000 Job		JobAvg		4,200
	$ 500,000 Job		JobAvg		8,000
	$1,000,000 Job		JobAvg		15,100
	$5,000,000 Job		JobAvg		60,000
	As a % of Labor (No Hoisting Equipment)				5%
.12	SMALL TOOLS AND SUPPLIES				
	(See 1-6A & 7A: Rental Rates, Purchase Prices)				
	$ 100,000 Job		JobAvg		1,500
	$ 500,000 Job		JobAvg		4,000
	$1,000,000 Job		JobAvg		6,700
	$5,000,000 Job		JobAvg		30,000
	As a Percentage of Labor		JobAvg		2%
.13	HAULING EQUIPMENT AND TOOLS				
	$ 100,000 Job		JobAvg	1,000	620
	$ 500,000 Job		JobAvg	2,000	1,600
	$1,000,000 Job		JobAvg	3,700	3,100
	$5,000,000 Job		JobAvg	12,000	8,500
.14	GAS AND OIL FOR EQUIPMENT				
	$ 500,000 Job		JobAvg		2,200
	$1,000,000 Job		JobAvg		2,800
	$5,000,000 Job		JobAvg		12,000
	As a Average of Equipment Cost		JobAvg		17%
.15	REPAIRS TO EQUIPMENT AND TOOLS				
	$ 100,000 Job		JobAvg		700
	$ 500,000 Job		JobAvg		1,250
	$1,000,000 Job		JobAvg		2,300
	$5,000,000 Job		JobAvg		7,500
	As an Average of Equipment Cost				10%
.16	PHOTOGRAPHS - 2 Views, 4 Copies		Month		150
.17	SCHEDULING - C.P.M., Pert, Network, Analysis				
	$ 500,000 Job		JobAvg		4,700
	$1,000,000 Job		JobAvg		8,400
	$5,000,000 Job		JobAvg		14,500
	Add for Update, Monitor		Each		780
.18	COMPUTER COSTS		Employee/Wk		10
.19	PERFORMANCE BOND - SUBCONTRACTORS		ContrAmt		1.5%
.20	PUNCH LIST AND FINAL OUT		ContrAmt		.5%

DIVISION #1 - GENERAL REQUIREMENTS

TOOLS & EQUIPMENT

See 103.9 for Towers, Cranes and Lift Equipment

Div. 1 General Conditions	Approximate Cost New	Fair Rental* Rate per Mo.
Engineering Instruments - Transits	1,270	260
Levels 18"	1,030	240
Fans - 15,000 CFM - 36"	1,190	410
Generators - 3500 Watt - Portable	1,300	390
5000 Watt - Portable	1,680	440
Heaters, Temp - Oil 100M to 300 BTU	1,410	460
LP Gas 90M BTU	390	210
150M BTU	430	250
350M BTU	770	360
Laser - Rotating	4,940	620
Light Stands - Portable - 500 watt Quartz	730	270
Pumps - Submersible 1/2 HP Elect 2"	450	330
Centrifugal 2" 8,000 Gal	1,050	200
3" 17,000 Gal	1,080	570
Diaphragm 2" - 3" x 3" - Pneumatic	1,510	470
3" - 3" x 3" - Gas	1,570	610
Submersible - 5 HP 3"	1,620	520
Hose - Discharge - 3" - 25'	110	60
Suction - 3" - 20'	140	70
Vacuum Cleaners - Wet Dry - 5 Gal	650	165

Div. 2 Excavation (Including Demolition)

	Approximate Cost New	Fair Rental Rate
Air Tools - Breakers Light Duty - 35 to 40#	1,040	270
Heavy Duty - 60 to 90#	1,430	350
Rock Drill - 40#	1,930	360
Chipping Hammer - 7# to 12#	830	280
Clay Digger	780	260
Hose - 3/4" - 50'	140	60
Compressors 125 cfm Gas - Tow	11,570	820
185 cfm Diesel - Trailer Mounted	14,710	850
26' Conveyor - 2 HP Electric	9,700	1,010
Electric Breakers - 60#	2,270	420
Jacks - Hydraulic - 20 Ton - 11 HP	870	330
Screw - 20 Ton	390	90
Saws - Chain 18"	600	410
Concrete Asphalt 14" Blade	1,730	260
24" Plate - Vibratory Gas 170#	2,270	660
Tampers - Rammer Gas 135#	2,490	760

Div. 3 Concrete

	Approximate Cost New	Fair Rental Rate
Bucket & Boot - 1 CuYd	2,220	490
1 1/2 CuYd	2,810	500
2 CuYd	3,580	770
Buggies - Manual - 6 to 8 CuFt	510	190
Power Operated - 16 CuFt	6,490	880
Conveyors - 32' Hydraulic and Belt - Gas	10,170	1,260
50' Hydraulic and Belt - Gas	22,500	2,700
Core Drill - Diamond - 15 Amp	3,520	570
with Trailer	10,170	930
Crack Chaser	4,540	1,390
Drill - Cordless 3/8" Reversing	310	100
Heavy Duty 1/2" Reversing	400	155
3/4" Reversing	730	200
Sander - Hand - 9"	360	155
Grinder - Ceiling 7' to 11' - Elec	2,380	450
Floor - Elec - 1 1/2 HP	3,300	670
Hammer - Drill - 3/4" Variable Speed	510	195
Roto Chipping - 1 1/2"	540	505
Hopper - Floor 30 CuFt	1,190	240
Mixer - 6 CuFt	2,490	495
Planer - 10'	4,650	740
Scarifier & Scabblers - Single Bit	1,190	750
5 Bit Floor - 175 cfm	8,440	2,270
Stripper - Floor	4,060	440

*Weekly Rent 40% of monthly, Daily Rent 15% of monthly, Hourly Rent 2% of monthly.

TOOLS & EQUIPMENT

	Approximate Cost New	Fair Rental* Rate per Mo.
Div. 3 **Concrete, Cont'd...**		
Saws - Rotary Hand - 7 1/4"	195	135
9 1/4" - 8 1/4"	240	145
Table 14" Radial Arm 3 HP	1,850	310
Floor - Gas 11 HP	1,600	670
Gas 18 HP	4,430	710
Electric 8 HP 14"	1,870	670
Cut off 14" Electric	730	490
Screeds - Vibrating 6'	930	695
12 1/2' Beam Type	2,010	705
25' Beam Type	4,330	800
Troweling Machines - Gas 36" 4 Blade 7 HP	1,750	515
48" 4 Blade 6 HP	2,010	580
Trunks & Tremmies - 12" and Hopper	185	70
Vibrators - Flexible Head - 1 HP	1,130	340
2 HP	1,240	370
High cycle - 180 Cycle	3,300	570
Back Panel 2 1/2 HP	770	695
Wheelbarrows	120	60
Div. 4 **Masonry**		
Hoist Electric - One ton	1,080	175
Mixer - Mortar - 6 Cu Ft - Gas 7 HP	2,060	440
Elec 1 1/2 HP	2,180	410
8 Cu Ft - Gas 7 HP	2,470	460
12 Cu Ft - Gas or Electric	3,710	970
Pallet Jack	760	310
Pump Grout - Hydraulic 10 GPM	6,390	1,440
Saws - Table - 1 1/2 HP - 14"	2,210	410
5 HP - 14"	3,190	460
Scaffold - 5' - 6" with Braces	80	3.70
6' - 6" with Braces	80	4.10
Wheels	90	11.30
Brackets	20	2.10
Plank - Aluminum	90	5.15
16' Laminated	40	3.10
Base - Adj	25	1.65
Splitter - 10,000#	1,750	390
Rolling Towers	360	100
Swing Stage - Motorized with deck-cables-safety	9,270	1,240
Div. 6 **Carpentry**		
Door Hanging Eq. (Router, Mortiser, Template)	310	100
Drills - Heavy Duty (See Div. 3)		
Fasteners - Power - Drywall	150	50
Hammer - Drill 1/2"	320	175
Miter Box - 14" Power	420	340
Nailers and Staplers - Spot with compressor	1,850	290
Planers	515	155
Sanders - Disc 9"	270	100
Belt 3" - Heavy Duty	310	130
Floor	430	340
Saws - Band	310	260
Chain	360	340
Rotary, Hand - 7 1/4"	200	100
8 1/4"	230	135
Table - Fixed 10"	410	145
Jig	210	80
Reciprocating	460	230
Cut-off - 12" Elec.	2,060	390
Scaffold - Rolling	460	115
Screwdriver - Variable Speed - Drywall	260	115
Stud Drivers - Low Velocity	290	125
High Velocity	410	145
Wrench - 1/2" Impact - Air	300	145
1" Impact - Air	620	500

*Weekly Rent 40% of monthly, Daily Rent 15% of monthly, Hourly Rent 2% of monthly.

0201.0 DEMOLITION & CLEARING (Op.Eng., Truck Dr. & Lab.)

		UNIT	COST with MACHINE
.1	STRUCTURE MOVING - Wood Frame	SqFt	16.50
	With Masonry	SqFt	18.50
.2	CLEARING AND GRUBBING		
	Trees - Trunk	Dia/Inch	16.50
	Stump - Removed	Dia/Inch	13.50
	Chipped - Below Grade	Dia/Inch	7.75
	Add for Hauling Away and Dumping	Dia/Inch	6.75
	Shrubs & Brush - Light	Acre	2,420.00
	Medium	Acre	3,400.00
	Heavy	Acre	4,550.00
.3	DEMOLITION AND LOAD (See .34 for Disposal)		
.31	Total Building		
	Wood - Mainly Housing	CuFt/Bldg	.34
	Masonry - Load Bearing	CuFt/Bldg	.39
	Concrete - Frame	CuFt/Bldg	.50
	Steel - Frame	CuFt/Bldg	.39
	Add for Floor Above 2 Stories	CuFt/Bldg	.07

.32 Selective Building Removals (No Cutting/Disposal)
(See .35 - Cut and Drill)
(See .34 - Disposal/Haul Away)
(See .33 - Site Removal)

	Unit	Labor Only	Machine Only	Unit	Labor Only	Machine Only
Concrete:						
8" Walls Reinforced	CuYd	200.00	56.00	SqFt	7.30	2.10
Non-Reinforced	CuYd	120.00	50.00	SqFt	5.70	1.75
12" Walls Reinforced	CuYd	360.00	48.00	SqFt	15.20	3.25
Footings - 24" x 12"	CuYd	320.00	180.00	SqFt	11.00	6.70
6" Struc. Slab Reinforced	CuYd	125.00	35.00	SqFt	4.60	1.30
8" Struc. Slab Reinforced	CuYd	180.00	59.00	SqFt	6.60	1.95
4" Slab on Ground Reinforced	CuYd	59.00	19.50	SqFt	2.20	.70
Non-Reinforced	CuYd	46.00	16.50	SqFt	1.70	.62
6" Slab on Ground Reinforced	CuYd	73.00	25.00	SqFt	2.70	.90
Non-Reinforced	CuYd	52.00	23.00	SqFt	1.90	.82
9" Stairs Reinforced	CuYd	220.00	90.00	SqFt	8.00	3.10
Masonry:						
4" Brick or Stone Walls	CuYd	42.00	17.50	SqFt	1.50	.44
and 8" Backup	CuYd	71.00	21.50	SqFt	2.60	.77
Block or Tile Partitions	CuYd	71.00	11.50	SqFt	2.60	.41
6" Block or Tile Partitions	CuYd	36.00	14.50	SqFt	1.35	.51
8" Block or Tile Partitions	CuYd	44.00	16.50	SqFt	1.60	.60
12" Block or Tile Partitions	CuYd	56.00	20.50	SqFt	2.10	.72
Add for Plastered Type				SqFt	.50	.14

Misc - Hand Work (Add for Equipment & Scaffold)	UNIT	Labor	
Acoustical Ceilings - Attached (Incl. Iron)	SqFt	.70	-
Suspended (Incl. Grid)	SqFt	.50	-
Asbestos - Ceilings and Walls	SqFt	17.00	-
Columns and Beams	SqFt	42.00	-
Pipe	LnFt	52.00	-
Tile Flooring	SqFt	1.90	-
Cabinets and Tops	LnFt	12.50	-
Carpet	SqFt	.40	
Ceramic and Quarry Tile	SqFt	1.50	-
Doors and Frames - Metal	Each	62.00	-
Wood	Each	54.00	-
Drywall Ceilings - Attached (Including Grid)	SqFt	.80	-
Wood or Metal Studs - 2 Sides	SqFt	.90	-
Paint Removal - Doors and Windows	SqFt	.80	-
Walls	SqFt	.70	-
Plaster on Wood or Metal Studs	SqFt	1.25	-
Ceilings - Attached (Incl. Iron)	SqFt	1.25	-
Roofing - Built-Up	SqFt	1.15	-
Shingles - Asphalt and Wood	SqFt	.40	-
Terrazzo Flooring	SqFt	2.00	-
Vinyl Composition Flooring (No Mastic Removal)	SqFt	.40	-
Wall Coverings	SqFt	.80	-
Windows - Metal or Wood	Each	42.00	-
Wood Flooring	SqFt	.40	-

0201.0   DEMOLITION & CLEARING, Cont'd...

.33 Site Removals
(See .34 for Disposal)
(See .35 for Cutting Additions)

	UNIT	(1) LABOR ONLY	MACHINE ONLY
Concrete:4" Sidewalks - Reinforced	SqFt	2.30	.72
Non -Reinforced	SqFt	1.80	.69
6" Drives - Reinforced	SqFt	2.70	.90
Non-Reinforced	SqFt	2.10	.95
Curb - 6" x 18"	LnFt	6.20	1.75
and Gutter	LnFt	10.10	2.40
Asphalt:2"	SqFt	1.40	.45
Curb	LnFt	3.30	.77
Fencing: 8" Metal	LnFt	2.10	.50

.34 Disposal or Haul Away (Including Truck or Box & Driver)
Haul - No Dump Charges Included

	UNIT	COST
Concrete Truck Measure - 75¢ a minute or	CuYd/Mile	.88
Masonry - 75¢ a minute or	CuYd/Mile	.85
Wood - 75¢ a minute or	CuYd/Mile	.80
Box Rent (Included Above) - 30 Cu.Yd.	Box	410.00
Clean Material - 20 Cu.Yd.	Box	380.00
10 Cu.Yd.	Box	325.00
Dump Charges - Concrete	CuYd	7.85
Building Materials	CuYd	11.35
Tree and Brush Removal	CuYd	16.00

.35 Saw Cutting/Core Drilling/Torch Cutting/Blasting
Saw Cutting (includes Operator):

	UNIT		COST
Slabs - Asphalt	LnFt	per inch	1.35
Concrete - Structural	LnFt	per inch	2.50
Hollow	LnFt	per inch	1.05
Slabs on Grd/Non - Rein.	LnFt	per inch	.88
/with Mesh	LnFt	per inch	1.10
Walls - Concrete - Reinforced	LnFt	per inch	3.70
Non - Reinforced	LnFt	per inch	3.00
Masonry - Hollow	LnFt	per inch	2.10
Solid	LnFt	per inch	2.80

Core Drilling:

	UNIT	COST
Solid Slab - 2" Diameter	Inch	5.15
3" Diameter	Inch	5.85
4" Diameter	Inch	7.75
6" Diameter	Inch	10.50
8" Diameter	Inch	14.10
Hollow Core Slab - 2" Diameter	Inch	3.10
3" Diameter	Inch	3.30
4" Diameter	Inch	4.75
6" Diameter	Inch	8.85
Torch Cutting - Steel per Inch	LnFt	6.10
Blasting - Unrestricted	CuYd	130.00
Restricted	CuYd	225.00

Cut Openings:

	UNIT	COST
Concrete (see .32)	SqFt	-
Sheet Rock Partitions	SqFt	3.10
Wood Floors	SqFt	2.60

No Disposal or Haul Away Included (see .34)

(1) With Pneumatic Tools

0202.0 EARTHWORK (Op. Eng., Truck Driver & Lab.)

.1 GRADING

Machine	UNIT [1]	COST	UNIT [1]	COST
Strip Top Soil - 4"	CuYd	6.30	SqYd	.70
Spread Top Soil				
4" Site Borrow	CuYd	7.00	SqYd	.80
Off-Site Borrow ($13 CuYd)	CuYd	26.00	SqYd	3.00

Rough Grading - Cut and Fill	UNIT	SOFT [1]	MED. [1]	HARD [1]
Dozer - To 200'	CuYd	4.40	4.75	5.25
To 500'	CuYd	4.90	5.75	8.80
Scraper - Self Propelled - To 500'	CuYd	4.15	4.50	5.05
To 1,000'	CuYd	5.00	5.60	6.80
Grader - To 200'	CuYd	4.40	5.00	7.15
Add for Compaction (See 0202.4)				
Add for Hauling Away (See 0202.5)				
Add for Truck Haul on Site	CuYd	3.50	-	-
Add for Borrow Brought In				
Loose Fill – 3.00 Ton	CuYd	12.20	-	-
Crushed Stone - 5.50 Ton	CuYd	16.20	-	-
Gravel - 4.30 Ton	CuYd	14.20	-	-

Hand and Machine	UNIT	HAND LABOR	MACHINE
Fine Grading - 4" Fill - Site	CuYd	14.30	7.80
or SqFt		.20	.11
4" Fill - Building	CuYd	25.80	11.80
or SqFt		.30	.15

.2 EXCAVATION - Dig & Cast or Load (No Hauling)

Soil			
Open - Soft (Sand) with Backhoe or Shovel	CuYd	26.00	4.10
Medium (Clay)	CuYd	35.40	5.00
Hard	CuYd	52.00	7.24
Add for Clamshell or Dragline	CuYd	-	1.65
Deduct for Front End Loader	CuYd	-	1.40
Deduct for Dozer	CuYd	-	.32
Trench or Pocket - Soft with Backhoe or Shovel	CuYd	28.10	6.05
Medium	CuYd	36.40	8.00
Hard	CuYd	51.00	9.50
Add for Clamshell or Dragline	CuYd	-	1.60
Augered - 12" diameter	CuYd	58.20	11.25
24" diameter	CuYd	44.70	7.70
Add for Frost	CuYd	-	9.00
Rock - Soft - Dozer	CuYd	-	39.00
Hammer	CuYd	-	97.00
Medium - Blast	CuYd	-	118.00
Hammer	CuYd	-	195.00
Hard - Blast	CuYd	-	260.00
Hammer	CuYd	-	355.00
Swamp	CuYd	-	11.25
Underwater	CuYd	-	14.50

.3 BACKFILL (Not Compacted and Site Borrow)	CuYd	12.50	3.24
Add for Off-Site Borrow	CuYd	-	12.00

Add to <u>All Above</u> for Mobilization Average   5%

---

[1] Machine and Operators

0202.0　EARTHWORK, Cont'd...

		UNIT	(1) LABOR	(2) COST
.4	COMPACTION (Incl. Backfilling & Site Borrow)			
	Labor Only			
	Building to 85 - 24" Lifts	CuYd	17.70	-
	to 95 - 12" Lifts	CuYd	20.80	-
	to 100 - 6" Lifts	CuYd	25.00	-
	Labor Compaction & Machine Backfill Combined			
	Building to 85 - 24" Lifts	CuYd	10.90	3.55
	to 90 - 18" Lifts	CuYd	11.40	3.85
	to 95 - 12" Lifts	CuYd	12.20	3.75
	to 100 - 6" Lifts	CuYd	13.30	4.20
	Subgrade (Including Grading and Rollers)	CuYd	-	4.85
	Machine Only (No Grading)			
	Site to 85 - 24" Lifts	CuYd		4.00
	to 90 - 18" Lifts	CuYd		4.10
	to 95 - 12" Lifts	CuYd		4.70
	to 100 - 6" Lifts	CuYd		6.10
	Add to Above for Off-site Borrow	CuYd		13.50
.5	DISPOSAL (Haul Away) Country	CuYd/Mile		.85
	City	CuYd/Mile		1.00
.6	TESTS			
	Field Density - Compaction	Each		40.00
	Soil Gradation	Each		60.00
	Density (Proctor)	Each		98.00
	Moisture and Specific Gravities	Each		105.00
	Hydrometer (Sand, Silt and Clay)	Each		115.00
	Rock -2" Core	LnFt		73.00
	4" Core	LnFt		125.00
	Add for Soil Penetration	LnFt		8.25
	Add for Mileage	Mile		.65

0203.0　PILE AND CAISSON FOUNDATIONS (L&M)
(Operating Engineers and Iron Workers)

		UNIT		COST
.1	PILE, CONCRETE			
.11	Augured or Cast in Place -12"	LnFt		25.00
.12	Precast Prestressed -10"	LnFt		22.00
	12"	LnFt		26.00
	14"	LnFt		28.00
	16"	LnFt		33.00
.13	Pipe Casing Pulled - Cast - in - Place - 10"	LnFt		24.00
	12"	LnFt		24.00
.2	STEEL			
.21	Steel Pipe -10"	LnFt		29.00
	12"	LnFt		33.00
	14"	LnFt		38.50
	16"	LnFt		41.50
	Concrete - Filled - 10"	LnFt		32.00
	12"	LnFt		39.00
	14"	LnFt		46.00
	16"	LnFt		53.50
.22	Steel H Section 8" - 36#	LnFt		26.00
	10" - 42#	LnFt		29.00
	12" - 53#	LnFt		36.00
	14" - 73#	LnFt		38.00
	14" - 89#	LnFt		46.50
.23	Helical Pier Foundation			
	8" -10" - 12"	LnFt		28.00
	10" - 12" - 14"	LnFt		30.00
.3	WOOD (Treated) to 40' (Incl. Tests & Cutoffs)			
	10"	LnFt		21.00
	12"	LnFt		22.00
	14"	LnFt		25.00
	16"	LnFt		26.00
	Add for Mobilization			10%

---
(1) Hand Work
(2) Machine and Operators

		UNIT	COST
0203.0	**PILE & CAISSON, Cont'd...**		
.4	CAISSONS -20" Concrete Filled	LnFt	37.00
	24"	LnFt	43.00
	30"	LnFt	58.50
	36"	LnFt	74.00
	42"	LnFt	96.00
	48"	LnFt	120.00
	54"	LnFt	165.00
	60"	LnFt	196.00
	Add for Bells	Each	2,100.00
	Add for Wet Ground	LnFt	6.80
	Add for Obstructions - Hand Removal	CuFt	68.00
	Add for Obstructions - Machine Removal	CuFt	12.50
	Add for Reinforced Steel	Ton	1,750.00
	Add for Mobilization		10%
0204.0	**EARTH & WATER RETAINER WORK**		
.1	STEEL SHAFT PILING (Including Bracing) (L&M)		
	Heavy -27# -12"-16' Full Salvage	SqFt	20.50
	40# -15"-16' Full Salvage	SqFt	22.00
	57# -18"-16' Full Salvage	SqFt	23.00
	Add per Foot Longer than 16'	SqFt	2.40
	Add for No Salvage	SqFt	9.50
	Light -12 ga - 18" Black to 8' Full Salvage	SqFt	17.50
	10 ga - 18" Black to 8' Full Salvage	SqFt	18.50
	8 ga - 18" Black to 8' Full Salvage	SqFt	23.00
	Add for No Salvage	SqFt	7.90
	Add for Galvanized	SqFt	30%
.2	WOOD SHEET PILING & BRACING		
	6' Deep	SqFt	6.30
	8' Deep	SqFt	6.60
	10' Deep	SqFt	7.20
	12' Deep	SqFt	7.70
.3	H PILES & WOOD SHEATHING (4" Lbr.)		
	10' Deep	SqFt	22.50
	15' Deep	SqFt	24.75
	20' Deep	SqFt	30.00
	25' Deep	SqFt	34.00
	Deduct for Salvage	SqFt	40%
.4	UNDERPINNING	CuYd	800.00
.5	RIP RAP & LOOSE STONE WALLS		
	Machine Placed	CuYd	27.50
	Hand Placed	CuYd	63.50
	and Grouted	CuYd	160.00
.6	CRIBBING		
	6" Open to 10'	SqFt	25.20
	8" Open	SqFt	33.50
0205.0	**SITE DRAINAGE (Including Building Foundations)**		
.1	DITCHING AND BACKFILL (Open) - See 0202.2		
.2	DEWATERING		
	Pumping -2" Pump	Day	64.00
	3" Pump	Day	98.00
	4" Pump	Day	134.00
	Well Points - Ln.Ft. Header - first month	Month	139.00
	Add for Each Additional Month	Month	77.00
	Add for Attending Time	Hour	51.50

0205.0   SITE DRAINAGE, Cont'd...

.3   CULVERTS & PIPING (No Excavation - See 0202.2)

.31   Corrugated Galvanized Metal

	UNIT	LABOR	MATERIAL
Watertight (Bituminous Coated)			
12" Diameter with Bands & Gaskets	LnFt	5.05	9.75
15"	LnFt	5.50	14.00
18"	LnFt	6.00	17.30
24"	LnFt	7.10	23.75
30"	LnFt	8.50	30.00
36"	LnFt	10.10	37.00
48"	LnFt	20.00	57.00
Non - Watertight			
12" Diameter with Bands & Gaskets	LnFt	4.10	8.20
15"	LnFt	4.90	9.00
18"	LnFt	5.70	12.15
24"	LnFt	8.10	15.10
30"	LnFt	10.20	18.00
36"	LnFt	11.20	30.00
48"	LnFt	11.90	41.00
Add for Oval Arch Shape	LnFt	20%	-
Aprons			
18"	Each	19.80	76.50
24"	Each	22.90	112.50
30"	Each	24.20	180.00
36"	Each	28.30	300.00

.32   Reinforced Concrete Pipe - #3 - Class 5

	UNIT	LABOR	MATERIAL
12" Diameter	LnFt	6.60	12.60
18"	LnFt	8.90	20.00
24"	LnFt	12.70	26.50
27"	LnFt	15.20	40.00
30"	LnFt	19.20	49.00
36"	LnFt	23.60	53.00
48"	LnFt	35.70	84.00
Add for Each Added Foot in Depth	LnFt	5%	-
Add for Apron 36" (Flared End)	Each	198.00	525
Add for Trash Guards (Galvanized)	Each	166.00	900

.33   Vitrified Clay 12 "

	UNIT	LABOR	MATERIAL
Vitrified Clay 12 "	LnFt	7.00	13.50
24"	LnFt	11.40	50.00

.4   CATCH BASINS & MANHOLES (No Excavation)

	UNIT	LABOR	MATERIAL
48" Cast in Place (Concrete)	LnFt	180.00	192.00
48" Brick or Block	LnFt	170.00	172.00
48" Precast Concrete	LnFt	115.00	100.00
48" Precast Concrete Collar	LnFt	145.00	172.00
Add for Cover - Precast Concrete	Each	79.00	156.00
Add for Base - Precast Concrete	Each	104.00	159.00
Add for Covers & Grates - H.D.C.I.	Each	47.30	190.00
Add for Covers & Grates - L.D.C.I.	Each	47.30	190.00
Add for Covers - H.D. Watertight	Each	47.30	325.00
Add for Steps	Each	-	16.25
Add for Adjusting Rings 2"	Each	16.70	16.25

.5   FOUNDATION DRAINAGE (Subdrainage)

	UNIT	LABOR	MATERIAL
4" Clay Pipe	LnFt	1.40	1.90
4" Corrugated - Perforated	LnFt	1.20	1.15
4" Plastic Pipe - Perforated	LnFt	1.20	1.42
Solid	LnFt	1.20	1.10
6" Clay Pipe	LnFt	1.60	2.10
6" Corrugated - Perforated	LnFt	1.30	1.75
6" Plastic Pipe - Perforated	LnFt	1.30	3.20
Solid	LnFt	1.30	2.70
Add for Porous Surround 2'x 2' ($8.00 CuYd)	LnFt	1.70	2.95

0206.0 PAVEMENT, CURBS AND WALKS

.1 PAVING (PARKING LOTS AND DRIVEWAYS)

	UNIT	COST
.11 Bituminous (Material $185/Ton, 5% Asphalt, 10-Mile Delivery)		
1 1/2" Wearing 10.5 SqYd/Ton	SqYd	7.50
2" Wearing 9.0 SqYd/Ton	SqYd	9.20
2 1/2" Wearing 7.5 SqYd/Ton	SqYd	10.50
3" Wearing 6.0 SqYd/Ton	SqYd	12.50
Add for Paths and Small Driveways	SqYd	6.90
Add for Patching	SqYd	15.00
Add for Asphalt Content per 1%	SqYd	2.90
Add for Over 10-mile Delivery - Ton/Mile	SqYd	.50
Deduct for Base Asphalt	SqYd	10%
Add for Seal Coat	SqYd	2.30
Add for Striping - Paint	LnFt	.32
Add for Striping - Plastic	LnFt	.66
Base Course for Above - Add:		
4" Sand & Gravel $10.00 Ton	SqYd	5.30
4" Crushed Stone $12.00 Ton	SqYd	6.30
6" Sand & Gravel $10.00 Ton	SqYd	6.50
6" Crushed Stone $12.00 Ton	SqYd	7.80
Add per Mile over 10 Miles	SqYd	.48
4" Sand & Gravel	Ton	10.00
4" Crushed Stone	Ton	11.00
6" Sand & Gravel	Ton	9.60
6" Crushed Stone	Ton	10.50
Add per Ton Mile Over 10 Miles	Ton	.48
.12 Concrete (4000# Ready Mix, $74 CuYd - Machine Placed)		
6" Reinforced with 6 x 6, 8-8 Mesh	SqYd	25.50
7" Reinforced with 6 x 6, 6-6 Mesh	SqYd	26.50
8" Reinforced with #4 Rods - 12" O.C.	SqYd	30.00
9" Reinforced with #5 Rods - 12" O.C.	SqYd	32.50
10" Reinforced with #6 Rods - 8" O.C.	SqYd	33.90
12" Reinforced with #8 Rods - 8" O.C.	SqYd	43.00
Add for Base - Same as Base Prices Above		
Add to Above for Hand Placed	SqYd	25%
Add for Driveways	SqYd	50%
.13 Stabilized Aggregate (Delivery by Dump Truck)		
4" Gravel - $10.00 Ton - 3/4" Compacted	SqYd	6.00
4" Crushed Stone - $11.00 Ton - 3/4" Compacted	SqYd	6.80
6" Gravel - $10.00 Ton - 3/4" Compacted	SqYd	6.60
6" Crushed Stone - $11.00 Ton - 3/4" Compacted	SqYd	8.80
6" Pulverized Concrete	SqYd	9.30
Add for Soil Cement Treatment	SqYd	1.10
Add for Oil Penetration Treatment	SqYd	3.80
Add for Calcium Chloride Treatment	SqYd	.58
Add per CuYd Mile Over 10 Miles	SqYd	.48
.14 Brick - 4" x 8" x 2 1/2"	SqYd	85.00
Add for Sand Bed - Compacted	SqYd	7.90
Add for Mortar Setting - Bed & Joints	SqYd	8.50

0206.0 PAVEMENT, CURBS AND WALKS, Cont'd...

.2 CURBS & GUTTERS (Cost Incl. Excavation & Equip.)

.21 Concrete - Cast in Place

	UNIT	LABOR	MATERIAL
Curb			
6" x 12" Small Job - 200' Day	LnFt	6.80	3.40
6" x 18"	LnFt	8.10	4.00
6" x 24"	LnFt	10.20	5.10
6" x 30"	LnFt	12.00	6.10
Add for Reinforced - Two #5 Rods	LnFt	.80	.80
Add for Gutter - 6" x 12"	LnFt	5.04	2.70
Add for Gutter - 6" x 18"	LnFt	5.30	3.70
Add for Large Job - Over 200' Day	LnFt		10%
Add for Formless 1000' Day Up	LnFt		20%
Add for Curved or Radius Work	LnFt		40%
Curb & Gutter Rolled			
6" x 12" Small Job	LnFt	8.50	4.90
6" x 18"	LnFt	10.00	6.70
6" x 24"	LnFt	12.00	8.60
Deduct for Large Job - Over 200' Day	LnFt	-	10%
Deduct for Formless 1000' Day Up	LnFt	-	25%
Add for Reinforced - Two #5 Rods	LnFt	.80	.80
Add for Curved or Radius Work	LnFt	-	40%
Add for Approaches - 8' x 16' x 6'	SqFt	4.30	2.55
.22 Concrete - Precast & Pinned - 10" x 10'	LnFt	2.30	8.20
9" x 10'	LnFt	2.10	7.40
.23 Asphalt - 6" x 8'	LnFt	1.30	2.20
Add for Curved Work	LnFt	-	30%
.24 Granite - 6" x 16"	LnFt	6.50	29.00
.25 Timbers, Treated - 6" x 6"	LnFt	2.30	4.00
6" x 8"	LnFt	3.10	5.75
.26 Plastic - 6" x 6"	LnFt	2.10	6.80
.3 WALKS AND DRIVEWAYS			
Bituminous - 1 1/2" with 4" base	SqFt	.60	.90
2" with 4" base	SqFt	.60	.95
Concrete - 4" - Broom Finish	SqFt	1.70	1.40
5" - Broom Finish	SqFt	1.80	1.80
6" - Broom Finish	SqFt	1.90	1.80
Add Mesh 6" x 6", 10 - 10	SqFt	.20	.15
Add for Exposed Aggregate - Washed	SqFt	.80	.08
Add for Coloring (Acrylic)	SqFt	.45	.75
Add for Base - 4" Sand or Gravel	SqFt	.30	.10
Precast Block - Colored 1" with 2" Sand Cushion	SqFt	1.60	1.00
Colored 2" with 2" Sand Cushion	SqFt	1.80	1.20
Crushed Rock - 4" Compacted	SqFt	.40	.35
Flagstone - 1 1/4" with Sand Bed	SqFt	4.50	9.00
1 1/4" with Mortar Setting Bed	SqFt	6.30	10.00
Brick - 4" x 8" x 2 1/4" with 4" Sand Bed	SqFt	4.50	3.70
4" x 8" x 2 1/4" with Mortar Setting Bed	SqFt	5.20	5.10
Add for Herringbone or Weave Pattern	SqFt	1.50	1.70
Wood - 2" T&G on 6" x 6" Timbers	SqFt	1.70	3.10
2" Boards on 4" x 4" Timbers	SqFt	1.50	2.50
Asphalt Block - 6" x 12" x 3"	SqFt	2.70	6.00
Slate - 1 1/4"	SqFt	6.80	9.20
.4 STAIRS – EXTERIOR	SqFt	7.90	10.00

0207.0 FENCING (L&M) (Ironworkers or Carpenters)

	UNIT	COST
.1 CHAIN LINK (Galvanized 9 ga) Including Intermediate		
Posts and Concrete Embedded		
5' High - 2" Mesh and 2" O.D. Pipe	LnFt	15.00
6' High	LnFt	16.00
7' High	LnFt	17.00
8' High	LnFt	19.00
10' High	LnFt	35.00
Add for 1 - or 3 - Strand Barbed Wire	LnFt	3.15
Add for Vinyl Coated Wire	LnFt	15%
Add for Aluminum Wire	LnFt	25%
Add for Wood Slats	LnFt	50%
Add for Aluminum Slats	LnFt	75%
Add for Posts - Corner, End and Gate:		
5' High - 3" O.D.	Each	46.00
6' High - 3" O.D.	Each	51.00
7' High - 3" O.D.	Each	65.00
8' High - 3" O.D.	Each	77.00
10' High - 3" O.D.	Each	110.00
Add for Gate Frames:		
5' High	LnFt	53.50
6' High	LnFt	56.00
7' High	LnFt	63.00
8' High	LnFt	79.00
10' High	LnFt	94.50
.2 WELDED WIRE (Galvanized 11 ga) Including Intermediate		
Posts and Concrete Embedded		
4' High - 2" x 4"	LnFt	12.60
5' High	LnFt	14.20
6' High	LnFt	14.90
Add for Posts:		
4' Long	Each	27.30
5' Long	Each	29.90
6' Long	Each	31.50
Add for Gate Frames:		
4' Long	LnFt	27.30
5' Long	LnFt	31.50
6' Long	LnFt	35.00
Add for Slats	LnFt	6.00
.3 MESH WIRE (Galvanized 14 ga)		
3' High	LnFt	6.50
4' High	LnFt	8.00
5' High	LnFt	10.00
.4 WOOD FENCING		
Rail - 4' Cedar - 3 Boards	LnFt	17.00
Redwood - 3 Boards	LnFt	19.00
Pine, Painted - 3 Boards	LnFt	17.00
Vertical - 6' Pine, Painted	LnFt	21.00
Redwood	LnFt	26.00
Cedar	LnFt	26.00
Weave - 6' Redwood	LnFt	27.00
8' Redwood	LnFt	33.00
Picket - 4' Cedar	LnFt	14.00
6' Cedar	LnFt	17.00
Split Rail - 4' - 3 Rail	LnFt	9.50
Add for Post Set in Concrete	Each	5.75
.5 GUARD RAILS - Corrugated - Galvanized with Wood Posts	LnFt	33.00
Galvanized with Steel Posts	LnFt	36.00
Wire Cable - with Wood Posts, 3 - Strand	LnFt	17.00
with Steel Posts, 3 - Strand	LnFt	18.00
with no posts, 3-strand	LnFt	7.90

0208.0   RECREATIONAL FACILITIES

		UNIT	COST
.1	PLAYING FIELDS AND OUTDOOR COURTS		
.11	Football Fields - Field Size - 300' x 160		
	Minimum Use Size - 306' x 180'		
	Artificial Turf	Each	725,000.00
	Natural Turf	Each	340,000.00
.12	Tennis Courts -Court Size - 78' x 36'		
	Minimum Use Size - 108' x 48'		
	Asphalt with Color Surfacing - 1 Court	Each	28,000.00
	2 Courts	Each	23,500.00
	3 Courts	Each	22,500.00
	Incl. 3" Asphalt, 4" Gravel Base & Striping		
	Synthetic	Each	37,000.00
	Concrete	Each	32,000.00
	Add for Practice Boards	Each	3,000.00
	Add for Net Posts (4" Pipe with Ratchet)	Pair	750.00
	Add for Steel nets	Each	750.00
.13	Track and Field		
	Track - 440 yard - Track Size 21' x 1,320'		
	Synthetic Turf - 1" Polyurethane	Each	163,000.00
	1" Polyurethane	SqYd	1,700.00
	3" Bituminous Base	SqYd	8.70
	6" Gravel Base	SqYd	6.40
	Rubberized Asphalt	Each	74,000.00
	1" with 12% Resiliency	SqYd	12.70
	Add Bituminous Base - same as above	SqYd	8.10
	Cinder	Each	64,600.00
	High Jump - 50' Radius with 12' x 16' P.T.	Each	12,000.00
	Long Jump - 200' x 4' Runway with 20' x 8' P.T.	Each	5,500.00
	Pole Vault - 130' x 4' Runway with 16' x 16' P.T.	Each	3,500.00
.14	Basketball Courts -		
	Concrete - 4" Grade School - Court 42' x 74'	Each	20,000.00
	High School - Court 50' x 84'	Each	23,500.00
	College - Court 50' x 94'	Each	28,000.00
	Asphalt - 1 1/2" - Grade School	Each	10,000.00
	High School	Each	11,000.00
	College	Each	13,000.00
	Add for Back Stops	Each	2,000.00
.15	Volley Ball Courts - Court Size 30' x 60'	Each	11,500.00
	Minimum Use Size - 36' x 66'		
	Concrete - 4"	Each	10,500.00
	Asphalt - 1 1/2"	Each	8,000.00
	Add for Posts and Inserts	Pair	700.00
.16	Shuffleboard Courts - 6' x 52'		
	Concrete - 4"	Each	1,500.00
	Asphalt - 1 1/2"	Each	1,000.00
.17	Miniature Golf (9 - Hole) Bases - Concrete	Each	12,000.00
	Equipment and Carpet	Each	9,500.00
.18	Horse Shoe Courts - 10' x 40'	Each	700.00
	See Division 11 for Playground Equipment		
.19	Baseball and Softball Fields		
	45' Radius with Backstop	Each	15,000.00
	65' Radius with Backstop	Each	19,000.00

		UNIT	COST
0208.0	**RECREATIONAL FACILITIES, Cont'd...**		
.2	RECREATIONAL EQUIPMENT		
	Climbers - Arch	Each	570.00
	Dome	Each	670.00
	Circular	Each	1,200.00
	Catwalks	Each	760.00
	Slides - Straight - 6'	Each	1,000.00
	8'	Each	1,300.00
	10'	Each	1,900.00
	Spiral - 7'	Each	4,700.00
	10'	Each	6,900.00
	Spring Equipment - Single	Each	450.00
	2 Unit	Each	650.00
	4 Unit	Each	1,200.00
	Swings - 2 Leg - 2 Seat - 8' High	Each	740.00
	2 Leg - 4 Seat	Each	1,080.00
	3 Leg - 3 Seat - 8' High	Each	825.00
	6 Seat	Each	1,300.00
	Add for 12' High	-	20%
	Add for Nursery Seats	Each	310.00
	Add for Saddle Seats	Each	700.00
	Add for Tire Swings	Each	180.00
	Teeter Totters	Each	1,100.00
	Whirls - Small - 6'	Each	910.00
	Large - 10'	Each	1,650.00
.3	SITE FURNISHINGS		
	Benches - Steel Leg		
	Stationary - with Black Wood Slats - 8'	Each	450.00
	with Black Aluminum Slats - 8'	Each	610.00
	Portable - 8'	Each	290.00
	Player - No Back, Wood Seat - 8'	Each	240.00
	No Back, Wood Seat - 14'	Each	380.00
	Bike Racks		
	Permanent - 10'	Each	620.00
	20'	Each	960.00
	Portable - 10'	Each	360.00
	Bleachers, Elevated		
	5 - Row x 15' Steel - Seats 50	Each	3,800.00
	10 - Row x 15' Steel - Seats 100	Each	6,600.00
	15 - Row x 15' Steel - Seats 150	Each	9,200.00
	Litter Receptacles		
	Pedestal - 24"	Each	350.00
	36"	Each	430.00
	Stoves	Each	430.00
	Tables - Steel Frame - Wood Slat - 8'	Each	460.00
	Aluminum Slat - 8'	Each	490.00
	All Wood	Each	305.00
	All Aluminum	Each	500.00
.4	SHELTERS	SqFt	15.50

0209.0	LANDSCAPING (L&M) (Laborers)	UNIT	COST	UNIT	COST
.1	SEEDING (.80 lb) - Machine	SqYd	.50	Acre	2,200.00
	Hand	SqYd	1.15	Acre	5,400.00
	Add Fine Grading - Hand	SqYd	1.00	Acre	4,700.00
	Add for 30 - Day Maintenance	-	-	Acre	1,510.00
	Deduct for Rye and Wild Grasses	-	-	Acre	680.00
.2	SODDING - Flat ($.80 per SqYd)	SqYd	2.75	-	-
	Slope (Pegged)	SqYd	3.40	-	-
	Add Fine Grading - Hand	SqYd	1.70	-	-
	Add for 30 - Day Maintenance	SqYd	.50	-	-
	Remove and Haul Away Old Sod	SqYd	1.30		
.3	DISCING	SqYd	1.05	Acre	5,000.00
.4	FERTILIZING	SqYd	.35	Acre	1,290.00
				Ton	1,040.00
.5	TOP SOIL - 4" Hand - Only	SqYd	3.55	Acre	19,800.00
	Machine and Hand	SqYd	2.50	Acre	13,000.00
		CuYd	31.20	-	-
.6	TREES AND SHRUBS				
	Trees - 2"			Each	580.00
	3"			Each	710.00
	4"			Each	950.00
	5"			Each	1,200.00
	6"			Each	1,800.00
	Shrubs - Small - 1' to 3'			Each	26.00
	Large - 3' to 5'			Each	52.00
.7	BEDS				
	Wood Chips, Cedar, 2" - $12 CuYd			SqYd	3.40
	Mulch, Redwood Bark - $30 CuYd			SqYd	7.00
	Stone Aggregate - $15 CuYd			SqYd	3.85
	Planting Soil, 24" - $15 CuYd			SqYd	4.40
.8	WOOD CURBS AND WALLS				
	Curbs - 4" x 4" - Fir or Pine Treated			LnFt	2.90
	Cedar			LnFt	3.60
	6" x 6" - Fir or Pine Treated			LnFt	7.30
	Cedar			LnFt	8.10
	Walls - 4" x 4" - Fir or Pine, Incl. Dead Men			SqFt	7.60
	6" x 6" - Fir or Pine, Incl. Dead Men			SqFt	11.45
	Cedar, Including Dead Men			SqFt	17.70
.9	SPRINKLER SYSTEM, WATERED AREA			CSF	34.30
0210.0	**SOIL STABILIZATION**				
.1	CHEMICAL INTRUSION			CuFt	18.70
	Pressure Grout			Gal	5.90
.2	CONCRETE INTRUSION			CuFt	34.30
.3	VIBRO FLOTATION			-	-
0211.0	**SOIL TREATMENT**				
.1	PESTICIDE			SqFt	.31
.2	VEGETATION PREVENTATIVE			SqFt	.10
0212.0	**RAILROAD WORK**				
.1	NEW WORK			LnFt	161.00
.2	REPAIR WORK			LnFt	23.00
0213.0	**MARINE WORK**				
0214.0	**TUNNEL WORK**				

0201.0 DEMOLITION

.32   Selective Building Removals -
No Cutting or Disposal Included (see 0201.34 & 0201.35)

	UNIT	COST
Concrete - Hand Work (see 0201.32 for Machine Work)		
8" Walls - Reinforced	SqFt	12.00
Non - Reinforced	SqFt	8.50
12" Walls - Reinforced	SqFt	21.00
12" Footings x 24" wide	LnFt	19.00
x 36" wide	LnFt	26.00
16" Footings x 24" wide	LnFt	33.00
6" Structural Slab - Reinforced	SqFt	7.80
8" Structural Slab - Reinforced	SqFt	9.70
4" Slab on Ground - Reinforced	SqFt	3.65
Non - Reinforced	SqFt	2.70
6" Slab on Ground - Reinforced	SqFt	4.30
Non - Reinforced	SqFt	3.20
Stairs - Reinforced	SqFt	13.30
Masonry - Hand Work		
4" Brick or Stone Walls	SqFt	2.45
4" Brick and 8" Backup Block or Tile	SqFt	4.50
4" Block or Tile Partitions	SqFt	2.40
6" Block or Tile Partitions	SqFt	2.60
8" Block or Tile Partitions	SqFt	3.00
12" Block or Tile Partitions	SqFt	3.75
Miscellaneous - Hand Work (Including Loading)		
Acoustical Ceilings - Attached (Including Iron)	SqFt	.70
Suspended (Including Grid)	SqFt	.40
Asbestos - Pipe	LnFt	52.00
Ceilings and Walls	SqFt	16.70
Columns and Beams	SqFt	42.00
Tile Flooring	SqFt	1.90
Cabinets and Tops	LnFt	11.50
Carpet	SqFt	.35
Ceramic and Quarry Tile	SqFt	1.35
Doors and Frames - Metal	Each	59.30
Wood	Each	53.00
Drywall Ceilings - Attached	SqFt	.85
Drywall on Wood or Metal Studs - 2 Sides	SqFt	.95
Paint Removal - Doors and Windows	SqFt	.85
Walls	SqFt	.70
Plaster Ceilings - Attached (Including Iron)	SqFt	1.20
on Wood or Metal Studs	SqFt	1.15
Roofing - Builtup	SqFt	1.15
Shingles - Asphalt and Wood	SqFt	.40
Terrazzo Flooring	SqFt	1.90
Vinyl Flooring	SqFt	.40
Wall Coverings	SqFt	.75
Windows	Each	38.00
Wood Flooring	SqFt	.40
.33 Site Removals (Including Loading)		
4" Concrete Walks - Labor Only (Non-Reinforced)	SqFt	2.70
Machine Only (Non-Reinforced)	SqFt	.90
6" Concrete Drives - Labor Only (Non-Reinforced)	SqFt	3.40
Machine Only (Reinforced)	SqFt	1.20
6" x 18" Concrete Curb - Machine	LnFt	2.30
Curb and Gutter - Machine	LnFt	3.00
2" Asphalt - Machine	SqFt	.52
Fencing - 8' Hand	LnFt	3.10

		UNIT	COST
0202.0	**EARTHWORK**		
.1	GRADING - Hand - 4" - Site	SqFt	.31
	Hand – 4" Building	SqFt	.52
.2	EXCAVATION - Hand - Open - Soft (Sand)	CuYd	39.50
	Medium (Clay)	CuYd	50.00
	Hard (Shale)	CuYd	81.00
	Add for Trench or Pocket		15%
.3	BACK FILL - Hand - Not Compacted (Site Borrow)	CuYd	18.70
.4	BACK FILL - Hand - Compacted (Site Borrow)		
	12" Lifts - Building - No Machine	CuYd	31.00
	With Machine	CuYd	25.00
	18" Lifts - Building - No Machine	CuYd	30.00
	With Machine	CuYd	24.00
0205.0	**DRAINAGE**		
.4	BUILDING FOUNDATION DRAINAGE		
	4" Clay Pipe	LnFt	4.70
	4" Plastic Pipe - Perforated	LnFt	3.75
	6" Clay Pipe	LnFt	5.10
	6" Plastic Pipe - Perforated	LnFt	5.70
	Add for Porous Surround - 2' x 2'	LnFt	6.75
0206.0	**PAVEMENT, CURBS AND WALKS**		
.2	CURBS AND GUTTERS		
.21	Concrete - Cast in Place (Machine Placed)		
	Curb - 6" x 12"	LnFt	13.65
	6" x 18"	LnFt	15.75
	6" x 24"	LnFt	17.85
	6" x 30"	LnFt	21.00
	Curb and Gutter - 6" x 12"	LnFt	18.90
	6" x 18"	LnFt	22.05
	6" x 24"	LnFt	25.20
	Add for Hand Placed	LnFt	8.40
	Add for 2 #5 Reinf. Rods	LnFt	2.30
	Add for Curves and Radius Work	LnFt	40%
.22	Concrete Precast - 6" x 10" x 8"	LnFt	14.20
	6" x 9" x 8"	LnFt	13.20
.23	Bituminous - 6" x 8"	LnFt	5.20
.24	Granite - 6" x 16"	LnFt	44.00
.25	Timbers - Treated - 6" x 6"	LnFt	8.00
	6" x 8"	LnFt	12.00
.26	Plastic - 6" x 6"	LnFt	12.00
.3	WALKS		
	Bituminous - 1 1/2" with 4" Sand Base	SqFt	2.30
	2" with 4" Sand Base	SqFt	2.40
	Concrete - 4" - Broom Finish	SqFt	4.50
	5" - Broom Finish	SqFt	4.85
	6" - Broom Finish	SqFt	5.25
	Add for 6" x 6", 10 - 10 Mesh	SqFt	.50
	Add for 4" Sand Base	SqFt	.70
	Add for Exposed Aggregate	SqFt	1.20
	Crushed Rock - 4"	SqFt	.85
	Brick - 4" - with 2" Sand Cushion	SqFt	11.55
	4" - with 2" Mortar Setting Bed	SqFt	13.65
	Flagstone – 1 1/4" - with 4" Sand Cushion	SqFt	18.10
	1¼" - with 2" Mortar Setting Bed	SqFt	20.00
	Precast Block - 1" Colored with 4" Sand Cushion	SqFt	3.80
	2" Colored with 4" Sand Cushion	SqFt	4.40
	Wood - 2" Boards on 6" x 6" Timbers	SqFt	6.50
	2" Boards on 4" x 4" Timbers	SqFt	5.80
	Slate - 1 1/4" - with 2" Mortar Setting Bed	SqFt	23.00

* See Section 0505 for Permanent Forms of Corrugated Deck and Steel Lath.

0301.0 GENERAL CONCRETE WORK (S) (Cement Finishers & Laborers)

		UNIT	LABOR	MATERIAL
.1	CONCRETE PLACING & VIBRATING (3500# Concrete with 5.5 sack cement)			
.11	Footings - 1 1/2" Aggregate			
	Wall & Pad Types - Truck Chuted	CuYd	16.00	90.00
	Buggies	CuYd	20.60	90.00
	Crane	CuYd	21.80	90.00
.12	Wall & Grade Beams - 3/4" Aggregate			
	At Grade (to 8' deep) -Truck Chuted	CuYd	16.70	90.00
	Buggies	CuYd	22.60	90.00
	Crane	CuYd	21.80	90.00
	At Grade (over 8' deep, poured with trunks) - Truck Chuted	CuYd	17.70	90.00
	Buggies	CuYd	23.90	90.00
	Crane & Hoppers	CuYd	22.90	90.00
	Above Grade (deeper than 8') - Conveyors	CuYd	16.60	90.00
	Ramp & Buggies	CuYd	23.90	90.00
	Crane & Hoppers	CuYd	22.90	90.00
	Climbing Crane	CuYd	22.80	90.00
	Pumping	CuYd	18.30	90.00
.13	Column & Pedestals - 3/4" Aggregate - Buggies	CuYd	26.30	90.00
	Crane	CuYd	22.60	90.00
	Tower & Buggies	CuYd	26.40	90.00
	Fork Lift	CuYd	46.40	90.00
	Climbing Crane	CuYd	24.10	90.00
	Pumping	CuYd	19.50	90.00
.14	Beams - 3/4" Aggregate - Buggies	CuYd	25.00	90.00
	Crane	CuYd	22.90	90.00
	Tower & Buggies	CuYd	25.40	90.00
	Fork Lift	CuYd	45.80	90.00
	Climbing Crane	CuYd	22.50	90.00
	Pumping	CuYd	20.10	90.00
.15	Slabs - 6" Structure - 3/4" Aggregate - Buggies	CuYd	21.80	90.00
	Crane	CuYd	22.90	90.00
	Climbing Crane	CuYd	20.80	90.00
	Pumping	CuYd	19.60	90.00
.16	Stairs & Landings -			
	Structural - 3/4" Aggregate - Buggies	CuYd	25.00	90.00
	Truck Chuted	CuYd	20.80	90.00
	Climbing Crane	CuYd	22.90	90.00
	Pumping	CuYd	20.80	90.00
	Pan Filled - 1/2" Ready Mixed	CuYd	43.00	96.00
	Hand Mixed (Dry)	CuYd	67.10	90.00
.17	Curbs, Platforms & Misc. Small Pours - 1/2" Aggregate Buggies	CuYd	31.40	90.00
	Fork Lift	CuYd	43.70	90.00
.18	Slabs on Ground - 3/4" Aggregate - Truck Chuted	CuYd	17.30	90.00
	Buggies	CuYd	22.50	90.00
	Crane	CuYd	21.30	90.00
	Conveyors	CuYd	17.70	90.00
.19	Slabs-Over Metal Decks or Lath - 1/2" Aggregate Buggies	CuYd	26.00	90.00
	Tower & Buggies	CuYd	27.00	90.00
	Crane	CuYd	24.20	90.00
.20	Toppings - 1/2" Aggregate - Buggies	CuYd	25.50	94.00
	Towers & Buggies	CuYd	28.10	94.00

Conveying Equipment and Operator not included in above costs. See Page 3-4. Also other variations on Page 3-4

0301.0	GENERAL CONCRETE WORK, Cont'd...	UNIT	LABOR	MATERIAL
	Additions to Concrete Placing Work:			
	Add for Ea 500# Concrete above 3500# Concrete	CuYd	-	2.40
	Add or deduct for Sack Cement	CuYd	-	5.45
	Add for Non Corrosive	CuYd	-	8.85
	Add for High Early Cement Concrete	CuYd	-	8.85
	Deduct for 1 1/2" Aggregate	CuYd	-	2.10
	Add for 3/8" or 1/2" Aggregate	CuYd	-	3.95
	Add for Lightweight Aggregate (4000)	CuYd	3.40	17.70
	Add for Heavyweight Aggregate (Granite) (4000#)	CuYd	6.80	12.10
	Deduct for Fly Ash Concrete (3000#)	CuYd	-	3.10
	Add for Exposed Aggregate Mix	CuYd	-	10.60
	Add for Fibre Reinforcement Mix	CuYd	4.00	9.40
	Add for Less than 6 CuYd Delivery	Load	-	33.30
	Add for Hauls beyond 15 Miles	CuYd Mi	-	1.15
	Add for Time after 7 Minutes per Yard	Minute	-	99.00
	Add for Conveying Equipment and Operators:			
	Towers (Approx. 30 CuYd/ Hour)	CuYd	-	6.70
	Mobile Cranes (Approx. 25 CuYd/ Hour)	CuYd	-	7.70
	Tower Cranes (Approx. 20 CuYd/ Hour)	CuYd	-	8.32
	Fork Lifts (Approx. 5 CuYd/ Hour)	CuYd	-	7.80
	Conveyors (Approx. 50 CuYd/ Hour	CuYd	-	8.30
	Pumping (Approx. 35 CuYd/ Hour)	CuYd	-	4.85
	Add for Floors Above Grade - per Floor Placing	CuYd	1.30	-
	Add for Winter Work:			
	Productivity Loss	CuYd	5.70	-
	Heating Water and Aggregate	CuYd	-	8.30
	Calcium Chloride 1%	CuYd	-	2.85
	Insulation Blanket - Slabs (5 uses)	SqFt	.10	.16
	Walls & Beams (3 uses)	SqFt	.15	.12
	Heaters: Without Operators (Including Fuel - Floor Area)	CuYd	.50	1.90
		or SqFt	.10	.21
	Enclosures (3 uses)- Wall Area	CuYd	1.05	.40
		or SqFt	.10	.21
.2	FINISHING (Including Screeds and Bulkheads to 6")			
.21	Rough Screeding - Slabs	SqFt	.40	.08
	Stairs	SqFt	.70	.08
.22	Trowel Finishing - Slabs on Ground	SqFt	.60	.08
	Solid and Pan Slabs	SqFt	.60	.08
	Slab over Corrugated	SqFt	.60	.08
	Topping Slabs	SqFt	.60	.08
	Stairs	SqFt	1.05	.08
	Curbs and Bases	SqFt	1.05	.08
.23	Broom Finishing - Slabs on Ground	SqFt	.50	.08
	Solid and Pan Slabs	SqFt	.60	.08
	Slab over Corrugated	SqFt	.70	.08
	Topping Slabs	SqFt	.60	.08
	Stairs	SqFt	1.05	.08
.24	Float Finish - Slabs on Ground	SqFt	.50	.08
	Solid and Pan Slabs	SqFt	.50	.08
	Slab over Corrugated	SqFt	.50	.08
	Stairs	SqFt	.90	.08
.25	Special Finishing			
.251	Patch Walls, 2 Sides Tie Holes & Honeycomb	SqFt	.30	.09
.252	Rub Walls, 1 Side Carborundum for Fins	SqFt	.12	.05
	With Burlap and Grout	SqFt	.60	.10
.253	Level & Top Floors - Trowel Finish 1"	SqFt	1.00	.45
	With Epoxy 1/4"	SqFt	1.90	6.80
.254	Exposed Aggregate Slabs - Washed	SqFt	.80	.06
	Retardant	SqFt	.30	.11
	Add for - Seeding	SqFt	.40	.11
	Add to All Finishing Items Above			
	Winter Production Loss and Cost	SqFt	.30	.07
	Sloped Work	SqFt	.20	06
	Heavyweight Aggregates	SqFt	.24	.07

		UNIT	LABOR	MATERIAL
0301.0 GENERAL CONCRETE WORK, Cont'd...				
.255	Bushhammer - Green Concrete	SqFt	1.30	.12
	Cured Concrete	SqFt	1.90	.12
	Sand Blast - Light Penetration	SqFt	.95	.12
	Heavy Penetration	SqFt	1.60	.25
.3	SPECIALTIES			
.31	Abrasives - Non-Slip			
	Alo-Grit (.86 lb & 1/4 lb/SqFt)	SqFt	.22	.30
	Carborundum Grits (1.30 lb & 1/4 lb/SqFt)	SqFt	.22	.48
	Strips 3/8" x 1/4"	LnFt	.80	1.50
	Epoxy Coating (50.00 gal) & 50 SqFt/Gal	SqFt	.32	1.70
.32	Admixtures (per CuYd Concrete)			
	Accelerator (.06 oz)	CuYd	-	1.60
	Air Entraining (.04 oz)	CuYd	-	1.00
	Densifiers (.07 oz)	CuYd	-	2.10
	Retarders (.05 oz)	CuYd	-	1.00
	Water Reducing (.06 oz)	CuYd	-	2.85
.33	Colors			
	Dust on Type:			
	Black, Brown & Red (.50 lb) 50#/100 SqFt	SqFt	.20	.46
	Green and Blue (.60 lb) 50#/100 SqFt	SqFt	.20	.57
	Integral (Top 1"):			
	Black, Brown & Red (1.50 lb) 27#/100 SqFt	SqFt	.45	.77
	Green and Blue (4.25 lb) 27#/100 SqFt	SqFt	.45	1.65
	Full Thickness			
	Black, Brown & Red	CuYd	26.00	135.00
	Green and Blue	CuYd	26.00	175.00
.34	Curing			
	Curing Compounds			
	Resin (10.00 gal) 200 SqFt/gal	SqFt	.10	.07
	Hydrocide Res.Base (15.00 gal) 200 SqFt/gal	SqFt	.10	.09
	Rubber Base (8.00 gal) 200 SqFt/gal	SqFt	.10	.06
	Wax Base (3.00 gal) 200 SqFt/gal	SqFt	.10	.03
	Asphalt Base (4.00 gal) 200 SqFt/gal	SqFt	.10	.03
	Paper	SqFt	.10	.07
	Polyethylene - 4 mil	SqFt	.10	.06
	Water	SqFt	.10	.01
	Burlap	SqFt	1.10	.08
	Curing and Sealing	SqFt	.14	.08
.35	Expansion and Control Joints			
	Asphalt - Fibre - 1/2" x 4"	LnFt	.45	.27
	1/2" x 6"	LnFt	.45	.35
	1/2" x 8"	LnFt	.50	.49
	Polyethylene Foam - 1/2" x 4"	LnFt	.45	.45
	1/2" x 6"	LnFt	.45	.50
	1/2" x 8"	LnFt	.50	.65
	Sponge Rubber - 1/2" x 4"	LnFt	.45	2.20
	1/2" x 6"	LnFt	.45	3.40
	1/2" x 8"	LnFt	.50	4.70
	Paper - Fibre (No Oil) - 1/2" x 4"	LnFt	.45	.27
	1/2" x 6"	LnFt	.45	.37
	1/2" x 8"	LnFt	.50	.48
	Add for Cap	LnFt	.20	.32
	Add for 3/4" Thickness	LnFt	-	30%
	Add for 1" Thickness	LnFt	-	80%

See 0413.5 for Other Expansion Joint Costs.
See 0410.0 Mortars for Cement Prices.

0301.0 GENERAL CONCRETE WORK, Cont'd...

	UNIT	LABOR	MATERIAL
.36 Grouts - Non-Shrink			
Iron Oxide (.45/lb)			
Hand Mixed (1 Cem: 1 Sand: 1 Iron Oxide)	CuFt	7.30	32.00
Per 1"	SqFt	.95	2.55
Premixed (.45/lb)	CuFt	2.60	42.50
Aluminum Oxide (.45/lb)	CuFt	5.30	12.70
Non-Metallic, Premixed (.35/lb)	CuFt	3.85	32.00
.37 Hardeners and Sealers			
Acrylic Sealer (7.50 gal) 300 SqFt/gal	SqFt	.13	.06
Epoxy Sealer (25.00 gal) 300 SqFt/gal	SqFt	.13	.16
Urethane Sealer (9.50 gal) 400 SqFt/gal	SqFt	.13	.06
Liquid Hardeners (4.85 gal) 200 SqFt/gal	SqFt	.13	.05
.38 Joint Sealers			
Rubber Asphalt			
Hot 1/2" x 1/2" Joint (.70 lb)	LnFt	.70	.55
Cold 1/2" x 1/2" Joint (.54 lb)	LnFt	.50	.66
Epoxy (20.00 Qt)	LnFt	.64	1.80
.39 Moisture Proofing (Loose Laid for Slabs)			
Polyethylene 4 Mil	SqFt	.07	.03
6 Mil	SqFt	.07	.04
Asphalted Paper	SqFt	.07	.05
.4 EQUIPMENT (Conv., Finishing, Vibrating, etc.)			
See Divisions I-6A and I-7A			
.5 TESTS			
Cylinder - 6" x 12" (7-day and 28-day)	Ea	-	45.00
Add per Pickup	Ea	-	55.00

0302.0 CONCRETE FORM WORK (S) (Carpenters)
(Lumber @ 500.00 MBF & 3/4" BB Plywood @ .65 SqFt)
(Costs Include Erection, Stripping, Cleaning, Oiling)

	UNIT	LABOR	MATERIAL
.1 REMOVABLE FORMS (Expendable and Reusable)			
.11 Footings (2-1/2 BdFt/SqFt and 3 Uses)			
Wall Type - Constant Elevation	SqFt	2.50	.60
Pad Type	SqFt	2.60	.60
Add for Volume Elevations and Changes	SqFt	.20	-
Add for Deep Foundation (8' or more)	SqFt	.20	-
Add for Each Foot Form Deeper than 12"	SqFt	.12	.05
Add for Keyway	LnFt	.50	.12
.12 Walls & Grade Beams (2-1/2 BdFt/SqFt & 3 Uses)			
Straight Walls - 4' High	SqFt	2.60	.72
Add for Each Foot Higher than 4'	SqFt	.05	.04
Add for Walls Above Grade	SqFt	.06	-
Add for Deep Foundation (8' or more)	SqFt	.20	-
Add for Pilastered Wall, 24' O.C. Total Area	SqFt	.12	.03
Add for Pilastered Wall, Pilasters Only	SqFt	4.95	.65
Add for Openings - Opening Area	SqFt	3.30	.80
Add for Retaining and Battered Type Wall	SqFt	.95	.15
Add for Curved Wall	SqFt	2.05	.18
Add for Brick Ledge	LnFt	1.90	.20
Add for Parapet Wall - Hung	SqFt	3.00	.30
Add for Pit or Small Trench Walls	SqFt	1.80	.10
Add for Lined Forms - Hardwood Panels	SqFt	.40	.50
Gang Formed Walls - Make Up	SqFt	4.60	6.50
Move	SqFt	1.05	.25
3/4" B-B Plywood - Avg - 5 Ply - 8 Uses	SqFt	-	-
7 Ply - 8 Uses	SqFt	-	-
M.D.O. Plywood - Avg. - 20 Uses	SqFt	-	-

0302.0   CONCRETE FORM WORK, Cont'd...

	UNIT	LABOR	MATERIAL
.13 Columns & Pedestals			
Sq. & Rectangular (2 1/2 BdFt/ SqFt & 3 Uses)			
8" x 8"	SqFt	5.10	.90
12" x 12"	SqFt	4.90	.91
16" x 16"	SqFt	4.90	.92
20" x 20"	SqFt	4.70	.93
24" x 24"	SqFt	4.70	.94
Add per Foot - Work over 10' Floor Heights	SqFt	.40	-
Add per Floor above 20' Above Grade	SqFt	.20	-
Deduct for Ganged Formed (8 Uses)	SqFt	1.40	-
Round - Steel or Fiberglass (Rent and 3 Uses)			
12"	LnFt	7.80	4.50
16"	LnFt	7.60	5.00
20"	LnFt	8.80	6.00
24"	LnFt	13.00	7.00
30"	LnFt	16.90	8.50
36"	LnFt	21.00	10.20
Add per Foot - Work over 10" Floor Heights	LnFt	.40	.45
Round-Fibre (6" to 48" x 18' available)			
8" Cut Length Prices Used	LnFt	5.40	2.50
12"	LnFt	5.60	4.70
16"	LnFt	5.00	7.25
20"	LnFt	7.70	10.00
24"	LnFt	10.40	13.40
30"	LnFt	12.10	16.60
36"	LnFt	14.90	18.80
Add for Less than 100 Feet - One Size	LnFt	-	20%
Add for Seamless Fibre	LnFt	-	15%
Add for Conical Heads to Steel or Fibre	Each	104.00	60.00
Add for Beam Fittings or Other Openings	Each	114.00	65.00
.14 Beams (12" Floor Heights and 3 Uses Lumber)			
Spandrel Beams (Includes Shoring)			
12" x 48" (4 1/2 BdFt/ SqFt)	SqFt	5.50	1.20
12" x 42" (4 3/4 BdFt/ SqFt)	SqFt	5.50	1.25
12" x 36" (5 BdFt/ SqFt)	SqFt	5.70	1.30
12" x 30" (5 1/4 BdFt/ SqFt)	SqFt	5.80	1.30
8" x 42" (4 3/4 BdFt/ SqFt)	SqFt	5.80	1.25
8" x 36" (5 1/4 BdFt/ SqFt)	SqFt	6.00	1.30
Add for Decks and Safety Rail	SqFt	1.20	.40
Interior Beams			
16" x 30" (4 BdFt/ SqFt)	SqFt	5.50	1.15
16" x 24" (4 1/2 BdFt/ SqFt)	SqFt	5.60	1.20
12" x 30" (4 3/4 BdFt/ SqFt)	SqFt	5.50	1.25
12" x 24" (5 1/4 BdFt/ SqFt)	SqFt	5.60	1.30
12" x 16" (6 1/2 BdFt/ SqFt)	SqFt	6.20	1.45
8" x 24" (5 1/4 BdFt/ SqFt)	SqFt	5.90	1.35
8" x 16" (6 1/2 BdFt/ SqFt)	SqFt	6.20	1.45
Add for Beams Carrying Horizontal Shoring	SqFt	1.10	.35
Add per Foot for Floor Heights over 10'	SqFt	.50	.12
Add per Floor over 20' Above Grade	SqFt	.20	.11
Add for Splayed Beams	SqFt	1.80	.20
Add for Inverted Beams	SqFt	2.40	.20
Add for Mud Sills (3 Uses)	SqFt	.80	.40

0302.0 CONCRETE FORM WORK, Cont'd...	UNIT	LABOR	MATL
.15 Slabs (12' Floor Heights and 3 Uses Lumber)			
.151 Solid Slabs (Includes Shoring) (Metal Adj. Beams or Joists)			
Horizontal Shoring Method			
To 5" thick (2' OC x 10' Span) 2.5 BdFt/ SqFt	SqFt	2.20	.71
5" - 8" thick (2' OC x 15' Span) 2.8 BdFt/ SqFt	SqFt	2.30	.80
8" - 11" thick (2' OC x 20' Span) 3.1 BdFt/ SqFt	SqFt	2.50	.85
Add for Heights above 10' per foot	SqFt	.30	.09
Vertical Shoring Method			
(Wood or Metal Posts, Purlins & Joists)			
To 5" thick - 2.7 BdFt/SqFt - 4' x 5'6" OC	SqFt	2.30	.76
5" - 8" thick - 3.0 BdFt/SqFt - 4' x 5'0" OC	SqFt	2.50	.82
8" - 11" thick - 3.3 BdFt/SqFt - 4' x 4'6" OC	SqFt	4.10	.86
Add for Heights above 10' per foot	SqFt	.30	.09
Add for Adjustable Hardware	SqFt	-	.02
Add for Cantilevered Slabs	SqFt	1.50	.17
Add for Drop Panels - No Edge included	SqFt	.30	.12
Flying Form method (8 Uses)			
To 5" Thick	SqFt	1.80	.65
5" - 8" Thick	SqFt	1.90	.66
8" - 11" Thick	SqFt	2.00	.67
Add for Heights above 8' per foot	SqFt	.25	.07
Add for 2 Uses	SqFt	.24	.30
Add for 4 Uses	SqFt	.20	.20
.152 Pan Slabs - Cost same as solid slabs above plus pan forming costs below.			
Based on 3 Uses and lease of approximately 4,000 Square Feet			
20" Pan 8" + 2"	SqFt	1.05	.78
10" + 2"	SqFt	1.10	.80
12" + 2"	SqFt	1.10	.82
14" + 2"	SqFt	1.20	.85
30" Pan 8" + 2 1/2"	SqFt	1.00	.75
10"+2 1/2"	SqFt	1.00	.78
12"+2 1/2"	SqFt	1.10	.80
14"+2 1/2"	SqFt	1.10	.82
19" x 19" Dome Pan - 24" x 24" Joist Center			
6" + 2"	SqFt	1.00	.77
8" + 2"	SqFt	1.00	.79
10" + 2"	SqFt	1.00	.79
12" + 2"	SqFt	1.10	.83
30" x 30" Dome Pan - 36" x 36" Joist Center			
10" + 2 1/2"	SqFt	1.10	.85
12" + 2 1/2"	SqFt	1.20	.87
14" + 2 1/2"	SqFt	1.30	.91
Add for 2 Uses	SqFt	.10	.12
Add for 1 Use	SqFt	.10	.26
Deduct for 4 Uses	SqFt	.10	.07
Deduct for 5 Uses	SqFt	.05	.08
Pan Slabs: Based on 5 Uses & Lease of 4,000 SqFt			
40" x 40" Dome Pan - 16" + 3"	SqFt	1.40	1.10
48" x 48" Joist Center - 18" + 3"	SqFt	1.50	1.30
Deduct for 6 Uses	SqFt	.10	.12
Deduct for 7 Uses	SqFt	.05	.13
Add to above units if subcontracted		30%	10%

0302.0   CONCRETE FORM WORK, Cont'd...

		UNIT	LABOR	MATL
.16	Stairs and Landing (3 BdFt and 2 Uses)			
	Structural - Contact Area of			
	Soffits, Stringers and Risers	SqFt	4.70	1.35
	On Ground - Contact Area of			
	Stringers and Risers	SqFt	6.20	1.35
.17	Curbs & Platforms (2 BdFt and 2 Uses)	SqFt	4.30	.80
.18	Edge Forms/Bulkheads for Slabs (2 BdFt, 2 Uses)			
	Floor Supported	SqFt	4.20	.78
	Structural	SqFt	5.80	.87
.2	SHORING, SUPPORTS AND ACCESSORIES			
	(All items in this section are included in SqFt			
	costs of Section 0302.1. This section is for			
	cost-keeping & limited analyzing of variables.)			
.21	Horizontal Shoring			
	10' Span - Monthly Rent Cost	Each		1.95
	SqFt Contact Area	SqFt		.44
	15' Span - Monthly Rent Cost	Each		7.40
	SqFt Contact Area	SqFt		.55
	20' Span - Monthly Rent Cost	Each		8.60
	SqFt Contact Area	SqFt		.73
.22	Vertical Shoring (4' OC - 10' High) - Average	SqFt		.33
	Wood Posts with Ellis Shore Hardware			
	Single - W/T Head - New	Each		13.60
	LnFt Beam - 6 Uses	LnFt		.70
	Double - W/T Head & Bracing - New	Each		29.00
	LnFt Beam - 6 Uses	LnFt		1.25
	Metal Posts - Single - Monthly Rent Cost	Each		4.20
	LnFt Beam - 2 Uses per Month	LnFt		.93
	Double - W/T Head & Bracing	LnFt		7.50
	LnFt Beam - 2 Uses per Month	LnFt		1.66
	Tubular Frames - to 10'			
	Mo. Cost - Incl. Head & Base - 10,000#	Each		16.00
	LnFt - Average - 2 Uses per Month	LnFt		1.35
	Deduct for 6,000#	Each		25%
.23	Column Clamps and Steel Strapping			
	Clamps - Monthly Rent Cost - Steel	Each		4.90
	Lock Fast	Each		8.95
	Gang Form	Each		7.85
	Contact Area - 2 Uses per Month	SqFt.		.41
	Strapping - 3/4" x .025 (1.10 lb)	LnFt		.32
	3/4" x .023 (1.00 lb)	LnFt		.32
	Contact Area of Forms	SqFt		.22
.24	Wall and Beam Brackets			
	Brackets (2' OC) - Monthly Rent Cost	Each		.68
	New Cost	Each		6.50
	Contact Area - 4 Uses per Month	SqFt		.17
.25	Accessories - Beam Hangers			
	Tyloops, Lags, Washers & Bolts - Heavy	LnFt		1.00
	Light	LnFt		.75

0302.0 CONCRETE FORM WORK, Cont'd...

		UNIT	LABOR	MATERIAL
.3	SPECIALTIES			
.31	Nails, Wire and Ties			
	Nails 6 d common (50# box)	CWT	-	58.00
	8 d common	CWT	-	59.00
	16 d common	CWT	-	64.00
	8 d box	CWT	-	71.00
	16 d box	CWT	-	96.00
	9 ga concrete nails (3/4" to 3")	CWT	-	159.00
	Add for Coated Nails	CWT	-	60%
	Wire - Black Annealed 9 ga (100# Coil)	CWT	-	89.50
	16 ga (100# Coil)	CWT	-	86.00
	Average Nail and Wire Cost for Formwork	BdFt	-	.02
		or SqFt	-	.03
	Ties - Breakback -8" 3000# 5" ends	Each	-	1.00
	12" 3000# 5" ends	Each	-	.90
	16" 3000# 5" ends	Each	-	1.15
	Add for 5000#	Each	-	.16
	Add for 8" ends	Each	-	.09
	Average Tie Cost for Formwork (2' OC)			
	Wall Area	SqFt	-	.42
	Contact Area Form	SqFt	-	.23
	Gang Form Contact Area	SqFt	-	.24
	Coil Bolts - 8"	Each	-	1.45
	12"	Each	-	1.65
.32	Anchors and Inserts (including Layout)			
	Anchor Bolts (Concrete) -			
	1/2" x 12"	Each	1.20	.94
	5/8" x 12"	Each	1.30	2.20
	3/4" x 12"	Each	1.50	3.10
	Ceiling Type Inserts			
	Adjustable - 1/2" Bolt Size x 3'	Each	1.00	2.55
	5/8" Bolt Size x 3'	Each	1.10	2.55
	3/4" Bolt Size x 3'	Each	1.10	3.10
	Continuous Slotted	Each	.90	1.90
	Threaded - 1/2" Bolt Size	Each	1.00	4.25
	5/8" Bolt Size	Each	1.10	7.10
	3/4" Bolt Size	Each	1.20	8.30
	Hanger Wire Type - Drive In	Each	.90	.21
	Shell	Each	.90	.26
	Ferrule Type - 1/2"	Each	1.00	1.15
	5/8"	Each	1.05	1.40
	3/4"	Each	1.00	2.00
	T-Hanger - 4"	Each	1.00	1.10
	10"	Each	1.00	1.60
	14"	Each	1.20	2.20
	Wall and Beam Type Insert			
	Dovetail Slot - 24 ga (No Anchors)	LnFt	.40	.45
	22 ga (No Anchors)	LnFt	.50	.85
	Flashing Reglects	LnFt	.70	.75
	Shelf Angle Inserts - Add for Bolts,			
	Washers, and Nuts -5/8"	Each	1.00	3.20
	3/4"	Each	1.10	4.10

0302.0 CONCRETE FORM WORK, Cont'd...	UNIT	LABOR	MATERIAL
Bolts - 5/8" x 2"	Each	.90	1.40
3/4" x 2"	Each	.90	1.90
3/4" x 3"	Each	.90	2.20
Nuts - 5/8"	Each	.32	.31
3/4"	Each	.40	.42
Washers	Each	.10	.31
Threaded Rod - 3/8" x 36" (Galv)	Each	1.20	1.60
1/2" x 36" (Galv)	Each	1.30	2.90
5/8" x 36" (Galv)	Each	1.50	4.40
.33 Chamfers, Drips and Reveals (1 Use)			
Chamfers - 3/4" Metal	LnFt	.30	.60
Plastic with Tail	LnFt	.31	.65
without Tail	LnFt	.35	.50
Wood	LnFt	.30	.12
Reveals - 3/4" Plastic	LnFt	.45	1.40
Drips	LnFt	.40	.50
.34 Stair Nosings and Treads			
Nosings, Curb Bar - Steel - Galvanized	LnFt	1.30	10.00
Treads 3" x 1/2" - Cast Iron	LnFt	1.50	11.50
Extruded Aluminum	LnFt	1.50	8.00
Cast Aluminum	LnFt	1.50	10.40
.35 Water Stops			
Polyvinyl Chloride - 6" x 3/16"	LnFt	.90	1.50
6" Centerbulb	LnFt	1.00	2.70
9" x 3/16"	LnFt	1.10	2.20
9" Centerbulb	LnFt	1.20	3.45
Add for 3/8"	LnFt	.20	50%
Rubber (Neoprene) - 6" Centerbulb	LnFt	1.00	8.95
9" Centerbulb	LnFt	1.20	17.00
Add per Splice	Each	9.15	-
.36 Divider Strips - White Metal, 16 ga x 1 1/4"	LnFt	.75	1.00
1/2" x 1 1/4"	LnFt	.80	1.00
3/16" x 1 1/4"	LnFt	.80	.95
1/4" x 1 1/4"	LnFt	.80	1.70
Add for Brass 1/8"	LnFt	.15	.95
.37 Tongue and Groove Joint Forms			
Asphalt - 3 1/2" x 1/8"	LnFt	.80	.85
5 1/2" x 1/8"	LnFt	.90	1.00
Metal - 3 1/2"	LnFt	.80	1.05
5 1/2"	LnFt	.90	1.25
Wood - 3 1/2"	LnFt	.80	.31
5 1/2"	LnFt	.90	.45
Plastic - 3 1/2"	LnFt	.80	.95
Add for Stakes	Each	.90	.60
.38 Bearing Pads and Shims			
Vinyl - 1/8" x 6" x 24"	SqFt	.95	2.30
1/4" x 6" x 24"	SqFt	1.10	4.30
Neoprene - 1/8" x 36" (70 Duro)	SqFt	.80	5.50
1/4" x 36"	SqFt	.90	10.00

.4 EQUIPMENT
See Pages 1 - 6A and 1 - 7A. Average 5% Labor Cost.

Add to Labor Formwork Costs Above for Winter Construction 10% to 25%

0303.0 REINFORCING STEEL (S&L) (Ironworkers)

		UNIT	LABOR Subcont	MATERIAL Plain	MATERIAL Epoxy
.1	BARS (Based on Local Trucking)				
	1/4" to 5/8" Large Size Job (100 Tons Up)	Ton	530	1040	1,850
	Medium Job (20 - 99 Tons Up)	Ton	590	1080	1,900
	Small Size Job (5 - 19 Tons)	Ton	610	1140	2,010
	3/4" to 1 1/4" Large Job (100 Tons Up)	Ton	540	1040	1,820
	Medium Job (10 - 99 Tons)	Ton	550	1050	1,850
	Small Size Job (5 - 19 Tons)	Ton	540	1100	1,940
	1 1/2" to 2" Average	Ton	580	1070	1,880
	Add For Galvanizing	Ton	70	500	-
	Add for Bending - Light #2 to #5	Ton	-	270	-
	Heavy #6 and Larger	Ton	-	150	-
	Add for Size Extras - Light #2 to #4	Ton	-	165	-
	Heavy #3 and Larger	Ton	-	133	-
	Add for Spirals - Shop Assembled - Hot Rolled	Ton	-	185	-
	Cold Rolled	Ton	-	260	-
	Unassembled - Hot Rolled	Ton	-	158	-
	Cold Rolled	Ton	-	245	-
	Add for Splicing: #11 Bars - Buttweld	Each	38.00	3.25	-
	#14 Bars - Buttweld	Each	52.00	4.90	-
	#11 Bars - Mech. Buttweld	Each	54.00	12.50	-
	#14 Bars - Mech. Buttweld	Each	60.00	14.10	-

		UNIT	LABOR	MATERIAL
	BARS (Based on Local Trucking)			
	Tables of Weights & Prices by LnFt -	Ton	-	1,140.00
	Small job from warehouse stock for local delivery	Lb	-	.43
	# 2 Bar 1/4" or .250 .167 lb	LnFt	.17	.17
	# 3 Bar 3/8" or .375 .376 lb	LnFt	.20	.23
	# 4 Bar 1/2" or .500 .668 lb	LnFt	.26	.30
	# 5 Bar 5/8" or .625 1.043 lb	LnFt	.38	.36
	# 6 Bar 3/4" or .750 1.502 lb	LnFt	.52	.47
	# 7 Bar 7/8" or .875 2.044 lb			
	# 8 Bar 1" or 1.000 2.670 lb			
	# 9 Bar 1 1/8" or 1.128 3.400 lb			
	#10 Bar 1 1/4" or 1.270 4.303 lb			
	#11 Bar 1 3/8" or 1.410 5.313 lb			
	#14 Bar 1 1/2" or 1.693 7.650 lb			
	#18 Bar 2 1/4" or 2.257 13.600 lb			

		UNIT	LABOR	MATERIAL
.2	ACCESSORIES			
	Additional sizes, but below are close to standard and are included in tonnage costs above			
	1/4" to 1 1/2" Slab Bolsters	LnFt	-	.37
	1/2" to 2" Beam Bolsters - Upper & Lower	LnFt	-	.67
	2" to 3" Beam Bolsters - Upper & Lower	LnFt	-	1.10
	3" High Chairs - Continuous	LnFt	-	.60
	3/4" x 4" to 6" Joist Chairs	Each	-	.55
	1/2" Dowel Bar Tubes - Plastic and Metal	Each	.55	.34
	Add for Galvanized Accessories	-	-	.21
	Add for Plastic Accessories	-	-	.23
.3	POST TENSION STEEL - PRESTRESSED IN FIELD			
	Ungrouted - 100 kips	Lb	.90	2.00
	200 kips	Lb	.84	2.10
	Deduct for Added 100 kips	Lb	.02	-
	Add for Chairs	Lb	-	.15

		UNIT	LABOR	MATERIAL
0303.0	**REINFORCING STEEL, Cont'd...**			
.4	WIRE FABRIC (750 SqFt Roll or 120 SqFt Sheet)			
	6" x 6" x 10/10 (W 1.4)	SqFt	.17	.15
	6" x 6" x 8/8 (W 2.1)	SqFt	.18	.20
	6" x 6" x 6/6 (W 2.9)	SqFt	.22	.25
	6" x 6" x 4/4 (W 4.0)	SqFt	.26	.28
	4" x 4" x 4/4 (W 4.0)	SqFt	.33	.40
	4" x 6" x 8/8 (W 2.0)	SqFt	.23	.22
	Add for Epoxy Coated (120 SqFt Sheet)	SqFt	.02	.24
0304.0	**SPECIALTY PLACED CONCRETE (No Fees)**			
.1	LIFT SLAB CONSTRUCTION			
	Concrete - 6" Slab	SqFt		4.50
	Formwork	SqFt		1.40
	Reinforcing Steel	SqFt		1.60
	Lifting	SqFt		1.60
	Brace and Assemble	SqFt		1.05
			TOTAL	10.15
.2	POST TENSIONED OR STRESSED IN PLACE CONCRETE			
	Concrete - 6" Slab and Columns	SqFt		5.25
	Formwork (Assume Flying Forms)	SqFt		5.60
	Post Tensioning and Reinforcing Steel	SqFt		3.80
			TOTAL	14.65
.3	TILT UP CONSTRUCTION (Incl. Concrete Columns)			
	Concrete - 6" Slab	SqFt		5.00
	Formwork	SqFt		3.40
	Reinforcing Steel	SqFt		3.20
	Tilting Up and Bracing	SqFt		1.45
			TOTAL	13.05

		UNIT	1"	2"	3"
.4	PNEUMATICALLY PLACED CONCRETE (Gunite)				
	Walls - 1" Layers with Mesh	SqFt	3.60	5.60	6.90
	Columns - 1" Layers with Mesh	SqFt	6.95	7.60	8.80
	Roofs	SqFt	4.60	5.25	6.20

		Spans to Approximate	UNIT	COST
0305.0	**PRECAST PRESTRESSED CONCRETE (L&M)**			
.1	BEAMS AND COLUMNS			
	Beams	20'	LnFt	110.00
		30'	LnFt	130.00
	Columns - 12" x 12" x 12' with Plates		LnFt	139.00
	16" x 16" x 12' with Plates		LnFt	168.00
.2	DECKS (Flat) - 24", 40", 48", 72" and 96" Wide - 50 lb. Roof Load			
	4"	12'	SqFt	5.80
	6"	18'	SqFt	6.45
	8"	24'	SqFt	6.90
	10"	30'	SqFt	7.70
	12"	50'	SqFt	9.45
.3	DOUBLE T (Flat)			
	8' x 20" - 30" Deep - 60 lb. Roof Load	40'	SqFt	7.45
		50'	SqFt	7.90
		60'	SqFt	9.25
		70'	SqFt	10.10
		80'	SqFt	11.00
	SINGLE T			
	8' x 36" - 48" Deep	60'	SqFt	12.10
		80'	SqFt	13.00
		100'	SqFt	14.60
		120'	SqFt	16.50
	Add for Floor Decks (100# Load)		SqFt	10%
	Add for Sloped Installation to Decks & T's		SqFt	10%
	Add for 2" Topping for Floors - If Required		SqFt	3.85
	Add per Mobilization		Each	3,500.00

		UNIT	COST
0305.0	**PRECAST PRESTRESSED CONCRETE, Cont'd...**		
.4	WALLS		
	Add to Flat Decks 0305.2 Above	SqFt	2.10
	Add to Double T 0305.3 Above	SqFt	2.30
	Add for Core Wall Type	SqFt	2.10
	Add for Insulated Type	SqFt	2.20
0306.0	**PRECAST CONCRETE (M)**		
.1	BEAMS AND COLUMNS- Same as 0305.1		
.2	DECKS- Same as 0305.2		
.3	PANELS OR FACING UNITS (L&M)		
	Insulated - 8' x 16' x 12"		
	Exposed Aggregate		
	Gravel	SqFt	16.10
	Quartz & Marble	SqFt	18.60
	Trowel or Brush		
	Grey Cement	SqFt	15.70
	White Cement	SqFt	17.20
	Deduct for Non-Insulated 8' x 16' x 8"	SqFt	1.40
	Add for Banded	SqFt	.55
.4	PLANK (S)		
	2" x 24" 6' Span	SqFt	5.50
	3" x 24" 8' Span	SqFt	6.15

			LABOR	MATERIAL
.5	SPECIALTIES (S)			
	Curbs 6" x 10" x 8'	LnFt	2.40	7.65
	8" x 10" x 8'	LnFt	2.90	8.50
	Copings 5" x 13"	LnFt	6.50	10.60
	Sills & Stools 5" x 6"	LnFt	5.20	13.80
	Splash Blocks 3" x 36" x 16"	Each	10.70	26.50
	5" x 36" x 16"	Each	13.20	28.60
	8" x 36" x 16"	Each	17.50	33.90
	Medians	LnFt	9.80	42.40

		SPANS TO APPROX.	UNIT	COST
0307.0	**PRECAST CEMENTITIOUS PLANK (L&M)**			
.1	EXPANDED MINERALS (Includes Clips, Rods & Grout)			
	3" x 24"	6'-0"	SqFt	4.25
	4" x 24"	9'-6"	SqFt	4.60
.2	GYPSUM (Metal Edged)			
	2" x 15"	4'-0"	SqFt	4.35
	2" x 15"	7'-0"	SqFt	4.70
.3	WOOD FIBRE			
	2" x 32"	3'-0"	SqFt	4.00
	2 1/2" x 32"	3'-6"	SqFt	4.25
	3" x 32"	4'-0"	SqFt	4.70
0308.0	**POURED IN PLACE CEMENTITIOUS CONCRETE (L&M)**			
.1	EXPANDED MINERALS - 2"		SqFt	2.65
.2	EXPANDED MINERALS & ASPHALT - 2"		SqFt	2.90
.3	GYPCRETE - 1/4"		SqFt	1.35
	1"		SqFt	1.70

All examples below are representative samples and have great variables because of design efficiencies, size, spans, weather, etc. All figures include a contractor's fee of 10% for Footings and Slabs on Ground (low risk) and a 15% fee for Walls, Columns, Beams and Slabs (high risk). All totals include material prices as follows: Concrete $80.00 CuYd, Lumber $500.00 M.B.F. (3 uses), Plywood $1.10 SqFt, and Reinforcing Steel $1,080.00 Ton. Taxes and insurance on Labor added at 35%. Includes General Conditions at 10%. CuYd Costs are for information only--not quick estimating.

	Unit	Unit Cost With ReinSteel	Unit Cost Without ReinSteel	CuYd Cost With ReinSteel
FOOTINGS (Including Hand Excavation)				
Continuous 24" x 12" (3 # 4 Rods)	LnFt	23.00	20.80	310.00
36" x 12" (4 # 4 Rods)	LnFt	28.90	29.70	260.00
20" x 10" (2 # 5 Rods)	LnFt	19.60	18.70	370.00
16" x 8" (2 # 4 Rods)	LnFt	16.60	19.60	490.00
Pad 24" x 24" x 12" (4 # 5 E.W.)	Each	78.00	60.00	540.00
36" x 36" x 14" (6 # 5 E.W.)	Each	162.00	114.00	483.00
48" x 48" x 16" (8 # 5 E.W.)	Each	268.00	222.30	452.00
WALLS (#5 Rods 12" O.C. - 1 Face)				
8" Wall (# 5 12" O.C. E.W.)	SqFt	16.50	13.20	636.00
12" Wall (# 5 12" O.C. E.W.)	SqFt	17.60	16.00	465.00
16" Wall (# 5 12" O.C. E.W.)	SqFt	17.60	18.20	390.00
Add for Steel - 2 Faces - 12" Wall	SqFt	2.10	-	59.00
Add for Pilastered Wall - 24" O.C.	SqFt	1.00	-	26.00
Add for Retaining or Battered Type	SqFt	2.90	-	79.00
Add for Curved Walls	SqFt	5.40	-	156.00
COLUMNS				
Sq Cornered 8" x 8" (4 # 8 Rods)	LnFt	38.30	28.10	2,320.00
12" x 12" (6 # 8 Rods)	LnFt	64.80	52.40	1,730.00
16" x 16" (6 # 10 Rods)	LnFt	84.60	65.80	1,300.00
20" x 20" (8 # 20 Rods)	LnFt	122.00	84.20	1,200.00
24" x 24" (10 # 11 Rods)	LnFt	149.00	101.40	1,000.00
Round 8" (4 # 8 Rods)	LnFt	27.80	19.30	2,000.00
12" (6 # 8 Rods)	LnFt	43.50	27.00	1,400.00
16" (6 # 10 Rods)	LnFt	58.80	37.90	1,200.00
20" (8 # 20 Rods)	LnFt	83.90	56.00	1,100.00
24" (10 # 11 Rods)	LnFt	122.80	77.50	1,000.00
BEAMS				
Spandrel 12" x 48" (33 # Rein. Steel)	LnFt	151.00	117.30	1,010.00
12" x 42" (26 # Rein. Steel)	LnFt	130.10	105.00	1,000.00
12" x 36" (21 # Rein. Steel)	LnFt	106.40	89.10	950.00
12" x 30" (15 # Rein. Steel)	LnFt	95.80	88.70	930.00
8" x 48" (26 # Rein. Steel)	LnFt	123.60	112.70	1,200.00
8" x 42" (21 # Rein. Steel)	LnFt	118.00	106.20	1,380.00
8" x 36" (16 # Rein. Steel)	LnFt	109.00	92.10	1,470.00
Interior 16" x 30" (24 # Rein. Steel)	LnFt	86.50	79.30	700.00
16" x 24" (20 # Rein. Steel)	LnFt	85.30	74.90	850.00
12" x 30" (17 # Rein. Steel)	LnFt	93.40	75.40	1,000.00
12" x 24" (14 # Rein. Steel)	LnFt	71.20	62.90	960.00
12" x 16" (12 # Rein. Steel)	LnFt	59.90	49.10	1,190.00
8" x 24" (13 # Rein. Steel)	LnFt	71.10	59.80	1,400.00
8" x 16" (10 # Rein. Steel)	LnFt	53.00	47.10	1,500.00

SLABS

	Unit	Unit Cost With ReinSteel	Unit Cost Without ReinSteel	CuYd Cost With ReinSteel
Solid -				
4" Thick	SqFt	10.20	8.20	800.00
5" Thick	SqFt	11.90	9.30	730.00
6" Thick	SqFt	13.00	8.80	680.00
7" Thick	SqFt	14.60	12.00	630.00
8" Thick	SqFt	16.40	14.10	620.00
Deduct for Post Tensioned Slabs	SqFt	.94	.36	
Pan -				
Joist -20" Pan - 10" x 2"	SqFt	14.25	12.70	-
12" x 2"	SqFt	16.00	13.00	-
30" Pan - 10" x 2 1/2"	SqFt	14.30	12.30	-
12" x 2 1/2"	SqFt	16.00	13.75	-
Dome -19" x 19" - 10" x 2"	SqFt	15.60	12.30	-
12" x 2"	SqFt	16.10	12.50	-
30" x 30" - 10" x 2 1/2"	SqFt	14.00	12.30	-
12" x 2 1/2"	SqFt	15.30	12.40	-

COMBINED COLUMNS, BEAMS AND SLABS

	Unit	With ReinSteel	Without	CuYd
20' Span	SqFt	21.10	-	-
30' Span	SqFt	22.30	-	-
40' Span	SqFt	23.90	-	-
50' Span	SqFt	25.50	-	-
60' Span	SqFt	30.20	-	-

STAIRS (Including Landing)

	Unit	With ReinSteel	Without	CuYd Cost With ReinSteel
4' Wide 10' Floor Heights 16 Risers	Riser	185.00	-	1,530.00
5' Wide 10' Floor Heights 16 Risers	Riser	225.00	-	1,610.00
6' Wide 10' Floor Heights 16 Risers	Riser	255.00	-	1,560.00

SLABS ON GROUND

	Unit	Unit Cost With Mesh	CuYd Cost With Mesh
4" Concrete Slab (6 6/10 - 10 Mesh - 5 1/2 Sack Concrete, Trowel Finished, Cured & Truck Chuted)	SqFt	3.70	300.00
Add per Inch of Concrete	SqFt	.62	
Add per Sack of Cement	SqFt	.16	
Deduct for Float Finish	SqFt	.08	
Deduct for Brush or Broom Finish	SqFt	.06	
Add for Runway and Buggied Concrete	SqFt	.20	
Add for Vapor Barrier (4 mil)	SqFt	.17	
Add for Sub - Floor Fill (4" sand/gravel)	SqFt	.47	
Add for Change to 6 6/8 - 8 Mesh	SqFt	.09	
Add for Change to 6 6/6 - 6 Mesh	SqFt	.17	
Add for Sloped Slab	SqFt	.23	
Add for Edge Strip (sidewalk area)	SqFt	.25	
Add for 1/2" Expansion Joint (20' O.C.)	SqFt	.08	
Add for Control Joints (keyed/ dep.)	SqFt	.18	
Add for Control Joints (joint filled)	SqFt	.20	
Add for Control Joints - Saw Cut (20' O.C.)	SqFt	.34	
Add for Floor Hardener (1 coat)	SqFt	.17	
Add for Exposed Aggregate - Washed Added	SqFt	.47	
Retarding Added	SqFt	.44	
Seeding Added	SqFt	.46	
Add for Light Weight Aggregates	SqFt	.47	
Add for Heavy Weight Aggregates	SqFt	.32	
Add for Winter Production Loss/Cost	SqFt	.40	

See 0206.2 for Curbs, Gutters, Walks and other Exterior Concrete
See 0302.53 for Topping and Leveling of Floors

	UNIT	COST
TOPPING SLABS		
2" Concrete	SqFt	3.10
3" Concrete	SqFt	3.90
No Mesh or Hoisting		
PADS & PLATFORMS (Including Form Work & Reinforcing)		
4"	SqFt	7.30
6"	SqFt	9.20
PRECAST CONCRETE ITEMS		
Curbs 6" x 10" x 8"	LnFt	12.50
Sills & Stools 6"	LnFt	28.35
Splash Blocks 3" x 16"	Each	68.60
MISCELLANEOUS ADDITIONS TO ABOVE CONCRETE IF NEEDED		
Abrasives - Carborundum - Grits	SqFt	.94
Strips	LnFt	3.10
Bushhammer - Green Concrete	SqFt	2.00
Cured Concrete	SqFt	2.75
Champers - Plastic 3/4"	LnFt	1.10
Wood 3/4"	LnFt	.62
Metal 3/4"	LnFt	1.20
Colors Dust On	SqFt	.80
Integral (Top 1")	SqFt	1.50
Control Joints - Asphalt 1/2" x 4"	LnFt	.90
1/2" x 6"	LnFt	1.05
PolyFoam 1/2" x 4"	LnFt	1.20
Dovetail Slots 22 Ga	LnFt	1.60
24 Ga	LnFt	1.05
Hardeners Acrylic and Urethane	SqFt	.27
Epoxy	SqFt	.36
Joint Sealers Epoxy	LnFt	3.10
Rubber Asphalt	LnFt	1.60
Moisture Proofing - Polyethylene 4 mil	SqFt	.19
6 mil	SqFt	.23
Non-Shrink Grouts - Non - Metallic	CuFt	43.00
Aluminum Oxide	CuFt	31.00
Iron Oxide	CuFt	47.00
Reglets Flashing	LnFt	1.70
Sand Blast - Light	SqFt	1.50
Heavy	SqFt	2.75
Shelf Angle Inserts 5/8"	LnFt	5.50
Stair Nosings Steel - Galvanized	LnFt	7.50
Tongue & Groove Joint Forms - Asphalt 5 1/2"	LnFt	2.25
Wood 5 1/2"	LnFt	1.90
Metal 5 1/2"	LnFt	2.35
Treads - Extruded Aluminum	LnFt	10.25
Cast Iron	LnFt	11.45
Water Stops Center Bulb - Rubber - 6"	LnFt	11.75
9"	LnFt	22.00
Polyethylene - 6"	LnFt	5.70
9"	LnFt	5.80

The unit costs in this Division are priced as being done by masonry or General Contractors. See Section 4A for Total Subcontracted Cost. In general, the pricing is based on Modular Units, and materials F.O.B. job site in truckload lots. The basic labor units do include mortar mixing, low scaffolding, tending, and labor fringe benefits. Cleaning, high scaffold, equipment reinforcements, taxes and insurance, etc. must be added to basic labor and material units. The basis for Labor Unit Costs can be found as follows: as to labor rate mean, Page 4-1, and as to number of units placed per day, Table 4B. Unit Costs are based on an average crew of 4 Bricklayers to 3 Tenders (including Mortar Mixer and Operators) for Brick and Stone Work, and 1 Bricklayer to 1 Tender for Block and Tile Work.

0401.0 BRICK MASONRY (Bricklayers)
.1 FACE BRICK (See Table 4B for Mfg. Size)

	Nominal Dimensions	UNIT	LABOR	MATERIAL (Truckload)
.11 Conventional	8" x 2-2/3" x 4"	M pcs	870.00	560.00
Running Bond		M pcs	880.00	560.00
Common Bond (6 Cs. Headers)		M pcs	900.00	560.00
Stack Bond		M pcs	900.00	560.00
Dutch & English Bond		M pcs	950.00	560.00
Flemish				
.12 Economy	8" x 4" x 4"	M pcs	1,090.00	800.00
.13 Panel (Triple)	8" x 8" x 4"	M pcs	1,720.00	1,800.00
	8" x 16" x 4"	M pcs	2,840.00	3,500.00
.14 Norman	12" x 2-2/3" x 4"	M pcs	1,020.00	800.00
.15 King	10" x 2-5/8" x 4"	M pcs	950.00	560.00
.16 Norwegian	12" x 3-1/5" x 4"	M pcs	1,120.00	910.00
.17 Saxon-Utility 3" wall	12"x 4"x 3" (thin)	M pcs	1,360.00	1,040.00
4" wall	12"x 4"x 4"	M pcs	1,380.00	1,070.00
6" wall	12"x 4"x 6"	M pcs	1,650.00	1,520.00
8" wall	16"x 3-5/8"x 3-5/8"	M pcs	1,870.00	1,950.00
.18 Meridian	12" x 2-1/4 " x 4"	M pcs	860.00	1,550.00
.19 Adobe Brick - Mexican	8" x 2-3/8"x 4"	M pcs	940.00	700.00
	12"x 2-3/8"x 4"	M pcs	1,080.00	820.00
.2 COATED BRICK (Ceramic Veneer)		M pcs	970.00	1,200.00
.3 COMMON BRICK - Clay		M pcs	1,020.00	400.00
Concrete		M pcs	1,020.00	320.00
.4 FIRE BRICK - Light Duty (domestic)		M pcs	840.00	1,200.00
Medium Duty		M pcs	870.00	1,880.00
Heavy Duty		M pcs	900.00	2,440.00
Add for Fireplaces		M pcs	870.00	-
Add:Less than Truckload Lot(14M pcs)				15%
Add:Full Size Brick		M pcs	4%	8%
Add:Ceramic Coating - to Common Brick		M pcs	15%	80%
Deduct: 3" thick Brick (if available)		M pcs	4%	7%
Add:Ea. Addl. 10' in Fl. Hgt. (or floor)		M pcs	3%	-
Add:Hauling & Unloading if required		M pcs		See Table 4B
Add:Breakage & Cutting Allowance		-	-	3%
Add:Piers & Corbels		M pcs	15%	-
Add:Sills & Soldiers		M pcs	20%	-
Add:Floor Brick (over 2")		M pcs	10%	5%
Add:Weave & Herringbone Pattern		M pcs	20%	7%
Add:Stack bond		M pcs	8%	-
Add:Circular or Radius Work		M pcs	20%	-
Add:Rock Faced		M pcs	10%	-
Add:Two-Face Joint Striking		M pcs	15%	-
Add:Arches (including Formwork)		M pcs	75%	20%
Add:Sawing (Special or Excessive)		M pcs	25%	5%
Add:Winter Work (below 40 degrees)				
Production Loss		M pcs	10%	-
Encls - Wall Area - 1 Side & 3 Uses		Sq Ft	.26	.25
2 Sides & 3 Uses		Sq Ft	.36	.35
Heaters & Fuel - Wall Area		Sq Ft	.12	.25
Heat Mortar		Cu Yd	12.50	6.00
Deduct: Residential Work		-	10%	-

Crew - 4 Bricklayers to 3 Tenders (Incl. Mortar Mixers & Operators).
See Section 0905.7 for Thin Veneer Brick and Stone (under 2").
See Section 0206.2 for Paver Brick for Sitework.

0402.0   CONCRETE BLOCK (Bricklayers)

		UNIT	LABOR	MATERIAL StdWt	LtWt

.1   CONVENTIONAL
.11   Foundation or Not Struck - Deduct .35 from Labor Units below.
.12   Backup or Struck One Face - Deduct .20 from Labor Units below.
.13   Partition or Struck Two Faces Used for Labor Units below:

	UNIT	LABOR	StdWt	LtWt
12" x 8" x 16" Plain	Ea	2.70	1.60	2.05
Double or Single Corner	Ea	2.50	1.70	2.10
Bull Nose (Sgl or Dbl)	Ea	2.90	1.85	2.25
Bond Beam	Ea	2.80	1.75	2.15
Header	Ea	2.80	1.75	2.15
12" x 8" x 8" Half Length Block	Ea	2.65	1.60	2.15
12" x 4" x 16" Half High Block	Ea	2.65	1.65	2.05
12" x 8" x 8" Lintel	Ea	2.90	1.75	2.15
12" x 16" x 8" Lintel	Ea	3.10	1.85	2.35
12" x 8" x 16" Control Joint	Ea	2.90	1.85	2.40
Half Control Joint	Ea	2.65	1.85	2.50
Fire Rated (4 Hr.)	Ea	2.75	1.85	2.50
L Corner	Ea	2.90	1.70	2.20
Solid or Cap	Ea	2.80	1.95	2.45
8" x 8" x 16" Plain	Ea	2.60	1.10	1.55
Double or Single Corner	Ea	2.55	1.20	1.75
Bullnose (Sgl or Dbl)	Ea	2.70	1.45	1.95
8" x 8" x 8" Half Bullnose	Ea	2.60	1.45	1.95
8" x 8" x 16" Bond Beam	Ea	2.70	1.45	1.85
Header	Ea	2.70	1.10	1.85
8" x 8" x 8" Half Length Block	Ea	2.55	1.10	1.60
8" x 8" x 16" Half High Block	Ea	2.55	1.10	1.70
8" x 8" x 8" Lintel	Ea	2.65	1.35	1.80
8" x 16" x 8" Lintel	Ea	2.90	1.35	1.80
8" x 8" x 16" Control Joint	Ea	2.65	1.50	1.90
8" x 8" x 8" Half Control Joint	Ea	2.50	1.50	1.90
8" x 8" x 16" Fire Rated (2 Hr.)	Ea	2.60	1.35	1.75
(4 Hr.)	Ea	2.60	1.50	1.90
Solid or Cap	Ea	2.60	1.35	1.80
6" x 8" x 16" Plain	Ea	2.50	.97	1.35
Bull Nose (Sgl or Dbl)	Ea	2.50	1.35	1.75
6" x 8" x 8" Half Bullnose	Ea	2.50	1.35	1.75
6" x 8" x 16" Bond Beam or Lintel	Ea	2.50	1.20	1.60
6" x 8" x 8" Half Length Block	Ea	2.50	1.00	1.45
6" x 4" x 16" Half High Block	Ea	2.50	1.10	1.45
6" x 8" x 16" Fire Rated (2 Hr.)	Ea	2.50	1.20	1.55
L Corner	Ea	2.70	1.30	1.65
Solid or Cap	Ea	2.50	1.40	1.75
4" x 8" x 16" Plain	Ea	2.40	.80	1.10
Bull Nose	Ea	2.45	1.00	1.30
Bond Beam or Lintel	Ea	2.45	.92	1.20
4" x 8" x 8" Half Length Block	Ea	2.35	.77	1.20
4" x 8" x 16" Half High Block	Ea	2.35	.82	1.10
L Corner	Ea	2.65	.97	1.30
Solid or Cap	Ea	2.50	1.10	1.40

0402.0 CONCRETE BLOCK (Bricklayers)

		UNIT	LABOR	MATERIAL StdWt	LtWt
.13	Partition or Struck Two Faces , Cont'd...				
	16" x 8" x 16" Plain	Ea	3.20	1.95	2.65
	16" x 8" x 8" Half Length	Ea	3.00	1.90	2.60
	14" x 8" x 16" Plain	Ea	2.90	1.90	2.55
	14" x 8" x 8" Half Length	Ea	2.70	1.85	2.55
	14" x 8" x 16" Bond Beam	Ea	2.70	2.15	2.75
	10" x 8" x 16" Plain	Ea	2.65	1.35	1.95
	10" x 8" x 8" Half Length	Ea	2.50	1.40	1.95
	10" x 8" x 16" Bond Beam	Ea	2.70	1.65	2.15
	3" x 8" x 16" Plain	Ea	2.40	.77	1.65
	Solid	Ea	2.50	.82	1.30
	Add or Deduct to all Blockwork Above for:				
	Add: Full Size Block	Ea	.10	.08	-
	Add: Breakage and Cutting	Ea	.10	3%	3%
	Add: Jamb and Sash Block	Ea	.20	.13	.13
	Add: Stack Bond Work	Ea	.20	-	-
	Add: Radius or Circular Work	Ea	1.25	-	-
	Add: Pilaster, Pier or Pedestal Work	Ea	.60	-	-
	Add: Knock-out Block	Ea	.60	.13	.13
	Deduct: Light Weight Block-Installation	Ea	.10	-	-
	Add: Winter Production Loss (below 40°)	Ea	10%	-	-
	Add: Enclosures - Unit	Ea	.25	.10	.10
	Add: Enclosures - Wall Area 1 Side	SqFt	.30	.20	.20
	Add: Enclosures - Wall Area 2 Sides	SqFt	.40	.30	.30
	Add: Heating & Fuel - Wall Area	SqFt	.20	.25	.25
	Deduct: Residential Work	Ea	10%	-	-
	See 0410 for Core Filling for Reinforced Masonry				
	See 0411 for Filling for Insulated Masonry				
.2	ORNAMENTED OR SPECIAL EFFECT				
.21	Shadow wall and Hi-Lite Block				
	Add to Block Prices 0402.1	Ea	.25	.16	.17
.22	Scored Block				
	Add to Block Prices 0402.1 - 1 Score	Ea	.30	.12	.12
	- 2 Score	Ea	.35	.20	.20
.23	Break Off Block				
	Add to Block Prices 0402.1 - Broken	Ea	.25	.70	.70
	- Unbroken	Ea	.35	.64	.64
.24	Split Face Block				
	Add to Block Prices 0402.1	Ea	.25	.30	.32
.25	Rock Faced Block				
	Add to Block Prices 0402.1	Ea	.25	.20	.20
.26	Adobe (or Slump) Block				
	Add to Block Prices 0402.1				
	8" x 8" x 16"	Ea	.30	.35	-
	4" x 8" x 16"	Ea	.25	.25	-
.3	SCREEN WALL - 4" x 12" x 12"	Ea	2.50	2.00	-
.4	INTERLOCKING				
.41	Epoxy Laid				
	Add to Block Prices 0402.1	Ea	-	.17	.17
	Deduct from Labor Costs 0402.1	Ea	.50	-	-
.42	Panelized (No Head Joint Mortar)				
	Add to Block Prices 0402.1	Ea	-	.17	.17
	Deduct from Labor Costs 0402.1	Ea	.60	-	-

0402.0　CONCRETE BLOCK, Cont'd...

		UNIT	LABOR	MATERIAL
.5	**SOUND BLOCK**			
	Add to Block Prices 0402.1	Ea	.35	.92
	Add for Fillers	Ea	.20	.31
.6	**BURNISHED BLOCK - One Face Finish**			
	(Truckload Price)			
	Plain 12" x 8" x 16"	Ea	3.10	4.20
	8" x 8" x 16"	Ea	2.90	3.70
	6" x 8" x 16"	Ea	2.80	3.15
	4" x 8" x 16"	Ea	2.70	3.00
	2" x 8" x 16"	Ea	2.60	2.90
	Shapes 12"	Ea	3.60	5.20
	8"	Ea	3.50	4.00
	6"	Ea	3.40	3.50
	4"	Ea	3.30	3.15
	2"	Ea	3.10	3.10
	Add for Bond Beam	Ea	.45	1.00
	Add to above for Two Face Finish	Ea	.60	2.00
	Add to above for Scored Face	Ea	.40	.26
	Add for Color	Ea	-	.46
	Add for Bullnose	Ea	.45	.92
.7	**PREFACED UNITS - Ceramic Glazed**			
	(Truckload Price)			
	12" x 8" x 16" Stretcher	Ea	3.90	6.90
	Glazed 2 Face	Ea	4.50	10.60
	8" x 8" x 16" Stretcher	Ea	3.75	6.50
	Glazed 2 Face	Ea	4.10	10.10
	6" x 8" x 16" Stretcher	Ea	3.80	5.90
	Glazed 2 Face	Ea	4.10	10.00
	4" x 8" x 16" Stretcher	Ea	3.90	5.60
	Glazed 2 Face	Ea	4.15	10.10
	2" x 8" x 16" Stretcher	Ea	3.55	5.60
	4" x 16" x 16" Stretcher	Ea	6.55	19.40
	Add for Scored Block	Ea	.40	.46
	Add for Base Caps, Jambs, Headers	Ea	.75	2.05
	Add for Raked Joints and White Cement	Ea	.90	.26
	Add for Less than Truckload Lot	Ea	-	10%

Crew Ratio - 1 Block Layer to 1 Tender
(Tender includes Mixers & Operators)

Deduct 10% from Block Labor for Residential Construction

0403.0　**CLAY BACKING AND PARTITION TILE**

	UNIT	LABOR	MATERIAL
(Carload Price)			
3" x 12" x 12"	Sq Ft	2.10	2.00
4" x 12" x 12"	Sq Ft	2.20	2.10
6" x 12" x 12"	Sq Ft	2.40	2.50
8" x 12" x 12"	Sq Ft	2.50	3.20

	UNIT	LABOR	MATERIAL
0404.0 CLAY FACING TILE			
.1 6T SERIES (SELECT QUALITY - CLEAR & FUNCTIONAL)			
2" x 5-1/3" x 12" Soap Stretcher (Open Back)	Ea	2.80	3.60
Soap Stretcher (Solid Back)	Ea	2.90	3.70
4" x 5-1/3" x 12" 1 Face Stretcher	Ea	3.00	4.95
Select 2 Face Stretcher	Ea	3.10	6.20
6" x 5-1/3" x 12" Select 1 Face Bond Stretcher	Ea	3.00	5.35
8" x 5-1/3" x 12" Select 1 Face Bond Stretcher	Ea	3.10	6.65
Shapes- Group 1 Square and B/N Corners	Ea	3.20	5.40
2 Sills and 2" Base	Ea	3.30	5.75
3 Sills and 4" Base	Ea	3.30	7.05
4 Starters and Octagons	Ea	3.75	13.10
5 Radials and End Closures	Ea	3.65	22.45
Add for Less than Carload Lots	Ea	-	10%
Add for Designer Colors	Ea	-	20%
Add for Base Only	Ea	-	40%
.2 8W SERIES (SELECT QUALITY - CLEAR & FUNCTIONAL)			
2" x 8" x 16" Soap Stretcher (Open Back)	Ea	3.75	5.90
Soap Stretcher (Solid Back)	Ea	3.85	6.40
4" x 8" x 16" 1 Face Stretcher	Ea	3.80	6.60
Select 2 Face Stretcher	Ea	4.10	10.05
6" x 8" x 16" Select 2 Face 6" Bond Stretcher	Ea	3.75	8.70
8" x 8" x 16" Select 1 Face 8" Bond Stretcher	Ea	4.20	10.60
Shapes- Group 1 Square and B/N Corners	Ea	4.10	9.20
2 Sills and 2" Base	Ea	4.60	11.70
3 Sills and 4" Base	Ea	4.70	11.55
4 Starters and Octagons	Ea	5.10	17.85
5 Radials and End Closures	Ea	5.30	44.40
Add for Less than Carload Lots	Ea	-	40%
Add for Designer Colors	Ea	-	20%
Add for Base Only	Ea	25%	-
0405.0 GLASS UNITS			
4" x 8" x 4"	Ea	4.00	5.60
6" x 6" x 4"	Ea	4.30	5.70
8" x 8" x 4"	Ea	4.95	6.65
12" x 12" x 4"	Ea	6.45	17.35
Add for Solar Reflective Type	Ea	-	40%
Accessories: Reinforcing & Expansion Joint	Ea	-	2.25
0406.0 TERRA-COTTA			
Unglazed	SqFt	2.90	6.45
Glazed	SqFt	3.45	7.65
Colored Glaze	SqFt	3.55	11.50
0407.0 MISCELLANEOUS UNITS			
.1 COPING TILE - 9" Double Slant	LnFt	4.30	9.20
12" Double Slant	LnFt	4.80	12.25
Bell	LnFt	4.20	10.20
Corners & Ends = 4 x Above Material Prices			
.2 FLUE LINING - 8" x 8"	LnFt	4.10	5.40
8" x 12"	LnFt	4.40	9.70
12" x 12"	LnFt	4.85	11.40
16" x 16"	LnFt	8.50	17.35
18" x 18"	LnFt	9.80	19.40
20" x 20"	LnFt	16.40	36.70
24" x 24"	LnFt	21.85	44.90

0408.0 NATURAL STONE (M) (Bricklayers)
(See 0906.0 for Stone under 2")

		SQUARE FOOT		CUBIC FOOT	
		Labor	Matl.	Labor	Matl.
.1	CUT STONE				
.11	Limestone				
	Indiana (Standard) and Alabama				
	Face Stone 3"	9.70	19.80	38.00	79.00
	4"	10.80	21.60	32.00	64.00
	Sills and Light Trim	-	-	42.00	75.00
	Copings and Heavy Sections	-	-	38.50	73.00
	Add for Select	1.70	-	6.80	
	Minnesota, Texas, Wisconsin, etc.				
	Face Stone 3"	9.70	25.00	38.00	103.00
	4"	10.80	28.00	32.00	83.00
	Sills and Light Trim	-	-	32.00	101.00
	Copings and Heavy Sections	-	-	31.00	98.00
.12	Marble				
	Face Stone 2"	9.80	32.00	58.00	193.00
	3" and 4"	10.90	34.00	42.00	123.00
	Sills and Light Trim	-	-	43.00	129.00
	Copings and Heavy Sections	-	-	38.00	110.00
.13	Granite				
	Face Stone 2"	10.05	29.00	60.00	173.00
	3"	12.30	31.00	49.00	124.00
	4"	14.40	35.00	43.00	106.00
	Sills and Light Trim	-	-	51.00	116.00
	Copings and Heavy Sections	-	-	47.00	111.00
.14	Slate 1 1/2"	10.90	31.00	64.00	186.00
.2	ASHLAR STONE (40 SqFt/Ton - 4" sawed bed)				
.21	Limestone				
	Indiana - Random	10.20	10.80		
	Coursed (2"-5"-8")	10.50	12.05		
	Minn., Ala., Texas, Wisc., etc.)				
	Split Face-1 Size 7 1/2"	10.80	11.95		
	Coursed (2"-5"-8")	12.70	13.10		
	Sawed/Planed Face-Random	10.40	13.20		
	Coursed (2"-5"-8")	9.90	14.55		
.22	Marble- Sawed Random	11.20	21.10		
	Coursed	10.55	21.70		
.23	Granite- Bushhammered-Random	11.90	24.20		
	Coursed	12.50	25.50		
.3	ROUGH STONE (30 s.f. per Ton)				
.31	Flagstone and Rubble 2"	11.20	9.65		
.32	Field Stone or Boulders	10.40	8.35		
.33	Lt.Wt. Boulders (Igneous) (260 s.f. Ton)				
	2" to 5" Veneer (Sawed Back)	8.95	8.40		
	3" to 10" Boulders	10.70	8.30		
.34	Lt.Wt. Limestone (90 s.f. Ton)				
	2" to 4"	10.20	10.40		

0409.0 PRECAST VENEERS AND SIMULATED MASONRY

.1	ARCHITECTURAL PRECAST STONE				
	Limestone and Gravel	9.40	20.70		
	Marble	10.20	29.00		
	Granite and Quartz	10.30	27.00		
.2	PRECAST CONCRETE	9.00	16.20		
.3	MOSAIC GRANITE PANELS	12.80	33.40		

0410.0 MORTARS

(See Table 4B for Quantities per Unit)

Material Cost used for Units Below (Truckload Prices)

	UNIT	LABOR	MATERIAL
Portland Cement - Gray	Bag- 94#	12.20	10.80
White	Bag- 94#	14.40	21.20
Masonry Cement	Bag- 70#	12.00	8.30
High Early Cement	Bag- 94#	-	12.10
Lime, Hydrated	Bag- 50#	7.40	6.05
Silica Sand	Bag-100#	-	8.00
Fire Clay	Bag-100#	-	23.00
Sand	CuYd	-	24.00
Add for Less than Truckload	-	-	20%
Labor Incl. in Unit Costs: with Mortar Mixer	CuYd	30.00	-
Hand Mixed	CuYd	69.00	-

.1 PORTLAND CEMENT AND LIME MIX
(4.5 Bags Portland and 4.5 Bags Lime)

	UNIT	LABOR	MATERIAL
1:1:6 - Gray - Truckload	CuYd	30.00	103.00
Less than Truckload	CuYd	30.00	123.00
White	CuYd	30.00	145.00
Add for Using Silica Sand	CuYd	26.00	45.00

.2 MASONRY CEMENT MIX (9 Bags Cement)

	UNIT	LABOR	MATERIAL
1:3 - Truckload	CuYd	30.00	99.00
Less than Truckload	CuYd	30.00	110.00

	UNIT	LABOR	MATERIAL
.3 EPOXY CEMENT	CuYd	40.00	201.00
.4 FIRE RESISTANT CEMENT (Clay Mix 300# Mpc)	CuYd	40.00	111.00
.5 ADMIXTURES (Add to Mortar Prices above)			
Waterproofing (1# sack cmt & $ .40/lb)	CuYd	20.00	10.40
Accelerators (1 qt sack cmt & $1.00/lb)	CuYd	20.00	14.40
.6 COLORING (50# CuYd or 90# Mpc & $1.00/lb)	CuYd	23.00	55.40
Standard Brick	M Pcs	29.00	112.00
Add for Heating Mortar Materials	CuYd	15.00	10.60

10% allowed in above Prices for Shrinkage

0411.0 CORE FILLING FOR REINFORCED CONCRETE MASONRY

Based on 3500# Conc.@ $76 CuYd; Mortar @ $90 CuYd; and $26 CuYd to Mix

Deduct 50% from Labor Units if Truck Chuted or Pumped

	Void			Ready Mix		Job Mix	
	CuFt	%	Unit	L	M	L	M
12" x 8" x 16" Plain - 2 Cell	.46	48	Pc	.25	1.40	.45	2.00
	.51	53	SqFt	.30	1.55	.45	2.30
8" x 8" x 16" Plain - 2 Cell	.29	40	Pc	.20	.89	.25	1.25
	.32	44	SqFt	.20	.98	.30	1.40
6" x 8 " x16" Plain - 2 Cell	.20	40	Pc	.10	.64	.40	.89
	.22	44	SqFt	.15	.70	.40	1.00
12" x 8" x 16" Bond Beam	.48	50	Pc	.30	1.40	.75	2.10
	.52	55	SqFt	.30	1.55	.90	2.30
8" x 8" x 16" Bond Beam	.22	32	Pc	.15	.66	.20	1.00
	.24	35	SqFt	.15	.74	.20	1.10
6" x 8" x 16" Bond Beam	.12	25	Pc	.10	.35	.10	.53
	.14	27	SqFt	.10	.42	.15	.61
12" x 16" x 8" Lintel	.55	58	pc	.30	1.70	.50	2.45
	.60	63	SqFt	.35	1.20	.55	2.70
8" x 16" x 8" Lintel	.29	40	Pc	.25	.87	.25	1.30
	.32	44	SqFt	.20	.95	.30	1.40
16" x 8" x 18" Pilaster Block	1.02	72	Pc	.60	3.10	.90	4.50
	1.14	81	LnFt	.60	3.40	1.00	5.10
Add for Vertical Rein.			Pc	.30	.29	.30	.30
(1 #4 Rods 16" O.C.)			SqFt	.30	.30	.30	.30

0412.0 CORE & CAVITY FILL FOR INSULATED MASONRY

.1 LOOSE
.11 Core Fill

	R Value-No Insulation	R Value-Insulated	UNIT	LABOR	MATERIAL
12" Concrete Block	1.35	4.10	Pc	.40	.47
			SqFt	.40	.50
Lt. Wt. Concrete Block	2.40	8.70	Pc	.40	.47
			SqFt	.45	.50
10" Concrete Block	1.30	2.50	Pc	.35	.40
			SqFt	.40	.45
Lt. Wt. Concrete Block	2.30	6.00	Pc	.35	.41
			SqFt	.40	.46
8" Concrete Block	1.20	2.05	Pc	.30	.27
			SqFt	.30	.28
Lt. Wt. Concrete Block	2.30	5.30	Pc	.30	.26
			SqFt	.30	.27
6" Concrete Block	.95	1.90	Pc	.25	.20
			SqFt	.25	.21
Lt. Wt. Concrete Block	1.70	3.15	Pc	.25	.20
			SqFt	.25	.21

	R Value	UNIT	LABOR	MATERIAL
8" Brick	.90	SqFt	.25	.16
6" Brick	.69	SqFt	.20	.11
4" Brick	.46	SqFt	.20	.08
Add to above for Expanded Mica	-	-	10%	200%
Add to above for Perlite	-	-	-	100%
10% added for spillage				

.12 Cavity Fill - Per Inch Wall

		UNIT	LABOR	MATERIAL
Expanded Styrene	4.00	SqFt	.30	.23
Fiber Glass	2.30	SqFt	.30	.26
Rock Wool	3.05	SqFt	.30	.26
Cellulose	3.90	SqFt	.30	.24
Add per added inch	-	-	40%	100%
10% added for spillage				

.2 RIGID

		UNIT	LABOR	MATERIAL
Fiber Glass				
1" - 3# Density	4.60	SqFt	.35	.37
1.5"	6.85	SqFt	.40	.57
2"	9.15	SqFt	.45	.74
Expanded Styrene - Molded (White)				
1" - 1# Density	4.55	SqFt	.35	.17
1.5"	6.85	SqFt	.40	.24
2"	9.15	SqFt	.45	.32
Add for Embedded Nailer Type	-	-	-	.12
Expanded Styrene - Extruded (Blue)				
1" - 2# Density	5.70	SqFt	.35	.43
1.5"	8.50	SqFt	.40	.20
2"	11.35	SqFt	.45	.76
Expanded Urethane				
1"	7.50	SqFt	.35	.46
2"	15.00	SqFt	.45	.65
Perlite				
1"	2.90	SqFt	.35	.42
2"	5.85	SqFt	.45	.84
Add for Glued Applications	-	SqFt	.05	.03

0413.0 ACCESSORIES & SPECIALTIES - MATERIAL

	UNIT	LABOR	MATERIAL
.1 ANCHORS			
Dovetail-Brick 12 ga Galvanized x 3 - 1/2"	Ea	.20	.49
Brick 16 ga Galvanized x 3 - 1/2"	Ea	.20	.34
Brick 16 ga Galvanized x 5"	Ea	.20	.42
Stone - Stainless	Ea	.20	1.30
Rigid Wall - 1 - 1/4"x 3/6"x 8" - Galv	Ea	.20	1.10
Stic - Kips and Clamp	Ea	.25	.23
Strap Z - 1/8"x 1"x 6" or 8" - Galv	Ea	.45	1.30
1/8" x 1"x 6" - SS	Ea	.45	2.85
3/16" x 1 - 1/4" x 8" - Galv	Ea	.45	1.90
Split Tail - 3/16" x 1 - 1/4" x 6" - Galv	Ea	.45	1.85
1/8" x 1 - 1/2"x 6" - SS	Ea	.45	3.80
Wall Clips - 2"x 3"	Ea	.45	.23
Wall Plugs - Wood Filled	Ea	.45	.25
.2 TIES - WIRE			
Galv Z - 3/16" Wire - 6" & 8"	Ea	.20	.21
Zinc Z - 3/16" Wire - 6" & 8"	Ea	.20	.47
Copperweld Z - 3/16" Wire - 6"	Ea	.20	.53
3/16" Wire - 8"	Ea	.20	.63
Adjustable Rect. - 3/16" Wire 3 - 1/4"	Ea	.20	.36
3/16" Wire 4 - 3/4"	Ea	.20	.42
Corrugated-Strap - 26 ga - 7/8" x 7"	Ea	.20	.04
22 ga - 7/8" x 7"	Ea	.20	.05
16 ga - 7/8" x 7"	Ea	.25	.08
Hardware Cloth - 2" x 5" x 1/4" - 23 ga	Ea	.20	.16
23 ga x 1/4" x 30"	SqFt	.30	.63
.3 REINFORCEMENT			
#9 Welded Wire - Ladder Type - 4"	LnFt	.20	.18
6"	LnFt	.20	.19
8"	LnFt	.20	.21
10"	LnFt	.20	.22
12"	LnFt	.25	.23
16"	LnFt	.25	.32
Add for 3/16" Wire H.D.	LnFt	-	30%
Add for Truss Type	LnFt	-	20%
Add for Rect. Ties - Composite & Cavity	LnFt	.03	.06
Add for Rect. Adj. Ties - Comp & Cavity	LnFt	.03	.06
Reinforcement Rods - Horizontal Placement			
3/8" or #3 .376 lb	LnFt	.20	.25
1/2" or #4 .668 lb	LnFt	.25	.32
5/8" or #5 1.043 lb	LnFt	.40	.40
Add for Vertical Placement	LnFt	25%	-
.4 FIREPLACE AND CHIMNEY ACCESSORIES			
Ash Dumps and Thimbles - 6" x 8"	Ea	34.00	15.00
Clean Cut Doors, Cast Iron - 8" x 8"	Ea	31.00	25.00
12" x 12"	Ea	36.00	50.00
Dome Dampers, Cast Iron - 24" x 16"	Ea	28.00	57.00
30" x 16"	Ea	32.00	73.00
36" x 20"	Ea	48.00	104.00
42" x 20"	Ea	61.00	109.00
48" x 24"	Ea	86.00	151.00

0413.0 ACCESSORIES & SPECIALTIES, Cont'd...

		UNIT	LABOR	MATERIAL 1/2"	1"
.5	CONTROL AND EXPANSION JOINT MATERIAL				
	Asphalt - Fibre	SqFt	.60	1.60	2.70
	Polyethylene Foam	SqFt	.65	1.70	2.75
	Sponge Rubber	SqFt	.65	7.70	9.40
	Paper Fibre	SqFt	.60	1.10	1.90
	Also in Thk. of 1/8",1/4",3/8" & 3/4"				

		UNIT	LABOR	2 oz	3 oz
.6	FLASHING, THRU WALL				
	Copper Between Polyethylene	SqFt	.90	1.60	1.95
	Rein Paper - 2 oz/1.05	SqFt	.85	1.65	2.40
	Asphalted Fabric - 3 oz	SqFt	.85	2.40	3.10
	Poly Vinyl Chloride - 20 mil	SqFt	.70	-	.28
	30 mil	SqFt	.75	-	.49
	Add for Adhesives			.05	.05

0414.0 CLEANING & POINTING (See 0414 for Restoration)

		UNIT	LABOR		
.1	BRICK & STONE- Acid & Other Chemicals	SqFt	.50	-	.04
	Soap & Water	SqFt	.45	-	-
.2	BLOCK - 1 Face	SqFt	.25	-	-
.3	FACING TILE AND BLOCK				
	Point - White Cement and Sand	SqFt	.90	-	.10
	Silica Sand	SqFt	1.05	-	.16
	Add for Scaffold (See 0417)				

0415.0 MASONRY RESTORATION (L&M) (Bricklayers)

		UNIT	Cost
.1	RAKING, FILLING AND TUCKPOINTING		
	Limited - Standard Brick & 3/8" Joint	SqFt	3.45
	Heavy	SqFt	4.30
	All	SqFt	8.40
	Deduct for Stone	SqFt	20%
	Deduct for 4" x 12" Brick	SqFt	30%
	Add for Larger & Smaller Joints	SqFt	25%
.2	SAND BLAST		
.22	Brick -Wet	SqFt	1.90
	Dry	SqFt	1.80
.23	Block -Wet	SqFt	1.80
	Dry	SqFt	1.60
.3	STEAM CLEAN AND CHEMICAL CLEANING	SqFt	1.60
.4	HIGH PRESSURE WATER CLEANING (Hydro)	SqFt	1.15
.5	BRICK REPLACEMENT -Standard	Each	23.00
	4" x 12"	Each	28.00
	Add for Scaffolding	SqFt	.79
	Add for Protection	SqFt	.34
.6	WATER PROOFING - CLEAR	SqFt	.96
	See 0702.3 for Waterproofing Masonry		
	See 0711.0 for Caulking		

0416.0 INSTALLATION OF STEEL & MISC. EMBEDDED ITEMS
  See Division 0502

0417.0 EQUIPMENT AND SCAFFOLD

		UNIT	LABOR	MATERIAL
.1	EQUIPMENT AVERAGE OF LABOR			
	See 1-7A for Rental Rates			
.2	SCAFFOLD - INCLUDING PLANK			
	Tubular Frame- to 40' - Exterior	SqFt	.45	.24
	to 16' - Interior	SqFt	.40	.25
	Swing Stage (Incl. Outriggers & Anchorage)	SqFt	.40	.27

The costs below are average but can vary greatly with Quantity, Weather, Area Practices and many other factors. They are priced as total contractor's price with an overhead and fee of 10% included. Units include mortar, ties, cleaning, and reinforcing. Not included are scaffold, hoisting, lintels, accessories, heat, and enclosures. Also added are 30% Insurance on Labor; 10% for General Conditions, Equipment and Tools; and 5% on Material for Sales Taxes. Crew Size is based on 4 Bricklayers to 3 Tenders for Brick and Stone Work, and 4 Bricklayers to 4 Tenders for Block and Tile. See Table 3 for Production Standards. Deduct 5% for Residential Work.

Example: .1	Face Brick 8" x 2 2/3" x 4"	UNIT	LABOR	MATERIAL	TOTAL
.11	Running Bond	Each	.84	.56	1.40
	Mortar and Clean Brick	Each	.12	.12	.24
			.96	.68	1.64
	Add: 30% Labor Burden, 5% Sales Tax		.29	.04	.33
			1.25	.72	1.97
	Add: 10% General Conditions & Equipment				.20
					2.17
	Add: 10% Overhead and Fee				.23
	Total Brick Cost			Each Unit	2.40
				or SqFt	15.50

0401.0 BRICK MASONRY

		SqFt	Unit
.1	FACE BRICK	COST	
.11	Conventional (Modular Size)		
	Running Bond - 8" x 2 2/3" x 4"	15.80	2.40
	Common Bond - 6 Course Header	18.40	2.42
	Stack Bond	16.00	2.43
	Dutch & English Bond - Every Other Course Header	23.70	2.57
	Every Course Header	26.10	2.57
	Flemish Bond - Every Other Course Header	17.85	2.57
	Every Course Header	21.26	2.57
	Add: If Scaffold Needed	.80	.14
	Add: For each 10' of Floor Hgt. or Floor (3%)	.45	.05
	Add: Piers and Corbels (15% to Labor)	2.27	.20
	Add: Sills and Soldiers (20% to Labor)	2.16	.25
	Add: Floor Brick (10% to Labor)	1.58	.13
	Add: Weave & Herringbone Patterns (20% to Labor)	2.15	.25
	Add: Stack Bond (8% to Labor)	1.26	.10
	Add: Circular or Radius Work 20% to Labor)	3.15	.25
	Add: Rock Faced & Slurried Face (10% to Labor)	1.58	.13
	Add: Arches (75% to Labor)	4.85	.90
	Add: For Winter Work (below 40°)		
	Production Loss (10% to Labor)	1.58	.13
	Enclosures - Wall Area Conventional	1.58	.13
	Heat and Fuel - Wall Area Conventional	.33	.05
.12	Econo - 8" x 4" x 3"	13.00	2.90
.13	Panel - 8" x 8" x 4"	10.15	4.50
.14	Norman - 12" x 2 2/3" x 4"	13.05	2.78
.15	King Size - 10" x 2 5/8" x 4"	11.40	2.57
.16	Norwegian - 12" x 3 1/5" x 4"	10.90	2.90
.17	Saxon-Utility - 12" x 4" x 3"	10.20	3.40
	12" x 4" x 4"	10.30	3.43
	12" x 4" x 6"	12.90	4.30
	12" x 4" x 8"	15.60	5.20
.18	Adobe - 12" x 3" x 4"	17.55	2.60
.2	COATED BRICK (Ceramic)	20.95	3.10
.3	COMMON BRICK (Clay, Concrete and Sand Lime)	12.00	1.80
.4	FIRE BRICK -Light Duty	19.60	2.95
	Heavy Duty	25.10	3.80
	Deduct for Residential Work - All Above	-	5%

		UNIT	LABOR	MATERIAL	TOTAL
Example:	12" x 8" x 16" Concrete Block - Partition	Each	2.60	1.55	4.15
	Mortar (Labor in Block Placing Above)	Each	-	.24	.27
	Reinforcing Wire 16" O.C. Horizontal	Each	.12	.14	.26
	Clean Block - 2 Faces	Each	.40	-	.40
			3.12	1.83	5.08

Add: 30% Taxes and Insurance on Labor .84
Add: 5% Sales Tax on Material .14
6.06
Add: 10% General Cond., Equip. and Tools .61
6.76
Add: 10% Overhead and Profit .67
Total Block Cost   Each   7.23
                         or SqFt 8.13

Not Included - Scaffold, Hoisting Equipment, Lintels, Embedded Accessories, Insulation, Heat and Enclosures. (See "Adds" Below.)

0402.0 CONCRETE BLOCK

	Std Wt Cost		Lt Wt Cost	
.1 CONVENTIONAL (Struck 2 Sides - Partitions)	SqFt	Unit	SqFt	Unit
12" x 8" x 16" Plain	8.30	7.40	9.05	8.10
Bond Beam (with Fill-Reinforcing)	11.00	9.80	11.60	10.30
12" x 8" x 8" Half Block	8.30	7.35	7.80	6.95
Double End - Header	8.50	7.60	8.50	8.10
8" x 8" x 16" Plain	7.25	6.45	7.85	7.00
Bond Beam (with Fill-Reinforcing)	8.80	7.80	9.30	8.30
8" x 8" x 8" Half Block	7.10	6.30	7.20	6.40
Double End - Header	7.50	6.65	8.15	7.20
6 "x 8" x 16" Plain	6.70	6.00	7.30	6.50
Bond Beam (with Fill-Reinforcing)	7.60	6.80	7.15	7.20
Half Block	6.65	5.90	7.20	6.40
4" x 8" x 16" Plain	6.55	5.80	6.10	5.40
Half Block	5.75	5.10	6.35	5.65
16" x 8" x 16" Plain	9.35	8.30	10.20	9.05
Half Block	9.00	8.00	9.90	8.80
14" x 8" x 16" Plain	8.90	7.95	10.00	8.90
Half Block	8.45	7.50	8.85	7.85
10" x 8" x 16" Plain	7.75	6.90	8.55	7.60
Bond Beam (with Fill-Reinforcing)	8.85	7.90	10.10	9.00
Half Block	8.60	7.40	8.00	7.10
Deduct: Block Struck or Cleaned One Side	.28	.26	.28	.26
Deduct: Block Not Struck or Cleaned Two Sides	.44	.39	.44	.39
Deduct: Clean One Side Only	.20	.19	.20	.19
Deduct: Lt. Wt. Block (Labor Only)	.18	.17	.18	.17
Add: Jamb and Sash Block	.47	.42	.47	.42
Add: Bullnose Block	.68	.61	.68	.61
Add: Pilaster, Pier, Pedestal Work	.75	.67	.75	.67
Add: Stack Bond Work	.29	.27	.29	.27
Add: Radius or Circular Work	1.40	1.22	1.40	1.22
Add: If Scaffold Needed	.78	.68	.77	.68
Add: Winter Production Cost (10% Labor)	.46	.44	.43	.40
Add: Winter Enclosing - Wall Area	.46	.44	.43	.40
Add: Winter Heating - Wall Area	.42	.41	.41	.40
Add: Core & Beam Filling - See 0411 (Page 4A-18)				
Add: Insulation - See 0412 (Page 4A-18)				

Deduct for Residential Work - 5%

		Std Wt Cost		Lt Wt Cost	
		SqFt	Unit	SqFt	Unit
0402.0	**CONCRETE BLOCK, Cont'd...**				
.2	ORNAMENTAL OR SPECIAL EFFECT - Add to Units Above in 0402.1				
	Shadow Wall	.51	.45	.52	.47
	Scored Block	.56	.50	.57	.51
	Breakoff	1.40	1.22	1.25	1.12
	Split Face	.81	.71	.87	.75
	Rock Faced	.80	.69	.84	.74
	Adobe (Slump)	.85	.75	-	-
.3	SCREEN WALL - 4" x 12" x 12"	6.45	5.70	-	-
.4	INTERLOCKING - <u>Deduct</u> from Units 0402.1				
	Epoxy Laid	.54	.48	.48	.49
	Panelized	.80	.70	.71	.70
.5	SOUND BLOCK - <u>Add</u> to Block Prices 0402.1			1.85	1.65
.6	BURNISHED - 12" x 8" x 16"			12.05	10.70
	8" x 8" x 16"			11.20	10.00
	6" x 8" x 16"			10.30	9.20
	4" x 8" x 16"			9.60	8.60
	2" x 8" x 16"			8.70	7.75
	Add for Shapes			2.65	2.35
	Add for 2 Faced Finish			3.80	3.40
	Add for Scored Finish - 1 Face			.92	.82
.7	PREFACED UNITS -12" x 8" x 16" Stretcher			17.00	15.10
	(Ceramic Glazed) 12" x 8" x 16" Glazed 2 Face			22.95	20.40
	8" x 8" x 16" Stretcher			15.80	14.10
	Glazed 2 Face			21.75	19.40
	6" x 8" x 16" Stretcher			14.10	12.60
	Glazed 2 Face			21.60	19.30
	4" x 8" x 16" Stretcher			14.90	13.30
	Glazed 2 Face			20.60	18.30
	2" x 8" x 16" Stretcher			14.60	12.95
	4" x 16" x 16" Stretcher			37.85	33.70
	Add for Base, Caps, Jambs, Headers, Lintels			4.25	3.80
	Add for Scored Block			1.25	1.12

		COST	
		SqFt	Unit
0403.0	**CLAY BACKING AND PARTITION TILE**		
	3" x 12" x 12"	5.60	5.60
	4" x 12" x 12"	6.00	6.00
	6" x 12" x 12"	7.15	7.15
	8" x 12" x 12"	7.85	7.85
0404.0	**CLAY FACING TILE (GLAZED)**		
.1	6T or 5" x 12" - SERIES		
	2" x 5 1/3" x 12" Soap Stretcher (Solid Back)	20.60	9.20
	4" x 5 1/2" x 12" 1 Face Stretcher	22.00	9.80
	2 Face Stretcher	25.80	11.40
	6" x 5 1/3" x 12" 1 Face Stretcher	26.95	12.00
	8" x 5 1/3" x 12" 1 Face Stretcher	15.15	13.50
.2	8W or 8" x 16" - SERIES		
	2" x 8" x 16" Soap Stretcher (Solid Back)	15.60	13.80
	4" x 8" x 16" 1 Face Stretcher	16.10	14.30
	2 Face Stretcher	21.10	18.70
	6" x 8" x 16" 1 Face Stretcher	19.10	17.35
	8" x 8" x 16" 1 Face Stretcher	20.00	17.75
	Add for Shapes (Average)	50%	50%
	Add for Designer Colors	-	20%
	Add for Less than Truckload Lots	-	10%
	Add for Base Only	-	25%

				COST	
				SqFt	Unit
0405.0	**GLASS UNITS**				
	4" x 8" x 4"			53.00	13.50
	6" x 6" x 4"			55.00	14.00
	8" x 8" x 4"			34.00	15.30
	12" x 12" x 4"			31.00	31.00
0406.0	**TERRA-COTTA**				
	Unglazed			11.75	11.75
	Glazed			15.80	15.80
	Colored Glazed			19.10	19.10

			Ln Ft
0407.0	**FLUE LINING**		
	8" x 12"		19.70
	12" x 12"		20.90
	16" x 16"		33.35
	18" x 18"		35.10
	20" x 20"		68.15
	24" x 24"		88.15

				Sq Ft	Cu Ft
0408.0	**NATURAL STONE**				
.1	CUT STONE				
	Limestone- Indiana and Alabama - 3"			38.30	162.00
	4"			41.20	131.00
	Minnesota, Wisc, Texas, etc.- 3"			42.60	181.00
	4"			49.00	156.00
.12	Marble - 2"			53.40	403.40
	3"			55.00	233.00
.13	Granite - 2"			50.20	331.00
	3"			54.00	229.00
.14	Slate - 1 1/2"			53.00	350.00
.2	ASHLAR- 4" Sawed Bed				
.21	Limestone- Indiana - Random			30.00	93.00
	Coursed - 2" - 5" - 8"			29.00	92.00
	Minnesota, Alabama, Wisconsin, etc.				
	Split Face - Random			30.00	95.00
	Coursed			33.00	105.00
	Sawed or Planed Face - Random			32.00	102.00
	Coursed			34.00	108.00
.22	Marble - Sawed - Random			42.00	134.00
	Coursed			43.50	137.00
.23	Granite - Bushhammered - Random			44.00	140.00
	Coursed			47.00	149.00
.24	Quartzite			32.00	102.00
.3	ROUGH STONE				
.31	Rubble and Flagstone			30.00	95.00
.32	Field Stone or Boulders			29.00	92.00
.33	Light Weight Boulders (Igneous)				
	2" to 4" Veneer - Sawed Back			25.00	-
	3" to 10" Boulders			26.00	-
.34	Light Weight Limestone			28.00	-

		Unit	Cost
0409.0	**PRECAST VENEERS AND SIMULATED MASONRY**		
.1	ARCHITECTURAL PRECAST STONE- Limestone	SqFt	39.00
	Marble	SqFt	46.00
.2	PRECAST CONCRETE	SqFt	31.50
.3	MOSAIC GRANITE PANELS	SqFt	44.00
	See 0904 for Veneer Stones (under 2")		
0410.0	**MORTAR**		
	Portland Cement and Lime Mortar - Labor in Unit Costs	CuYd	118.00
	Masonry Cement Mortar - Labor in Unit Costs	CuYd	106.00
	Mortar for Standard Brick - Material Only	SqFt	.49

		COST	
		SqFt	Unit
0411.0	**CORE FILLING FOR REINFORCED CONCRETE BLOCK**		
	Add to Block Prices in 0402.0 (Job Mixed)		
	12" x 8" x 16" Plain (includes #4 Rod 16" O.C. Vertical)	3.60	3.20
	Bond Beam (includes 2 #4 Rods)	4.25	3.80
	8" x 8" x 6" Plain (includes #4 Rod 16" O.C. Vertical)	2.20	2.00
	Bond Beam (includes 2 #4 Rods)	1.80	1.60
	6" x 8" x 16" Plain	1.95	1.75
	Bond Beam (includes 1 #4 Rod)	1.00	.86
	10" x 8" x 16" Bond Beam (includes 2 #4 Rods)	3.85	3.40
	14" x 8" x 16" Bond Beam (includes 2 #4 Rods)	4.40	3.90
0412.0	**CORE AND CAVITY FILL FOR INSULATED MASONRY**		
	See Page 4-11 for R Values		
.1	LOOSE		
	Core Fill - Expanded Styrene		
	12" x 8" x 16" Concrete Block	1.35	1.20
	10" x 8" x 16" Concrete Block	1.20	1.05
	8" x 8" x 16" Concrete Block	.86	.77
	6" x 8" x 16" Concrete Block	.74	.65
	8"Brick - Jumbo - Thru the Wall	.65	.58
	6"Brick - Jumbo - Thru the Wall	.53	.46
	4"Brick - Jumbo	.45	.40
	Cavity Fill - per Inch		
	Expanded Styrene	.58	-
	Mica	.97	-
	Fiber Glass	.60	-
	Rock Wool	.60	-
	Cellulose	.58	-
.2	RIGID - Fiber Glass - 3# Density, 1"	1.00	-
	2"	1.58	-
	Expanded Styrene - Molded - 1# Density, 1"	.74	-
	2"	1.10	-
	Extruded - 2# Density, 1"	1.05	-
	2"	1.60	-
	Expanded Urethane - 1"	1.15	-
	2"	1.50	-
	Perlite - 1"	1.10	-
	2"	1.70	-
	Add for Embedded Water Type	.21	-
	Add for Glued Applications	.07	-
0413.0	**ACCESSORIES AND SPECIALTIES**		
	See Page 4-12		
0414.0	**CLEANING AND POINTING**		
	Brick and Stone - Acid or Chemicals	.81	-
	Soap and Water	.76	-
	Block & Facing Tile - 1 Face (Incl. Hollow Metal Frames)	.42	-
	Point with White Cement	1.60	-
0415.0	**MASONRY RESTORATION** - See 0415.0		
0416.0	**INSTALLATION OF STEEL** - See 0502.0		
0417.0	**SCAFFOLD**		
.1	EQUIPMENT, TOOLS AND BLADES		
	Percentage of Labor as an average	-	7%
	See 1 - 7A for Rental Rates & New Costs		
.2	SCAFFOLD- Tubular Frame - to 40 feet - Exterior	1.00	-
	Tubular Frame - to 16 feet - Interior	.95	-
	Swing Stage - 40 feet and up	1.05	-

<u>**TABLE B**</u>

Modular Manufactured			Mortar CuFt	Unit Per	Units Placed	Haul & Unload	Unit
Size - Inches			M	SqFt	ManDay	M PCs	Wt.
_l_	_h_	_d_					

0401.0 BRICK MASONRY

.1	Face Brick						
.11	Conventional						
	Running Bond	7-5/8 x 2-1/4 x 3-5/8	13	6.75	600	16.00	4.5
	Common Bond						
	Header Every 6th Course			ƒ1/6	570	-	-
	Header Every 7th Course			ƒ1/7	570	-	-
	Dutch and English Bond						
	Header Every Other Course			ƒ1/2	510	-	-
	Header Every Course			ƒ2/3	510	-	-
	Flemish Bond						
	Header Every Other Course			ƒ1/8	500	-	-
	Header Every Course			ƒ1/3	500	-	-
.12	Econo	7-5/8 x 3-5/8 x 3-5/8		4.50	430	20.00	6.0
.13	Panel	7-5/8 x 7-5/8 x 3-5/8		2.25	280	40.00	13.5
		7-5/8 x 15-5/8 x 3-5/8		1.25	180	80.00	27.0
.14	Norman	11-5/8 x 2-1/4 x 3-5/8	16	4.50	450	20.00	6.0
.15	King	9-5/8 x 3-1/2 x 3-5/8	16	4.70	440	22.00	4.5
.16	Norwegian	11-5/8 x 2-13/16 x 3-5/8	16	3.75	370	22.00	8.0
.17	Saxon 4"	11-5/8 x 3-5/8 x 3-5/8	19	3.00	320	26.00	9.0
	6"	11-5/8 x 3-5/8 x 5-5/8	28	3.00	260	35.00	13.5
	8"	11-5/8 x 3-5/8 x 7-5/8	38	3.00	200	50.00	18.0

Deduct from above dimensions for 1/2" Joint 1/8" x 1/8" x 1/8".
Add to above dimensions for full size 3/8" x 0" x 2/8".

.2	Coated Brick (Glazed)		12	6.75	510	17.00	4.5
.3	Common Brick						
	Clay	7-14 x 2-1/16 x 3-1/2	13	6.75	660	15.00	4.5
	Concrete		13	6.75	660	15.00	4.5
.4	Fire Brick	8-0 x 2- 1/4 x 3-1/2	13	6.65	660	15.00	7.0

0402.0 STANDARD AND LIGHT-WEIGHT CONCRETE BLOCK

	12" Plain	11-5/8 x 7-5/8 x 15-5/8	65	1.125	190	110.00	5.0
	1/2 Height	11-5/8 x 3-5/8 x 15-5/8		2.25		Lt Wt	38.0
	1/2 Length	11-5/8 x 7-5/8 x 7-5/8		2.25			
	8" Plain	7-5/8 x 7-5/8 x 15-5/8	55	1.125	200	80.00	36.0
	1/2 Height	7-5/8 x 3-5/8 x 15-5/8		2.25		Lt Wt	27.0
	1/2 Length	7-5/8 x 7-5/8 x 7-5/8		2.25			
	6" Plain	5-5/8 x 7-5/8 x 15-5/8	45	1.125	210	60.00	28.0
	1/2 Height	5-5/8 x 3-5/8 x 15-5/8		2.25		Lt Wt	21.0
	1/2 Length	5-5/8 x 7-5/8 x 7-5/8		2.25			
	4" Plain	3-5/8 x 7-5/8 x 15-5/8	35	1.125	210	50.00	24.0
	1/2 Height	3-5/8 x 3-5/8 x 15-5/8		2.25		Lt Wt	18.0
	1/2 Length	3-5/8 x 7-5/8 x 7-5/8		2.25			
	16" Plain	15-5/8 x 7-5/8 x 15-5/8	70	2.25	170	150.00	61.0
	14" Plain	13-5/8 x 7-5/8 x 15-5/8	65	2.25	180	90.00	56.0
	10" Plain	9-5/8 x 7-5/8 x 15-5/8	60	2.25	195	85.00	43.0

Average 2 cubic yards mortar per M Block.

TABLE B

		Modular Manufactured Size - Inches			Mortar CuFt	Unit Per	Units Placed	Haul & Unload	Unit
		l	h	d	M	SqFt	ManDay	M PCs	Wt.
0403.0	**CLAY BACKING & PARTITION TILE**								
	3"	3 x	11-1/2 x	11-1/2	18.7	1.00	260	25.0	13.0
	4"	4 x	11-1/2 x	11-1/2	22.2	1.00	250	29.0	15.0
	6"	6 x	11-1/2 x	11-1/2	16.0	1.00	230	38.0	20.0
0404.0	**CLAY FACING TILE (GLAZED)**								
	2" 6T	1-3/4 x	5-1/16 x	7-3/4	13	2.25	180	20.00	6.5
	4" 6T	3-3/4 x	5-1/16 x	11-3/4		2.25		30.00	10.5
	6" 6T	5-3/4 x	5-1/16 x	11-3/4		2.25		45.00	15.2
	8" 6T	7-3/4 x	5-1/16 x	11-3/4		2.25		55.00	19.0
	2" 8W	1-3/4 x	7-3/4 x	15-3/4	22	1.13	125	40.00	14.0
	4" 8W	3-3/4 x	7-3/4 x	15-3/4		1.13		60.00	21.0
	6" 8W	5-3/4 x	7-3/4 x	15-3/4		1.13		85.00	31.0
0405.0	**GLASS UNITS**								
	6" x 6"	5-3/4 x	5-3/4 x	3-7/8	12.5	4.00	140	18.00	4.0
	6" x 8"	7-3/4 x	7-3/4 x	3-7/8	16.0	2.25	125	26.00	7.0
	12" x 12"	11-3/4 x	11-3/4 x	3-7/8	23.3	1.00	90	33.00	16.0
0406.0	**TERRA-COTTA**								
	3"	3" x	12" x	12"	25	1.00		36.00	10.0
	4"	4" x	12" x	12"	30	1.00		40.00	13.0
	6"	6" x	12" x	12"	40	1.00		47.00	18.0
	8"	8" x	12" x	12"	60				
0407.0	**MISCELLANEOUS UNITS**								
	Coping Tile	9"			50	-	160	35.00	-
		12"			60	-	140	40.00	-
	Flue Lining	8" x	8"		50	-	160	35.00	-
		12" x	12"		55	-	130	45.00	-
		18" x	18"		65	-	60	55.00	-
		21" x	21"		75	-	40	70.00	-
		24" x	24"		90	-	30	90.00	-
0408.0	**NATURAL STONE**								
	Cut Stone				SqFt				CuFt
	Lime Stone				10.0	-	18	25.00	150.0
	Marble				10.0	-	13	25.00	160.0
	Granite				10.0	-	11	25.00	165.0
	Ashlar Stone				15.0	-	26	25.00	150.0
	Rough Stone - Flagstone				15.0	-	22	25.00	140.0
	Field Stone				15.0	-	22	25.00	160.0
	Light Weight Stone				15.0	-	24	25.00	220.0
0409.0	**PRECAST VENEERS**								
	Architectural Precast Stone				10.0	-	18	25.00	150.0
	Terra-Cotta				10.0	-	17	25.00	130.0
	Precast Concrete				10.0	-	24	25.00	150.0

0501.0 STRUCTURAL METAL (L+M) (Ironworkers)

		UNIT	LABOR	MATERIAL
.1	BEAMS AND COLUMNS		(Subcontracted)	
.11	Wide Flange Shapes, H-Bearing Piles			
	Light Weight Flange Columns & Misc. Columns			
	Light Beams - American Standard			
	Small Job (5 to 30 ton)	Ton	530.00	1,880.00
	Medium Job (30 to 100 ton)	Ton	520.00	1,800.00
	Large Job (100 ton and up)	Ton	485.00	1,780.00
.12	Junior Beams	Ton	500.00	1,900.00
.2	CHANNELS - American Std. - Junior -3" to 15"	Ton	680.00	1,700.00
	10" to 12"	Ton	660.00	1,900.00
.3	ANGLES (Equal and Unequal)	Ton	730.00	2,060.00
.4	STRUCTURAL T's (from wide Flange Shapes)			
	Light Shapes and American Standard	Ton	530.00	1,850.00
.5	STRUCTURAL TUBING (Steel Pipe, Square & Rectangular)	Ton	540.00	1,880.00
.6	PLATES AND BARS	Ton	560.00	1,970.00
.7	BOX GIRDERS	Ton	900.00	1,890.00
.8	TRUSSES	Ton	950.00	2,570.00
	Add for Welded Field Connections	Ton	210.00	-
	Add for High Strength Bolting	Ton	-	243.00
	Add for Riveted	Ton	510.00	-
	Add for Weathering Steel	Ton	-	345.00
	Add for Galvanizing	Ton	-	500.00

0502.0 MISCELLANEOUS METALS (L+M) (Ironworkers)

		UNIT	LABOR	MATERIAL
.1	BOLTS (with Nuts & Washers in Concrete or Masonry) See 0201.36 for Hole Drilling in Field			
	1/2" x 4"	Each	2.50	2.20
	5/8" x 4"	Each	2.65	2.40
	3/4" x 4"	Each	2.90	3.00
	1" x 4"	Each	3.10	4.00
.2	CASTINGS			
	Manhole Ring & Cover -24" Light Duty	Each	94.00	335.00
	24" Heavy Duty	Each	106.00	405.00
	Wheel Guards- 2' 6"	Each	98.00	250.00
.3	CORNER GUARDS- 3" x 3" x 1/4" Steel	LnFt	6.00	8.10
	4" x 4" x 1/4" Steel	LnFt	7.00	10.30
	Galv.	LnFt	6.25	12.40
.4	FIRE ESCAPES- 24" Steel Grate	Per Floor	1,180.00	3,600.00
		Tread	73.00	220.00
.5	FRAMES, CHANNEL- 6" - 8.2 lbs	LnFt	5.30	13.50
	8" - 11.5 lbs	LnFt	7.30	18.40
	10" - 15.3 lbs	LnFt	10.05	32.40
.6	GRATINGS- Steel - 1" x 1/8"	SqFt	2.60	9.70
	Aluminum - 1" x 1.8"	SqFt	2.60	19.90
	Cast Iron #2 - Light Duty	SqFt	2.60	13.30
	Heavy Duty	SqFt	2.30	26.00
.7	GRILLES	SqFt	4.00	11.50
.8	HANDRAILS - 1 1/2"			
	Wall Mounted - Single Rail- Steel	LnFt	7.30	13.50
	Aluminum	LnFt	8.70	49.00
	Floor Mounted - 2 Rail- Steel	LnFt	10.00	30.00
	3 Rail - Steel	LnFt	11.00	36.00
	Add for Galvanizing	LnFt	-	20%
.9	LADDERS - Steel	LnFt	13.40	45.50
	Aluminum	LnFt	12.90	6.10
.10	LINTELS, LOOSE	Ton	616.00	1,400.00
	3" x 3" x 1/4" - 4.9 lbs per foot	LnFt	2.10	5.30
	4" x 3" x 1/4" - 5.8 lbs per foot	LnFt	2.55	6.00
	4" x 3 1/2" x 1/4" - 6.2 lbs per foot	LnFt	2.70	6.30
	4" x X3 1/2" x 5/16" - 7.7 lbs per foot	LnFt	3.40	7.30
	4" x X3 1/2" x 3/8" - 9.1 lbs per foot	LnFt	4.20	8.50
	4" x 4" x 1/4" - 6.6 lbs per foot	LnFt	3.20	7.00
	Add for Punching Holes	Each	-	5.00
	Add for Galvanizing	LnFt	-	1.50

		UNIT	LABOR	MATERIAL
				(Subcontracted)
0502.0	**MISCELLANEOUS METALS (Cont'd...)**			
.11	PIPE GUARDS - 4" - 4' Above Grade &	LnFt	11.45	10.30
	(Bollards in Concrete) - 4' Below Grade	LnFt	12.20	13.30
.12	PLATE, CHECKERED - 1/4" - 10.2 lbs	SqFt	2.10	10.80
	1/8" - 6.2 lbs	SqFt	1.60	9.80
.13	STAIRS, METAL PAN - 4' Wide x 10' (No Concrete)	PerFl	1,030.00	5,000.00
	Including Supports	Tread	72.50	335.00
.14	STAIRS, CIRCULAR - 3' x 10' - Aluminum	PerFl	577.00	5,100.00
	Steel	PerFl	650.00	5,300.00
	Cast Iron	PerFl	702.00	5,670.00
.15	WIRE GUARDS	SqFt	2.60	13.00
.16	TRENCH FRAME AND COVER - 2'	LnFt	7.30	14.00
0503.0	**ORNAMENTAL METALS (M) (Ironworkers)**			
	Non Ferrous - See 0502.0			
0503.0	**OPEN WEB JOISTS (L+M) (Ironworkers)**			
.1	STANDARD BAR JOISTS (Spans to 48')			
	Small Jobs (to 20 ton) - Spans to 15'	Ton	400.00	1,400.00
	25'	Ton	400.00	1,350.00
	35'	Ton	385.00	1,300.00
	Medium Jobs (20 - 50 ton) - Spans to 15'	Ton	385.00	1,400.00
	25'	Ton	380.00	1,350.00
	35'	Ton	375.00	1,300.00
	48'	Ton	365.00	1,300.00
	Large Jobs (50 ton & up) - Spans to 15'	Ton	375.00	1,350.00
	25'	Ton	365.00	1,200.00
	35'	Ton	365.00	1,300.00
	48'	Ton	350.00	1,300.00
.2	LONG SPAN JOISTS (Spans 48' to 150')			
	Small Jobs (to 30 ton) - Spans to 60'	Ton	400.00	1,350.00
	Medium Jobs (30 -100 ton) - Spans to 60'	Ton	390.00	1,400.00
	80'	Ton	375.00	1,400.00
	100'	Ton	350.00	1,400.00
	Large Jobs (100 ton & Up) - Spans to 60'	Ton	370.00	1,500.00
	80'	Ton	365.00	1,500.00
	100'	Ton	360.00	1,500.00
	120'	Ton	350.00	1,550.00
	150'	Ton	340.00	1,600.00
0505.0	**METAL DECKING (L+M) (Sheet Metal Workers)**			
.1	SHORT SPAN (Spans to 6')			
	(Baked Enamel - Ribbed, V Beam & Seam)			
	1 1/2" Deep - 18 Ga	Sq	60.00	192.00
	20 Ga	Sq	55.00	150.00
	22 Ga	Sq	54.00	145.00
	Add for Galvanized	Sq	-	10%
.2	LONG SPAN (Spans to 12') (Enameled & Open Bottom)			
	3" Deep - 16 Ga	Sq	77.00	590.00
	18 Ga	Sq	72.00	530.00
	20 Ga	Sq	73.00	470.00
	22 Ga	Sq	70.00	390.00
	4 1/2" Deep - 16 Ga	Sq	83.00	700.00
	18 Ga	Sq	82.00	650.00
	20 Ga	Sq	80.00	590.00
	Add for Acoustical	Sq	-	20%
	Add for Galvanized	Sq	-	20%

		UNIT	LABOR	MATERIAL
			(Subcontracted)	
0505.0	**METAL DECKING (L+M) (Sheet Metal), Cont'd...**			
.3	CELLULAR - Electric and Air Flow			
	3" Deep - 16 - 16 Ga Galvanized	Sq	96.00	830.00
	18 - 18 Ga Galvanized	Sq	90.00	800.00
	4 1/2" Deep- 16 - 16 Ga Galvanized	Sq	112.00	1,150.00
	18 - 18 Ga Galvanized	Sq	105.00	940.00
.4	CORRUGATED METAL			
	Standard Spans to Approx.			
	Black - .015" 3' 6"	Sq	46.00	100.00
	Galvanized - .015" 3' 6"	Sq	46.00	115.00
	Heavy Duty			
	Black - 26 Ga 5' 0"	Sq	51.00	155.00
	Galvanized - 26 Ga 5' 0"	Sq	51.00	165.00
	Super Duty			
	Black - 24 Ga 7' 0"	Sq	54.00	155.00
	Galvanized - 24 Ga 7' 0"	Sq	54.00	165.00
	Black - 22 Ga 7' 6"	Sq	54.00	180.00
	Galvanized - 22 Ga 7' 6"	Sq	54.00	180.00
.5	BOX RIB			
	2" - 24 Ga	Sq	73.00	570.00
	22 Ga	Sq	77.00	600.00
	20 Ga	Sq	82.00	650.00
0506.0	**METAL SIDINGS & ROOFINGS (L+M) (Sheet Metal)**			
.1	INDUSTRIAL			
.11	Steel (24 Ga - See 0505 for Other Gauges)			
	Corrugated - Galvanized	Sq	90.00	155.00
	Ribbed - Enameled	Sq	83.00	150.00
	Add for Liner Panel	Sq	41.00	140.00
	Add for Insulation	Sq	35.00	37.00
.12	Aluminum- Corrugated	Sq	78.00	140.00
.2	ARCHITECTURAL (Prefinished)			
.21	Steel - Baked Enameled	Sq	119.00	250.00
	Porcelain Enameled	Sq	150.00	310.00
	Acrylic Enameled	Sq	142.00	270.00
	Plastic Faced	Sq	142.00	340.00
.22	Aluminum - Anodized	Sq	138.00	255.00
	Plastic Faced	Sq	140.00	340.00
	Porcelainized	Sq	147.00	330.00
	Add for Liner Panel and Insulation	Sq	55.00	150.00
.23	Stainless Steel	Sq	230.00	765.00
.24	Protected Metal (Asphalt on Steel with Finish)	Sq	170.00	535.00
	See 1310 for Metal Buildings			
0507.0	**LIGHT GAGE FRAMING (L+M) (Ironworkers)**			
	3 5/8"- 16 Ga	LnFt	.75	4.70
	6"- 16 Ga	LnFt	.80	5.85
	8"- 16 Ga	LnFt	.90	6.65
	10"- 16 Ga	LnFt	1.10	8.30
	Average - Wall	Lb	.40	1.20
	Average - Hanging	Lb	.90	1.40
0508.0	**EXPANSION CONTROL (L+M) (Ironworkers)**			
	4"- Aluminum	LnFt	8.70	50.00
	Bronze	LnFt	9.15	140.00
	Stainless Steel	LnFt	9.15	140.00
	2"- Aluminum	LnFt	7.10	45.00
	Bronze	LnFt	8.60	80.00
	Stainless Steel	LnFt	8.60	89.00

Sq. Ft. Cost

0501.0 Structural Steel Frame

To 30 Ton 20' Span	9.50
24' Span	10.00
28' Span	10.10
32' Span	12.10
36' Span	13.50
40' Span	14.60
44' Span	15.40
48' Span	16.60
52' Span	18.40
56' Span	20.70
60' Span	21.50
Deduct for Over 30 Ton	5%

0504.0 Open Web Joists

To 20 Ton 20' Span	3.10
24' Span	3.20
28' Span	3.20
32' Span	3.40
36' Span	3.65
40' Span	4.20
48' Span	5.25
52' Span	6.90
56' Span	6.40
60' Span	7.00
Deduct for Over 20 Ton	10%

0505.0 Metal Decking

1 1/2" Deep - Ribbed - Baked Enamel - 18 Ga	3.80
20 Ga	3.75
22 Ga	3.20
3" Deep - Ribbed - Baked Enamel - 18 Ga	7.60
20 Ga	7.30
22 Ga	6.65
4 1/2" Deep - Ribbed - Baked Enamel - 16 Ga	9.95
18 Ga	8.60
20 Ga	8.00
3" Deep - Cellular - 18 Ga	9.70
16 Ga	12.20
4 1/2" Deep - Cellular - 18 Ga	13.80
16 Ga	15.70
Add for Galvanized	10%
Corrugated Black Standard .015	1.95
Heavy Duty - 26 Ga	2.10
S. Duty - 24 Ga	2.75
22 Ga	2.85
Add for Galvanized	15%

0506.0 Metal Sidings and Roofings

Aluminum- Anodized	5.00
Porcelainized	10.00
Corrugated	3.40
Enamel, Baked Ribbed	5.25
24 Ga Ribbed	3.60
Acrylic	6.15
Porcelain Ribbed	6.80
Galvanized- Corrugated	3.40
Plastic Faced	7.35
Protected Metal	8.95
Add for Liner Panels	2.80
Add for Insulation	.86

0601.0 ROUGH CARPENTRY (Carpenters)

		UNIT	LABOR	MATERIAL
.1	LIGHT FRAMING & SHEATHING (Standard - Hem-Fir)			
.11	Joists, Beams and Headers - 16" O.C. to 14'			
	2"x 6" Floor	BdFt	.70	.52
	2"x 8" Floor	BdFt	.70	.56
	2"x10" Floor	BdFt	.65	.57
	2"x12" Floor	BdFt	.70	.60
	Add for Ceiling Joists - 2nd Fl or Roof	BdFt	.15	-
	Add for Door, Window & Misc. Headers	BdFt	.45	-
	Add for Sloped Installations	BdFt	40%	-
	Add for Ledgers	BdFt	.30	-
.12	Studs, Plates and Miscellaneous Framing - 16" O.C.			
	2" x 2"	BdFt	1.00	.54
	2" x 3"	BdFt	.90	.53
	2" x 4"	BdFt	.80	.51
	2" x 6"	BdFt	.80	.52
	Add for 2nd Floor and Above per Floor	BdFt	.15	-
	Add for Bolted Plates or Sills	BdFt	.70	-
	Add for Each 1' Above 8' in Length	BdFt	.05	-
	Add for Fire Stops, Fillers, and Nailers	BdFt	.45	-
	Add for Soffit & Suspended Framing 2"x 4"	BdFt	1.05	-
	See 0602 for Metal Studs and Plates			
.13	Bridging - 16" O.C.			
	1" x 3" Wood Diagonal	Set	1.70	.42
	2" x 4" Diagonal	Set	1.90	1.00
	1" Metal Diagonal - 18 Ga	Set	1.70	1.30
	2" x 8" Solid	BdFt	2.00	.70
.14	Rafters and Field-Made Trussed Rafters - 16" O.C.			
	(See 0605 for Prefabrication)			
	2" x 4"	BdFt	1.00	.51
	2" x 6"	BdFt	1.00	.52
	2" x 8"	BdFt	1.00	.56
	2" x 10"	BdFt	.90	.60
	2" x 4" Trusses - Make up in Field	BdFt	.80	.76
	Erection	BdFt	.55	-
	Add for Hips and Valleys	BdFt	.55	-
	Add for Bracing	BdFt	1.05	.65
.15	Stairs			
	2" x 10" and 2" x 12" for Stringers	BdFt	2.30	.60
	1" x 8" and 2" x 10" for Risers & Stairs	BdFt	1.60	.61
	Average for Stringers, Treads and Risers	BdFt	1.90	.75
	Add to Above Framing Where Applicable:			
	Circular Installations	BdFt	60%	-
	Diagonal Installations	BdFt	10%	7%
	Kiln Dry Lumber	BdFt	-	15%
	Construction Grade Lumber	BdFt	-	.06
	Lumber Over 14'	BdFt	-	.05
	Winter Construction	BdFt	10%	-
	Add for Pressure Treating			
	2" x 4" - 2" x 6" - 2" x 8"	BdFt	-	.22
	2" x 10" - 2" x 12"	BdFt	-	.29
	Add for Fire Treating - .40	BdFt	-	.19
	- Dricon	BdFt	-	.35

0601.0   ROUGH CARPENTRY, Cont'd...

		UNIT	LABOR	MATERIAL
.16	**Sub Floor Sheathing (Structural)**			
	1" x 8" and 1" x 10" #3 Pine	BdFt	.50	.70
	1/2" x 4' x 8' Plywood - CD Exterior	SqFt	.45	.55
	5/8" x 4' x 8' Plywood - CD Exterior	SqFt	.50	.63
	3/4" x 4' x 8' Plywood - CD Exterior	SqFt	.50	.75
	3/4" x 4' x 8' Plywood - T&G, CD Exterior	SqFt	.55	.90
	1/2" x 4' x 8' OSB Board	SqFt	.50	.75
	5/8" x 4' x 8' OSB Board	SqFt	.50	.90
	3/4" x 4' x 8' OSB Board, T&G	SqFt	.55	1.10
.17	**Floor Sheathing (Over Sub Floor)**			
	With Partitions in Place			
	1/4" x 4' x 8' Plywood - CD	SqFt	.50	.41
	3/8" x 4' x 8' Plywood - CD	SqFt	.50	.42
	1/2" x 4' x 8' Plywood - CD	SqFt	.50	.55
	5/8" x 4' x 8' Plywood - CD	SqFt	.55	.63
	3/8" x 4' x 8' Particle Board	SqFt	.50	.50
	1/2" x 4' x 8' Particle Board	SqFt	.50	.55
	5/8" x 4' x 8' Particle Board	SqFt	.55	.61
	3/4" x 4' x 8' Particle Board	SqFt	.55	.67
.18	**Wall Sheathing**			
	1" x 8" and 1" x 10" #3 Pine	BdFt	.55	.70
	3/8" x 4' x 8' Plywood - CD Exterior	SqFt	.60	.44
	1/2" x 4' x 8' Plywood - CD Exterior	SqFt	.55	.55
	5/8" x 4' x 8' Plywood - CD Exterior	SqFt	.55	.63
	3/4" x 4' x 8' Plywood - CD Exterior	SqFt	.60	.73
	1/2" x 4' x 8' Fiberboard Impregnated	SqFt	.50	.27
	25/32" x 4' x 8' Fiberboard Impregnated	SqFt	.55	.31
	1" x 2' x 8' T&G Styrofoam	SqFt	.55	.35
	2" x 2' x 8' T&G Styrofoam	SqFt	.75	.62
	1/2" x 4' x 8' OSB Board	SqFt	.55	.75
	5/8" x 4' x 8' OSB Board	SqFt	.55	.90
	3/8" x 4' x 8			
.19	**Roof Sheathing - Flat**			
	1" x 6" and 1" x 8" #3 Pine	BdFt	.55	.70
	1/2" x 4' x 8' Plywood - CD Exterior	SqFt	.50	.55
	5/8" x 4' x 8' Plywood - CD Exterior	SqFt	.60	.63
	3/4" x 4' x 8' Plywood - CD Exterior	SqFt	.55	.75
	Add for Sloped Installation	SqFt	.20	-
	Add Steep Sloped Installation (over 5-12)	SqFt	.35	-
	Add for Dormer Work	SqFt	.70	-
	Add to Above Sheathing where Applicable:			
	Fire Treating	SqFt	-	.40
	Pressure Treating	SqFt	-	.30
	Winter Construction	SqFt	10%	-
	Plywood - AC Exterior (Good One Side)	SqFt	-	.28
	Plywood - AD Exterior (Good One Side)	SqFt	-	.34
	Diagonal Installations	SqFt	8%	7%
	Plywood 10' Lengths	SqFt	-	.22

Recommended 10% Decrease on Labor Units for Residential Construction

0601.0 ROUGH CARPENTRY, Cont'd...

.2 HEAVY FRAMING AND DECKING (Construction-Grade Fir, Air Dried S4S)

See 0604.0 for Laminated Heavy Framing & Decking.

See 0606.0 for Wood Treatments.

See 0109.8 for Wood Curbs and Walls.

	UNIT	LABOR	MATERIAL
.21 Columns and Posts			
4"x 4"	MBF	655.00	870.00
4"x 6"	MBF	650.00	890.00
6"x 6"	MBF	615.00	990.00
8"x 8"	MBF	600.00	1,400.00
12"x12"	MBF	570.00	1,680.00
Add for Fitting at Base and Heat	MBF	200.00	-
Beams and Joists			
4" x 4"	MBF	655.00	870.00
4" x 6"	MBF	650.00	890.00
4" x 8"	MBF	645.00	960.00
4" x10"	MBF	600.00	1,040.00
6" x 6"	MBF	610.00	990.00
6" x 8"	MBF	600.00	1,110.00
6" x10"	MBF	590.00	1,165.00
8" x12"	MBF	580.00	1,350.00
Add to 0601.21 Above for:			
Rough Sawn	MBF	-	135.00
Mill Cutting to Length and Shape	MBF	-	130.00
Nails	MBF	-	70.00
Hauling & Unloading (if Quoted Cars)	MBF	-	90.00
Equipment & Operator Cost - Fork Lift	MBF	-	78.00
Equipment & Operator Cost - Crane	MBF	-	110.00
Add for Red Cedar	MBF	-	1,300.00
Add for Redwood	MBF	-	1,600.00
.22 DECKING			
Tongue & Groove			
Fir, Hemlock & Spruce, Construction Grade (SPF)			
4" x 4"	MBF	420.00	970.00
2" x 6" and 2" x 8"	MBF	395.00	725.00
3" x 6"	MBF	420.00	870.00
4" x 6"	MBF	430.00	980.00
Cedar - #3 and better			
3" x 4"	MBF	405.00	1,660.00
4" x 4" - 4" x 6" - 4" x 8" and 4" x 10"	MBF	400.00	1,840.00
White Pine			
3" x 6" and 3" x 8"	MBF	405.00	1,680.00
4" x 6" and 4" x 8"	MBF	420.00	1,820.00
Add for D Grade	MBF	-	1,200.00
2" x 6" Panelized Decking - 1 1/2" x 20"			
Premium Grade	SqFt	.90	2.30
Architectural Grade	SqFt	.90	2.00
Add for Select Grade	MBF	-	5%
Add for Hemlock	MBF	-	50.00
Add for Hip Roof	MBF	79.00	-
Add for Specified Lengths	MBF	-	35.00
Add for End Matched	MBF	-	45.00
Add for Hauling and Unloading	MBF	-	90.00
Add for Nails	MBF	-	60.00

See 0604 for Laminated Decking

See 0604.3 for Square Foot Deck Costs

0601.0 ROUGH CARPENTRY, Cont'd...

.3 MISCELLANEOUS CARPENTRY

.31 Blocking and Bucks (2" x 4" or 2" x 6")	UNIT	LABOR	MATERIAL
Doors and Window Bucks			
Erected Before Masonry	BdFt	1.70	.55
or, Each	28.00	9.00	
Bolted to Masonry or Steel	BdFt	2.30	.55
or, Each	39.50	9.00	
Nail Driven to Steel Studs or Masonry	BdFt	1.50	.55
or, Each	31.00	9.00	
Roof Blocking - Pressure Treated			
Edges - Bolted to Concrete	BdFt	1.70	.85
Nailed to Wood	BdFt	.90	.80
Openings - Nailed	BdFt	1.90	.80
Add for 2" x 8" or 2" x 10"	BdFt	-	.05
Add to 0601.31 for Bolts - 4' O.C.	BdFt	-	.33
.32 Grounds, Furring, Sleepers & Nailers #3 Pine			
1" x 8" Fastened to Wood	LnFt	.60	.50
1" x 6" Fastened to Wood	LnFt	.60	.36
1" x 4" Fastened to Wood	LnFt	.55	.24
1" x 3" Fastened to Wood	LnFt	.55	.22
1" x 3" Fastened to Concrete/ Masonry			
Nailed	LnFt	.70	.33
Gun Driven (Incl Fasteners)	LnFt	.60	.39
Pre Clipped	LnFt	.90	.36
Add for Ceiling Work	LnFt	.20	-
2" x 4" Not Suspended Framing	BdFt	1.70	.52
Suspended Framing	BdFt	2.10	.52
2" x 2" Not Suspended Framing	BdFt	2.15	.56
Suspended Framing	BdFt	3.10	.56
.33 Cant Strips			
Pressure Treated			
Cut from 4" x 4" - At Roof Edges	BdFt	.55	.45
or, LnFt	.75	.66	
4" x 4" - At Roof Openings	BdFt	.80	.45
or, LnFt	1.05	.66	
6" x 6" - At of Edges	BdFt	1.90	2.10
or, LnFt	1.30	1.45	
6" x 6" - At Roof Openings	BdFt	2.20	2.20
or, LnFt	1.25	1.45	
Add for Bolting (Bolts - 4' O.C.)	BdFt	.80	.58
Not Treated			
Cut from 4" x 4" - At Roof Edges	BdFt	.55	.37
or, LnFt	.70	.55	
6" x 6" - At Roof Edges	BdFt	1.90	1.70
or, LnFt	1.30	1.10	
.34 Building Papers and Sealers			
15" Felt (432 Sq.Ft. to Roll)	SqFt	.10	.03
20" Felt (432 Sq.Ft. to Roll)	SqFt	.10	.04
30" Felt (216 Sq.Ft. to Roll)	SqFt	.12	.06
Cotton and Glass Asphalt Saturated	SqFt	.09	.06
Polyethylene - 4 mil	SqFt	.10	.03
6 mil	SqFt	.10	.04
30# Red Rosin Paper	SqFt	.10	.15
Sill Sealer 6" x 100'	SqFt	.30	.23

0602.0 FINISH CARPENTRY (Carpenters)

.1 FINISH SIDINGS AND FACING MATERIAL (Exterior)
(See Quick Estimating for Square Foot Costs)

	UNIT	LABOR	MATERIAL
.11 Boards, Beveled and Lap Siding			
Cedar - Beveled - Clear 1/2" x 4"	BdFt	1.30	1.85
1/2" x 6"	BdFt	1.20	2.00
Beveled - Rough Sawn 7/8" x 8"	BdFt	1.20	1.70
7/8" x 10"	BdFt	1.05	2.70
7/8" x 12"	BdFt	1.00	2.85
Board- Rough Sawn 3/4" x 12"	BdFt	1.00	2.75
Redwood Beveled- Clear Heart			
1/2" x 6"	BdFt	1.15	2.25
1/2" x 8"	BdFt	1.10	2.35
5/8" x 10"	BdFt	1.05	3.10
3/4" x 6"	BdFt	1.10	2.90
3/4" x 8"	BdFt	1.00	3.00
Board - Clear Heart 3/4" x 6"	BdFt	1.00	3.40
3/4" x 8"	BdFt	.95	4.60
Board, - T&G 1" x 4" & 6"	BdFt	1.00	3.90
Rustic Beveled - 1" x 8" & 10"	BdFt	1.00	4.10
5/4"x 6" & 8"	BdFt	.95	4.00
Add for Metal Corners	Each	1.00	.40
Add for Mitering Corners	Each	3.40	-
.12 Plywood - Siding			
Fir - AC - Smooth One Side 1/4"	SqFt	.70	.75
3/8"	SqFt	.70	.86
Fir - Rough Faced 3/8"	SqFt	.70	.92
Fir - AC - Smooth One Side 1/2"	SqFt	.75	.85
5/8"	SqFt	.75	.94
3/4"	SqFt	.80	1.02
Fir - Grooved and Rough Faced 5/8"	SqFt	.80	1.10
Cedar - Rough Sawn 3/8"	SqFt	.70	1.25
5/8"	SqFt	.80	1.70
3/4"	SqFt	.80	1.52
Cedar - Grooved & Rough Faced (4" & 8") 5/8"	SqFt	.80	1.55
Add for 4' x 10' and 4' x 9' Sheets	SqFt	-	.15
Add for Wood Batten Strips 1" x 2" Pine	LnFt	.70	.32
Add for Horizontal Joint Flashing (Spline)	LnFt	.55	.40
Add for Medium Density Fir	SqFt	.02	.16
.13 Hardboard - Paneling and Lap Siding (Primed)			
7/16" - Rough Textured 4' x 8' Paneling	SqFt	.60	1.05
7/16" - Grooved 4' x 8' Paneling	SqFt	.70	1.05
7/16" - Stucco Board 4' x 8' Paneling	SqFt	.70	1.15
Lap Siding - 7/16" x 8"	BdFt	.90	.78
7/16"x 12"	BdFt	1.00	.80
Add for Prefinishing	BdFt	-	.18
.14 Shingles - Wood			
16" Red Cedar - 12" to Weather - #1	SqFt	.95	2.00
#2	SqFt	.90	1.58
#3	SqFt	.80	1.21
Fancy Butt Red Cedar 7" #1	SqFt	.95	4.20
Red Cedar Hand Split - #1 1/2" to 3/4"	SqFt	1.10	1.63
3/4" to 1 1/4" - #1	SqFt	1.15	1.95
3/4" to 1 1/4" - #2	SqFt	1.10	2.05
3/4" to 1 1/4" - #3	SqFt	1.10	1.95
Add for Fire Retardant	SqFt	-	.45
Add for 3/8" Backer Board	SqFt	.35	.27
Add for Metal Corners	Each	.92	.40
Add for Ridges, Hips and Corners	LnFt	1.55	.90
Add for 8" to Weather	SqFt	25%	-

See Division 0708 for Roof Shingles
No Finish Included in Above Costs

0602.0 FINISH CARPENTRY, Cont'd...

.15 Facias and Trim	UNIT	LABOR	Pine #2	Cedar #3	Plywood 5/8" ACX
All Sizes (average)	BdFt	.90	.80	1.85	.90
1" x 3"	LnFt	.60	.20	.45	.22
1" x 4"	LnFt	.65	.24	.55	.30
1" x 6"	LnFt	.80	.35	.95	.45
1" x 8"	LnFt	.85	.50	1.30	.60
1" x 12"	LnFt	.90	.80	1.85	.90
Add for Clear Grades			400%	100%	-

.16 Soffits	UNIT	LABOR	MATERIAL
1/2" Plywood Fir ACV	SqFt	1.15	.70
Aluminum	SqFt	1.15	1.45
Plastic - Egg Crate	SqFt	1.15	1.50

.2 FINISH WALLS AND CEILING MATERIALS (Interior)

.21 Boards (See Quick Est. - Size/Cutting Allowance Added)		LABOR	MATERIAL
Cedar - #3 Grade - 1" x 6"	SqFt	.95	1.90
Knotty 1" x 6"	SqFt	.90	2.00
1" x 8"	SqFt	.90	2.20
D Grade 1" x 4"	SqFt	.95	2.85
1" x 6"	SqFt	.90	2.95
1" x 8"	SqFt	.90	2.85
Aromatic 1" x 6"	SqFt	.95	2.95
Redwood - Constr.1" x 6"	SqFt	1.00	2.15
1" x 8"	SqFt	.90	2.40
Add for Clear	SqFt	10%	100%
Fir - Beaded 5/8" x 4"	SqFt	1.00	2.00
#2 Grade 1" x 6"	SqFt	.95	2.15
1" x 8"	SqFt	.90	2.10
1" x 10"	SqFt	.85	2.15

.22 Hardboard & Pressed Woods (4' x 8' Panels)		LABOR	MATERIAL
Tempered 1/8"	SqFt	.60	.29
1/4"	SqFt	.70	.48
Pegboard (Perforated)1/8"	SqFt	.60	.30
1/4"	SqFt	.70	.46
Plastic Faced 1/4"	SqFt	.70	1.10
Flake Board 1/8"	SqFt	.55	.34
Add for Metal or Plastic Mouldings	LnFt	.50	.44
Add for Pre-finished	SqFt	-	.20

.23 Plywood Paneling (4'x 8' Panels, Prefinished)		LABOR	MATERIAL
Birch, Natural 1/4"	SqFt	.95	1.00
3/4"	SqFt	1.10	1.80
White Select 1/4"	SqFt	1.00	1.85
Oak, Red - Rotary Cut 1/4"	SqFt	1.00	1.15
3/4"	SqFt	1.10	2.05
White 1/4"	SqFt	1.00	2.05
Cedar, Aromatic 1/4"	SqFt	1.00	1.70
Cherry 3/4"	SqFt	1.10	2.35
Pecan 3/4"	SqFt	1.10	2.35
Walnut 1/4"	SqFt	.95	2.35
3/4"	SqFt	1.10	3.60
Mahogany, Lauan 1/4"	SqFt	.95	.75
3/4"	SqFt	1.10	1.30
African 3/4"	SqFt	1.10	2.65
Knotty Pine 1/4"	SqFt	.95	1.70
3/4"	SqFt	1.10	3.00
Slat Wall - Painted 3/4"	SqFt	1.10	1.70
Oak 3/4"	SqFt	1.15	2.65
Add for V Groove and T&G	SqFt	-	.30
Add for Glued-On Applications	SqFt	.20	.12
Add for 10' Lengths	SqFt	.15	.28

0602.0 FINISH CARPENTRY, Cont'd...

.24 Gypsum Board and Framing
(See 0902 - Subcontracted Work Costs)
(See 0902 - Metal Framing SqFt Costs)
Finish Board (Walls to 8' - Screwed On)

	UNIT	LABOR	MATERIAL
3/8" 4' x 8' and 12'	SqFt	.40	.31
1/2" 4' x 8' and 12'	SqFt	.40	.32
5/8" 4' x 8' and 12	SqFt	.40	.33
1" 4' x 8' and 12' Core Board	SqFt	.45	.60
1" 4' x 8' and 12' Bead Board	SqFt	.40	.60
Add for Adhesive Application	SqFt	.10	.02
Deduct for Nail-on Application	SqFt	.02	-
Add for: Fire Resistant Board	SqFt	.02	-
Add for: Foil Backed (Insulating)	SqFt	.02	.09
Add for: Moisture Resistant Type 5/8" & 1/2"	SqFt	.02	.12
Add for: Work Above 8'	SqFt	.02	.08
Add for: Work Over 2-Story per Story	SqFt	.10	-
Add for: Ceiling Work - To Wood	SqFt	.10	-
To Steel	SqFt	.15	-
Add for: Resilient Clip Application	SqFt	.40	-
Add for: Small Cut Up Areas	SqFt	.40	.08
Add for: Beam and Column Work	SqFt	.40	.06
Add for: Circular Construction	SqFt	.55	.06
Add for: Vinyl Faced Board	SqFt	.45	.08
3/8" x 4' x 8' - Cost Variable	SqFt	.45	.85
1/2" x 4' x 8' - Cost Variable	SqFt	.45	.95
Metal Framing (Studs, Runners and Channels)			
Studs 25-Gauge 1 5/8"	LnFt	.60	.36
2 1/2"	LnFt	.60	.39
3 5/8"	LnFt	.65	.42
6"	LnFt	.60	.57
8"	LnFt	.65	.60
Studs 209A 1 5/8"	LnFt	.55	.47
2 1/2"	LnFt	.60	.54
3 5/8"	LnFt	.60	.61
6"	LnFt	.60	.79
8"	LnFt	.65	.88
7/8" Furring Channels	LnFt	.60	.39
1 1/2" Furring Channels (Cold Rolled)	LnFt	.60	.53
Resilient Channels	LnFt	.55	.41
Add for Over 10' Lengths	LnFt	.20	.11
Add for 20-Gauge 6" Material	LnFt	.20	.53
Add for 16-Gauge 8" Material	LnFt	.30	1.15
Metal Trim			
Casing Bead	LnFt	.80	.26
Corner Bead	LnFt	.60	.17
L & J Bead 3/8" - 1/2" - 5/8"	LnFt	.60	.25
Expansion Bead - Metal	LnFt	.60	.68
Plastic	LnFt	.60	.35
Metal Mouldings	LnFt	.90	.61
Taping and Sanding	SqFt	.35	.08
Texturing	SqFt	.45	.09
Thin Coat Plaster — or Skin Coat	SqFt	1.00	.32
Sound Deadening Insulation - 2 1/2"	SqFt	.35	.29
3 1/2"	SqFt	.40	.29
6"	SqFt	.40	.39

.25 Cement Board

	UNIT	LABOR	MATERIAL
1/2" 3' x 5 1/2'	SqFt	.40	1.25
1/2" 4' x 8'	SqFt	.40	1.25

0603.0   MILLWORK & CUSTOM WOODWORK (M) (Carpenters)   MATERIAL

.1   CUSTOM CABINET WORK
      See Division 11 - Stock Cabinets (Medium etc)

Base Cabinets 35" High x 24" Deep -	UNIT	LABOR	Prefinished Red Oak or Birch	Plastic Laminate
18" W	LnFt	19.80	119.00	114.00
24" W	LnFt	19.80	114.00	109.00
30" W	LnFt	18.70	110.00	105.00
36" W	LnFt	18.70	105.00	100.00
36" Wide Sink Fronts	LnFt	17.50	74.00	69.00
42"	LnFt	17.50	82.00	74.00
36" Wide Corner Cabinet	LnFt	18.60	133.00	128.00
Add for Lazy Susan	Each	24.80	121.00	114.00
Add per Drawer	Each	4.20	25.50	25.50
Upper Cabinets - 12" Deep				
30" High 18" Wide	LnFt	19.80	87.00	84.00
24" W	LnFt	19.80	82.00	79.00
30" W	LnFt	18.70	80.00	75.00
36" W	LnFt	18.70	75.00	72.00
24" High 18" Wide	LnFt	18.70	74.00	71.00
24" W	LnFt	18.70	69.00	66.00
30" W	LnFt	18.70	67.00	64.00
36" W	LnFt	17.50	66.00	63.00
15" High 18" Wide	LnFt	17.50	68.00	65.00
24" W	LnFt	17.50	65.00	62.00
30" W	LnFt	16.10	64.00	61.00
36" W	LnFt	16.10	63.00	60.00
Utility Cabinets - 84" H x 24" D				
18" Wide	LnFt	23.40	175.00	151.00
24" W	LnFt	23.40	165.00	148.00
Add - Prefinished Interior	-	-	8%	-
Deduct - Prefinished to Unfinished	-	-	12%	-
Add for Plastic Lam. Interior	-	-	-	100%
Add to Above for Special Hdwe.	Unit	8.60	-	25.50
Add - White/Birch/White Oak/Maple	-	-	-	20%
Add - Walnut	-	-	-	100%
China or Corner Cabinet 84"H x 36"W	Each	125.00	690.00	685.00
Oven Cabinet 84" High x 27" High	Each	119.00	540.00	525.00
Vanity Cabinets 30" High x 21" Deep				
30" Wide	LnFt	37.00	115.00	112.00
36" W	LnFt	38.00	112.00	109.00
48" W	LnFt	42.00	108.00	107.00

.2   COUNTER TOPS, 25" with Back Splash 4"   MATERIAL

	UNIT	LABOR	MATERIAL
Plastic Laminated 1 1/2"	LnFt	11.75	34.00
Deduct for No Back Splash	LnFt	2.60	5.70
Plastic Laminated Vanity Top	LnFt	10.60	38.00
Marble	LnFt	11.10	73.00
Artificial	LnFt	11.10	63.00
Wood Cutting Block, 1 1/2"	LnFt	11.20	69.00
Stainless Steel	LnFt	13.00	120.00
Polyester-Acrylic Solid Surface	LnFt	11.75	135.00
Granite - Artificial - 1 1/4"	LnFt	14.25	75.00
3/4"	LnFt	13.00	57.00
Quartz	LnFt	13.00	70.00
Plastic (Polymer)	LnFt	13.00	46.00

0603.0 MiLLWORK & CUSTOM WOODWORK, Cont'd...

.3   CUSTOM DOOR FRAMES & TRIM

	Unit	Labor	Birch	Fir	Poplar	Oak	Pine	Maple
Custom Jamb & Stop								
4 5/8" x 2'6" x 3/4" x 6'8"	Each	$45	$128	$65	$66	$118	$119	-
x 2'8" x 3/4"	Each	47	130	67	69	120	120	-
x 3'0" x 3/4"	Each	48	126	72	70	121	124	-
5 1/4" x 2'6" x 3/4" x 6'8"	Each	47	138	77	70	125	121	-
x 2'8" x 3/4"	Each	48	141	79	70	128	122	-
x 3'0" x 3/4"	Each	49	145	82	73	146	129	-
6 3/4" x 2'6" x 3/4" x 6'8"	Each	49	190	-	-	190	144	-
x 2'8" x 3/4"	Each	50	195	-	-	192	145	-
x 3'0" x 3/4"	Each	51	197	-	-	194	148	-
Stock Jamb & Stop								
4 5/8" x 2'6" x 3/4" x 6'8"	Each	43	113	38	-	110	71	-
x 2'8" x 3/4"	Each	44	115	39	-	112	73	-
x 3'0" x 3/4"	Each	43	117	40	-	115	76	-
5 1/4" x 2'6" x 3/4" x 6'8"	Each	44	124	44	53	124	77	-
x 2'8" x 3/4"	Each	45	127	45	54	127	78	-
x 3'0" x 3/4"	Each	47	131	46	56	137	80	-
6 3/4" x 2'6" x 3/4" x 6'8"	Each	47	155	-	-	172	108	-
x 2'8" x 3/4"	Each	48	157	-	-	175	110	-
x 3'0" x 3/4"	Each	49	165	-	-	177	113	-
Fire Rated Jamb & Stop								
4 5/8" x 3'0" x 1 1/16"	Each	48	200	-	-	182	-	-
5 1/4" x 3'0" x 1 1/16"	Each	49	213	-	-	195	-	-
6 3/4" x 3'0" x 1 1/16"	Each	51	218	-	-	200	-	-
Trim Only -11/16" x 2 1/4"	Each	44	121	32	43	105	85	-
(2 sides) - 3/4" x 3 1/2"	Each	51	195	38	60	137	110	-

.4   MOULDINGS & TRIM-STOCK

	Unit	Labor	Birch	Fir	Poplar	Oak	Pine	Maple
Apron 7/16" x 2"	LnFt	.95	1.75	-	.51	1.08	.74	-
11/16" x 2 1/2"	LnFt	1.15	3.92	-	-	1.67	1.36	1.50
Astragal 1 3/4" x 2 1/4"	LnFt	1.20	-	-	-	5.85	4.80	-
Base 7/16" x 2 3/4"	LnFt	.95	3.93	.68	.82	1.43	1.24	1.51
9/16" x 3 1/4"	LnFt	1.00	3.35	-	1.10	2.56	1.48	1.63
Base Shoe 7/16" x 2 3/4"	LnFt	.95	-	-	.40	.80	.50	.83
Batten Strip 5/8" x 1 5/8"	LnFt	.85	-	-	-	1.25	1.03	-
Brick Mould 1 1/4" x 3"	LnFt	1.25	-	1.10	-	-	1.60	-
Casing 11/16" x 2 1/4"	LnFt	1.00	1.55	.82	.75	1.18	1.18	1.14
3/4" x 3 1/2"	LnFt	1.10	2.75	.92	.81	2.30	2.10	-
Chair Rail 5/8" x 1 3/4"	LnFt	.90	2.00	-	1.27	1.90	1.53	-
or Dado 11/16" x 2 1/4"	LnFt	.90	2.68	-	-	2.35	1.55	-
Closet Rod 1 5/16"	LnFt	1.40	-	.92	-	1.40	-	-
Corner Bead 3/4" x 3/4"	LnFt	.85	-	-	.69	1.22	.93	1.20
1 1/8" x 1 1/8"	LnFt	.90	-	-	1.21	1.76	1.62	1.68
Cove Mould 3/4" x 7/8"	LnFt	1.30	1.32	-	.59	.92	.74	1.04
Crown & Cove 9/16" x 2 3/4"	LnFt	1.40	3.17	-	1.15	2.00	1.80	2.20
9/16" x 3 5/8"	LnFt	1.50	3.90	-	-	3.32	2.35	-
11/16" x 4 5/8"	LnFt	1.50	-	-	-	3.90	3.60	-
Drip Cap 11/16" x 1 3/4"	LnFt	1.05	-	-	-	-	1.60	-
Half Round 1/2" x 1"	LnFt	1.20	-	-	-	-	1.15	-
Hand Rail 1 5/8" x 1 3/4"	LnFt	1.65	-	1.49	-	-	1.70	-
Hook Strip 5/8" x 2 1/2"	LnFt	1.00	-	.92	1.00	-	1.12	-
Picture Mould 3/4" x 1 1/2"	LnFt	1.00	1.00	-	-	1.12	1.12	-
Quarter Round 3/4" x 3/4"	LnFt	.85	-	.42	.59	.93	.60	.93
1/2" x 1/2"	LnFt	.80	-	.33	-	-	.40	-
Sill Casement 3/4" x 1 7/8"	LnFt	1.35	-	-	-	-	1.60	-
Stool 11/16" x 2 1/2"	LnFt	1.35	3.67	1.18	1.48	3.20	2.05	-

Above prices based on 200 LnFt. Deduct for Over 200 LnFt - 20%.
Add for Walnut Trim - 100% Add for Custom Trim – 50%

0603.0   MILLWORK & CUSTOM WOODWORK, Cont'd...

		Unit	Labor			Birch	Oak	Pine	Walnut
.5	STAIRS								
	Treads 1 1/6" x 10 1/4"	LnFt	2.15				4.70	3.80	-
	Risers 3/4" x 7 1/2"	LnFt	1.90				5.15	2.70	-
	Skirt Bds 9/16" x 9 1/2"	LnFt	2.40				6.60	2.80	-
	Nosings 1/8" x 3 1/2"	LnFt	1.70				3.30	2.00	-
.6	SHELVING								
	12" Deep	SqFt	5.25	-	-	34.30	25.42	13.20	78.00
	8"	SqFt	5.35	-	-	29.00	3.25	12.00	64.00
.7	CUSTOM PANELING	SqFt	3.20	-	-	20.20	14.06	-	24.00
.8	THRESHOLDS 3/4" x 3 1/2"								
	Standard	LnFt	7.80	-	-	-	5.80	-	-
	With Vinyl	LnFt	7.80	-	-	-	6.50	-	-

0604.0   GLUE LAMINATED (M) (Carpenters) (F.O.B. Cars)

		UNIT	LABOR	MATERIAL
.1	ARCHES AND RIGID FRAMES: Arches	MBF	700.00	1,940.00
	Rigid Frames	MBF	710.00	2,120.00
.2	BEAMS, JOISTS & PURLINS: 4" x 6", 8"& 10"	MBF	710.00	2,450.00
	6" x 6", 8" & 10"	MBF	710.00	2,310.00
	8" x 6", 8" & 10"	MBF	700.00	2,220.00
.3	DECKS: Doug.Fir - 3" x 6" (2 1/4"x 5 1/4")	SqFt	2.00	5.40
	4" x 6" (3" x 5 1/4")	SqFt	2.10	5.75
	Cedar - 3" x 6" (2 1/4"x 5 1/4")	SqFt	2.15	6.40
	4" x 6"	SqFt	2.30	7.00
	Pine - 3" x 6" (2 1/4"x 5 1/4")	SqFt	2.05	4.65

0605.0   PREFABRICATED WOOD & PLYWOOD COMPONENTS (See 0601.22, Job Fabricated)

.1	WOOD TRUSSED RAFTERS			
	4 -12 Pitch 24" O.C. With 2' Overhang 57 lb. Loading			
	16' Span	Each	35.00	69.00
	20'	Each	38.40	71.00
	22'	Each	38.90	73.00
	24'	Each	41.80	77.00
	26'	Each	42.90	84.00
	28'	Each	47.90	100.00
	30'	Each	52.60	112.00
	32'	Each	58.60	124.00
	Add for 5-12 Pitch	Each	5%	15%
	Add for 6-12 Pitch	Each	12%	25%
	Add for Gable End Type (Flying)	Each	22.50	35.60
	Add for 16" O.C.	Each	-	10%
	Add for Hip Ends - 24' Span	Each	175.00	425.00
	Add for Energy Type	Each	-	10%
.2	WOOD FLOOR AND ROOF TRUSS JOISTS			
.21	Open Wood Web - Gusset Plate Connection			
	24" O.C. Up to 23' Span x 12" - Single Chord	LnFt	1.65	5.25
	to 24' Span x 15"	LnFt	1.70	5.35
	to 27' Span x 18"	LnFt	1.75	5.45
	to 30' Span x 21"	LnFt	1.95	5.70
	to 25' Span x 15" - Double Chord	LnFt	1.85	4.85
	to 30' Span x 18"	LnFt	2.25	4.95
	to 35' Span x 21"	LnFt	2.65	5.15
	Open Metal Web - Pin Connection			
	to 25' Span x 18"	LnFt	1.75	5.05
	to 30' Span x 22"	LnFt	1.90	5.15
	to 35' Span x 30"	LnFt	2.10	5.25
	to 40' Span x 30"	LnFt	2.60	5.40

0605.0 PREFABRICATED WOOD & PLYWOOD COMPONENTS, Cont'd...

		UNIT	LABOR	MATERIAL
.22	Plywood Web			
	24" O.C. Up to 15' Span x 9 1/2"	LnFt	1.40	3.05
	to 19' Span x 11 7/8"	LnFt	1.45	3.15
	to 21' Span x 14"	LnFt	1.60	3.50
	to 22' Span x 16"	LnFt	1.80	3.70
.3	LAMINATED VENEER STRUCTURAL BEAMS			
.31	Micro Lam (Plywood) 7 1/4" x 1 3/4"	LnFt	1.40	3.25
	9 1/2" x 1 3/4"	LnFt	1.50	4.60
	11 7/8" x 1 3/4"	LnFt	1.55	5.25
	14" x 1 3/4"	LnFt	1.65	6.35
	16" x 1 3/4"	LnFt	1.75	7.20
	18" x 1 3/4"	LnFt	1.95	8.00
.32	Glue Lam (Dimension Lumber)			
	9" x 3 1/2" Industrial	LnFt	1.50	9.85
	12" x 3 1/2"	LnFt	1.60	11.90
	15" x 3 1/2"	LnFt	1.65	14.00
	9" x 5 1/8"	LnFt	1.50	13.50
	12" x 5 1/8"	LnFt	1.70	16.80
	15" x 5 1/8"	LnFt	1.90	21.00
	18" x 5 1/8"	LnFt	2.05	25.90
	24" x 5 1/8"	LnFt	2.45	32.50
	Add for Architectural Grade	LnFt	.30	10%
	Add for 6 3/4"	LnFt	.30	5.00
	Add for Pine Treated	LnFt		4.00
.4	DECKS - 4' x 30' with Plywood 2 Sides - Insulated	SqFt	1.25	6.40

0606.0 WOOD TREATMENTS (Preservatives)

		UNIT	LABOR	MATERIAL
	SALTS - PRESSURE (Water Borne)			
	Dimension 2 x 4-2 x 6 and 2 x 8, 2 x 10-2 x 12	BdFt	-	.19
	2 x 10 and 2 x 12	BdFt	-	.29
	Plywood 5/8" CDX	SqFt	-	.26
	SALTS - NON PRESSURE	BdFt	-	.15
	CREOSOTE (Penta)	BdFt	-	
	FIRE RETARDANTS - PRESSURE			
	Dimension and Timbers	BdFt	-	.38
	Plywood 5/8" CDX	SqFt	-	.38

0607.0 ROUGH HARDWARE

		UNIT	LABOR	MATERIAL
.1	NAILS, BOLTS, ETC. Job Average	SqFt & BdFt	-	.02
	Common (50# Box) 8 Penny	CWT	-	58.75
	16 Penny	CWT	-	55.00
	Finish #3	CWT	-	69.00
	Add for Coated	CWT	-	60%
.2	JOIST HANGERS	Each	1.65	1.15
.3	BOLTS - 5/8" x 12"	Each	1.95	1.75

0608.0 EQUIPMENT (Saws, Woodworking, Drills, Etc.)

		UNIT	LABOR	MATERIAL
	Average Job - As a Percentage of Labor	-	-	3%
	Heavy Equipment in Division 2			
	See 1-6A and 1-7A for Rental Rates			

Recommend 10% Decrease on Labor Units for Residential Construction

The costs below are average, priced as total contractor/subcontractor costs with an overhead of 5% and fee of 10% included. Units include fasteners and equipment, 35% taxes and insurance on labor, and 10% General Conditions and Equipment. Also included are nails, cutting, size and lap allowances. See Example on Page 4.

0601.0 ROUGH CARPENTRY

		UNIT	COST
.1	LIGHT FRAMING AND SHEATHING		
.11	Joists and Headers - Floor Area - 16" O.C.		
	2" x 6" Joists - with Headers & Bridging	SqFt	2.20
	2" x 8" Joists	SqFt	2.80
	2" x 10" Joists	SqFt	3.15
	2" x 12" Joists	SqFt	3.90
	Add for Ceiling Joists, 2nd Floor and Above	SqFt	8%
	Add for Sloped Installation	SqFt	15%
.12	Studs, Plates and Framing - 8' Wall Height - 16" O.C.		
	2" x 3" Stud Wall - Non-Bearing (Single Top Plate)	SqFt	1.43
	2" x 4" Stud Wall - Bearing (Double Top Plate)	SqFt	1.63
	2" x 4" Stud Wall - Non-Bearing (Single Top Plate)	SqFt	1.51
	2" x 6" Stud Wall - Bearing (Double Top Plate)	SqFt	2.00
	2" x 6" Stud Wall - Non-Bearing (Single Top Plate)	SqFt	1.94
	Add for Stud Wall - 12" O.C.	SqFt	8%
	Deduct for Stud Wall - 24" O.C.	SqFt	22%
	Add for Bolted Plates or Sills	SqFt	.12
	Add for Each Foot Above 8'	SqFt	.06
	Add to Above for Fire Stops, Fillers and Nailers	SqFt	.48
	Add for Soffits and Suspended Framing	SqFt	.65
.13	Bridging - 1" x 3" Wood Diagonal	Set	2.60
	2" x 8" Solid	Each	2.82
.14	Rafters		
	2" x 4" Rafter (Incl Bracing) 3 - 12 Slope	SqFt	1.90
	4 - 12 Slope	SqFt	2.05
	5 - 12 Slope	SqFt	2.15
	6 - 12 Slope	SqFt	2.50
	Add for Hip-and-Valley Type	SqFt	.45
	Add for 1' 0" Overhang - Total Area of Roof	SqFt	.17
	2" x 6" Rafter (Incl Bracing) 3-12 Slope	SqFt	2.38
	4-12 Slope	SqFt	2.43
	5-12 Slope	SqFt	2.50
	6-12 Slope	SqFt	2.60
	Add for Hip - and - Valley Type	SqFt	.55
.15	Stairs	Each Floor	472.00
.16	Sub Floor Sheathing (Structural)		
	1" x 8" and 1" x 10" #3 Pine	SqFt	1.66
	1/2" x 4' x 8' CD Plywood - Exterior	SqFt	1.34
	5/8" x 4' x 8'	SqFt	1.50
	3/4" x 4' x 8'	SqFt	1.72
.17	Floor Sheathing (Over Sub Floor)		
	3/8" x 4' x 8' CD Plywood	SqFt	1.26
	1/2" x 4' x 8'	SqFt	1.35
	5/8" x 4' x 8'	SqFt	1.46
	1/2" x 4' x 8' Particle Board	SqFt	1.08
	5/8" x 4' x 8'	SqFt	1.17
	3/4" x 4' x 8'	SqFt	1.38

0601.0 ROUGH CARPENTRY, Cont'd...

		UNIT	COST
.18	Wall Sheathing		
	1' x 8" and 1" x 10" - #3 Pine	SqFt	1.72
	3/8" x 4' x 8' CD Plywood - Exterior	SqFt	1.31
	1/2" x 4' x 8'	SqFt	1.42
	5/8" x 4' x 8'	SqFt	1.57
	3/4" x 4' x 8'	SqFt	1.83
	25/32" x 4' x 8' Fiber Board - Impregnated	SqFt	1.00
	1" x 2' x 8' T&G Styrofoam	SqFt	1.28
	2" x 2' x 8'	SqFt	1.87
.19	Roof Sheathing - Flat Construction		
	1" x 6" and 1" x 8" - #3 Pine	SqFt	1.69
	1/2" x 4' x 8' CD Plywood - Exterior	SqFt	1.45
	5/8" x 4' x 8'	SqFt	1.59
	3/4" x 4' x 8'	SqFt	1.85
	Add for Sloped Roof Construction (to 5-12 slope)	SqFt	.18
	Add for Steep Sloped Construction (over 5-12 slope)	SqFt	.30
	Add to Above Sheathing (0601.16 thru 0601.19)		
	AC or AD Plywood	SqFt	.30
	10' Length Plywood	SqFt	.23
.2	HEAVY FRAMING		
.21	Columns and Beams - 16' Span Average - Floor Area	SqFt	7.40
	20' Span	SqFt	7.72
	24' Span	SqFt	9.00
.22	Deck 2" x 6" T&G - Fir Random Construction Grade	SqFt	4.37
	3" x 6" T&G - Fir Random Construction Grade	SqFt	5.80
	4" x 6"	SqFt	7.40
	2" x 6" T&G - Red Cedar	SqFt	5.50
	Add for D Grade Cedar	SqFt	1.85
	2" x 6" T&G - Panelized Fir	SqFt	4.00
.3	MISCELLANEOUS CARPENTRY		

		EACH	or	BdFt
.31	Blocking and Bucks (2" x 4" and 2" x 6")			
	Doors & Windows - Nailed to Concrete or Masonry	52.00		2.50
	Bolted to Concrete or Masonry	58.50		3.50
	Roof Edges - Nailed to Wood	-		2.00
	Bolted to Concrete (Incl. bolts)	-		3.00

		LnFt	or	BdFt
.32	Grounds and Furring			
	1" x 6" Fastened to Wood	1.12		2.25
	1" x 4"	.97		3.00
	1" x 3"	.92		3.70
	1" x 3" Fastened to Concrete/Masonry - Nailed	1.45		5.65
	Gun Driven	1.35		5.40
	PreClipped	1.68		6.60
	2" x 2" Suspended Framing	1.45		4.40
	Not Suspended Framing	1.25		3.75
.33	Cant Strips			
	4" x 4" Treated and Nailed	1.70		-
	Treated and Bolted (Including Bolts)	2.45		-
	6" x 6" Treated and Nailed	3.40		-
	Treated and Bolted (Including Bolts)	4.30		-

		UNIT	COST
.34	Building Papers and Sealers		
	15" Felt	SqFt	.20
	Polyethylene - 4 mil	SqFt	.15
	6 mil	SqFt	.17
	Sill Sealer	SqFt	.75

0602.0 FINISH CARPENTRY

.1 FINISH SIDINGS AND FACING MATERIALS (Exterior)

.11 Boards and Beveled Sidings

	TO WEATHER	% ADDED	COST
Cedar Beveled - Clear Heart 1/2" x 4"	2 3/4"	51%	5.80
1/2" x 6"	4 3/4"	31%	5.05
1/2" x 8"	6 3/4"	23%	4.20
Rough Sawn 7/8" x 8"	6 3/4"	23%	4.35
7/8" x 10"	8 3/4"	19%	4.50
7/8" x 12"	10 3/4"	17%	4.50
3/4" x 12"	-	-	3.90
Redwood Beveled - Clear Heart			
1/2" x 6"	4 3/4"	31%	5.45
1/2" x 8"	6 3/4"	23%	5.40
5/8" x 10"	8 3/4"	19%	5.55
3/4" x 6"	4 3/4"	31%	5.65
3/4" x 8"	6 3/4"	23%	6.30
3/4" x 6" Board - Clear -		Varies	3.30
3/4" Tongue & Groove -		Varies	5.15
1" Rustic Beveled - 6" and 8"		Varies	5.75
5/4" Rustic Beveled - 6" and 8"		Varies	5.60

	UNIT	COST
Add for Metal Corners	Each	1.55
Add for Mitering Corners	Each	3.20

.12

	UNIT	COST
Plywood Fir AC Smooth -One Side 1/4"	SqFt	1.95
3/8"	SqFt	2.10
1/2"	SqFt	2.15
5/8"	SqFt	2.30
3/4"	SqFt	2.50
5/8" - Grooved and Rough Faced	SqFt	2.60
Cedar - Rough Sawn 3/8"	SqFt	2.50
5/8"	SqFt	2.60
3/4"	SqFt	3.10
5/8" - Grooved and Rough Faced	SqFt	3.10
Add for Wood Batten Strips, 1" x 2" - 4' O.C.	SqFt	.40
Add for Splines	SqFt	.40

.13 Hardboard - Paneling and Lap Siding (Primed)

		UNIT	COST
3/8" Rough Textured Paneling -	4' x 8'	SqFt	2.05
7/16" Grooved -	4' x 8'	SqFt	1.95
7/16" Stucco Board Paneling		SqFt	2.15
7/16" x 8" Lap Siding		SqFt	2.45
7/16" x 12" Lap Siding		SqFt	2.35
Add for Pre-Finishing		SqFt	.20

.14 Shingles

		UNIT	COST
Wood- 16" Red Cedar - 12" to Weather	- #1	SqFt	4.00
	- #2	SqFt	3.20
	- #3	SqFt	3.00
24" - 1/2" to 3/4" Red Cedar Hand Splits	- #1	SqFt	3.40
24" - 3/4" to 1 1/4" Red Cedar Hand Splits	- #1	SqFt	3.80
	- #2	SqFt	3.40
	- #3	SqFt	3.20
Add for Fire Retardant		SqFt	.47
Add for 3/8" Backer Board		SqFt	.80
Add for Metal Corners		Each	1.50
Add for Ridges, Hips and Corners		LnFt	4.15
Add for 8" to Weather		SqFt	25%

		COST		
		LN FT	or	SQ FT

0602.0 FINISH CARPENTRY, Cont'd...

	LN FT	SQ FT
.15 Facia - Pine #2 1" x 8"	1.90	2.84
Cedar #3 1" x 8"	2.90	4.25
Redwood - Clear 1" x 8"	4.10	6.20
Plywood 5/8" - ACX 1" x 8"	1.95	2.95
.16 Soffit - Plywood 1/2" - ACX 1/2" Fir ACX		3.20
Aluminum		3.20
Plastic (Egg Crate)		3.40

.2 FINISH WALLS (Interior) (15% Added for Size & Cutting)

	SQ FT
.21 Boards, Cedar - #3 1" x 6" and 1" x 8"	4.20
Knotty 1" x 6" and 1" x 8"	4.40
D Grade 1" x 6" and 1" x 8"	5.20
Aromatic 1" x 6" and 1" x 8"	5.40
Redwood - Construction 1" x 6" and 1" x 8"	4.60
Clear 1" x 6" and 1" x 8"	5.95
Fir - Beaded 5/8" x 4"	4.00
Pine - #2 1" x 6" and 1" x 8"	3.15
.22 Hardboard (Paneling) Tempered - 1/8"	1.30
1/4"	1.46
.23 Plywood (Prefinished Paneling) 1/4" Birch - Natural	3.08
3/4" Birch - Natural	4.05
1/4" Birch - White	3.80
1/4" Oak - Rotary Cut	2.95
3/4"	4.22
1/4" Oak - White	4.05
1/4" Mahogany (Lauan)	2.15
3/4"	3.18
3/4" Mahogany (African)	5.35
1/4" Walnut	5.83
.24 Gypsum Board (Paneling) - See 0902	

		COST	
		Prefinished Red Oak or Birch	Plastic Laminate
0603.0 MILLWORK & CUSTOM WOODWORK	**UNIT**		
.1 CUSTOM CABINET WORK (Red Oak or Birch)			
Base Cabinets - Avg. 35" H x 24" D with Drawer	LnFt	193.00	195.00
Sink Fronts	LnFt	115.00	117.00
Corner Cabinets	LnFt	250.00	255.00
Add per Drawer	LnFt	50.00	51.50
Upper Cabinets - Avg. 30" High x 12" Deep	LnFt	145.00	148.00
Utility Cabinets - Avg. 84" High x 24" Deep	LnFt	378.00	373.00
China or Corner Cabinets - 84" High	Each	695.00	713.00
Oven Cabinets - 84" High x 24" Deep	Each	475.00	472.00
Vanity Cabinets - Avg. 30" High x 21" Deep	Each	250.00	250.00
Deduct for Prefinishing Wood	Each	12%	-
.2 COUNTER TOPS - 25"			
Plastic Laminated with 4" Back Splash	LnFt	-	58.00
Deduct for No Back Splash	LnFt	-	10.30
Granite - 1 1/4" - Artificial	LnFt	-	115.00
3/4" - Artificial	LnFt	-	92.00
Marble	LnFt	-	110.00
Artificial	LnFt	-	96.00
Wood Cutting Block	LnFt	-	110.00
Stainless Steel	LnFt	-	170.00
Polyester-Acrylic Solid Surface	LnFt	-	188.00
Quartz	LnFt	-	100.00
Plastic (Polymer)	LnFt	-	72.00

(See 1103 for Stock Cabinets)

0603.0 MILLWORK & CUSTOM WOODWORK, Cont'd...

.3   CUSTOM DOOR FRAMES - Including 2 Sides Trim

	UNIT	COST
Birch	Each	305.00
Fir	Each	188.00
Poplar	Each	194.00
Oak	Each	240.00
Pine	Each	230.00
Walnut	Each	440.00

See 0802.87 for Stock Prehung Units

.4   MOULDINGS AND TRIM

	Birch	Fir	Poplar	Oak	Pine
Apron 7/16" x 2"	3.30	-	2.15	2.80	2.24
Astragal 1 3/4" x 2 1/4"	-	-	-	7.10	5.42
Base 7/16" x 2 3/4"	3.80	1.95	2.20	2.92	3.30
9/16" x 3 1/4"	5.05	-	-	4.44	4.50
Base Shoe 7/16" x 2 3/4"	-	-	1.92	2.60	2.70
Batten Strip 5/8" x 1 5/8"	-	1.56	-	2.90	2.35
Brick Mould 1 1/14" x 2"	-	2.72	-	-	2.73
Casing 11/16" x 2 1/4"	3.50	2.15	2.36	3.30	2.98
3/4" x 3 1/2"	4.78	2.72	2.40	4.75	4.12
Chair Rail 5/8" x 1 3/4"	3.80	-	3.00	3.82	3.00
Closet Rod 1 5/16"	-	2.78	-	-	3.40
Corner Bead 1 1/8" x 1 1/8"	-	2.40	3.00	3.70	4.22
Cove Moulding 3/4" x 3/4"	3.20	-	2.56	3.08	2.57
Crown Moulding 9/16" x 3 5/8"	5.76	-	3.74	4.70	3.95
11/16" x 4 5/8"	6.75	-	-	7.40	6.30
Drip Cap	-	-	-	-	3.10
Half Round 1/2" x 1"	-	-	-	-	3.63
Hand Rail 1 5/8" x 1 3/4"	-	4.17	4.55	7.30	4.00
Hook Strip 5/8" x 2 1/2"	-	2.25	2.58	-	2.70
Picture Mould 3/4" x 1 1/2"	2.28	-	-	3.32	3.00
Quarter Round 3/4" x 3/4"	-	1.34	1.70	2.66	2.10
1/2" x 1/2"	-	1.45	-	-	1.63
Sill 3/4" x 2 1/2"	-	2.72	-	-	3.62
Stool 11/16 x 2 1/2"	5.80	2.72	4.02	6.40	4.34

	UNIT	Birch	Oak	Pine
.5 STAIRS (Treads, Risers, Skirt Boards)	LnFt	40.00	32.00	23.50
.6 SHELVING (12" Deep)	SqFt	42.20	38.20	25.75
.7 CUSTOM PANELING	SqFt	29.10	21.50	18.00
.8 THRESHOLDS - 3/4" x 3 1/2"	LnFt	-	20.60	-

0604.0 GLUE LAMINATE

	UNIT	COST
Arches 80' Span	SqFt	10.20
Beams & Purlins 40' Span	SqFt	7.00
Deck Fir - 3" x 6"	SqFt	8.75
4" x 6"	SqFt	9.70
Deck Cedar - 3" x 6"	SqFt	10.30
4" x 6"	SqFt	11.10
Deck Pine - 3" x 6"	SqFt	8.00

0605.0 PREFABRICATED WOOD & PLYWOOD COMPONENTS

			UNIT	COST		UNIT	COST
.1	**WOOD TRUSSED RAFTERS -** 24" O.C. - 4 -12 Pitch						
	Span To 16'	w/ Supports	Each	140.00	or	SqFt	4.40
	20'	and	Each	150.00		SqFt	3.75
	22'	2' Overhang	Each	153.00		SqFt	3.50
	24'		Each	160.00		SqFt	3.32
	26'		Each	166.00		SqFt	3.20
	28'		Each	183.00		SqFt	3.28
	30'		Each	216.00		SqFt	3.60
	32'		Each	240.00		SqFt	3.75
	Add for 5-12 Pitch		Each	5%		SqFt	15%
	Add for 6-12 Pitch		Each	12%		SqFt	25%
	Add for Scissor Truss		Each	30.00		SqFt	.24
	Add for Gable End 24'		Each	65.00		SqFt	.44
.2	**WOOD FLOOR TRUSS JOISTS (TJI)**						
	Open Web - Wood or Metal - 24" O.C.						
	Up To 23' Span x 12"	Single	LnFt	8.72	or	SqFt	4.36
	To 24' Span x 15"	Cord	LnFt	8.94		SqFt	4.47
	To 27' Span x 18"		LnFt	9.16		SqFt	4.58
	To 30' Span x 21"		LnFt	9.70		SqFt	4.85
	To 25' Span x 15"	Double	LnFt	8.60		SqFt	4.34
	To 30' Span x 18"	Cord	LnFt	8.95		SqFt	4.48
	To 36' Span x 21"		LnFt	10.00		SqFt	5.00
	Plywood Web - 24" O.C.						
	Up To 15' x 9 1/2"		LnFt	5.60		SqFt	2.80
	To 19' x 11 7/8"		LnFt	5.65		SqFt	2.83
	To 21' x 14"		LnFt	6.30		SqFt	3.15
	To 22' x 16"		LnFt	7.00		SqFt	3.50
.3	**LAMINATED VENEER STRUCTURAL BEAMS**						
.31	Micro Lam - Plywood - 24" O.C.						
	9 1/2" x 1 3/4"		LnFt	7.80	or	SqFt	3.92
	11 7/8" x 1 3/4"		LnFt	8.44		SqFt	4.22
	14" x 1 3/4"		LnFt	10.00		SqFt	5.00
	16" x 1 3/4"		LnFt	11.10		SqFt	5.55
.32	Glue Lam- Dimension Lumber- 24" O.C.						
	9" x 3 1/2"		LnFt	14.60		SqFt	7.30
	12" x 3 1/2"		LnFt	16.90		SqFt	8.45
	15" x 3 1/2"		LnFt	18.80		SqFt	9.40
	9" x 5 1/2"		LnFt	19.00		SqFt	9.50
	12" x 5 1/2"		LnFt	23.20		SqFt	11.60
	15" x 5 1/2"		LnFt	29.40		SqFt	14.70
	18" x 5 1/2"		LnFt	35.60		SqFt	17.80
	Add for Architectural Grade		LnFt	25%			
	Add for 6 3/4"		LnFt	40%			

0606.0 WOOD TREATMENTS

		UNIT	COST
PRESERVATIVES – PRESSURE TREATED			
Dimensions		BdFt	.22
Timbers		BdFt	.34
FIRE RETARDENTS			
Dimensions & Timbers		BdFt	.43

0607.0 ROUGH HARDWARE

		UNIT	COST
.1	NAILS	SqFt or BdFt	.02
.2	JOIST HANGERS	Each	3.50
.3	BOLTS - 5/8" x 12"	Each	4.10

DIVISION #7 - THERMAL & MOISTURE PROTECTION

0701.0	WATERPROOFING (L&M) (Roofers)	UNIT	LABOR	MATERIAL
.1	MEMBRANE			
	1 Ply Membrane - Felt 15#	SqFt	.60	.45
	Fabric and Felt	SqFt	.80	.49
	2 Ply Membrane - Felt 15#	SqFt	1.00	.70
	Fabric and Felt	SqFt	1.20	.72
.2	HYDROLITHIC	SqFt	1.00	1.03
.3	ELASTOMERIC- Rubberized Asphalt .060M & Poly	SqFt	1.00	.70
	Liquid	SqFt	1.15	.85
.4	METALLIC OXIDE- 3 Coat	SqFt	.95	2.15
	3 Coat with Sand & Cement Cover	SqFt	1.20	2.40
.5	VINYL PLASTIC	SqFt	.60	1.40
.6	BENTONITE - 3/8"	SqFt	.85	.78

0702.0	DAMPPROOFING (Roofers or Laborers)	UNIT	LABOR	MATERIAL
.1	BITUMINOUS (Asphalt)			
.11	Trowel Mastics			
	Asphalt 1/16" (12 Sq.Ft. Gal.)	SqFt	.35	.29
	1/8" (20 Sq.Ft. Gal.)	SqFt	.40	.35
.12	Spray or Brush Liquid			
	Asphalt - 1 Coat - Spray	SqFt	.25	.20
	Spray	SqFt	.32	.25
	Brush	SqFt	.40	.28
.13	Hot Mop			
	Asphalt - 1 Coat - Including Primer	SqFt	.60	.47
	Fibrous Asphalt - 1 Coat	SqFt	.65	.50
.14	Trowel Mastics & Pre-formed Vapor Barriers			
	Mastic Fabric Mastic	SqFt	.60	.95
	and Polyvinyl Chloride	SqFt	.60	.78
.2	CEMENTITIOUS - 1 Coat - 1/2"	SqFt	.40	.20
	2 Coat - 1"	SqFt	.50	.24
.3	SILICONE (Masonry) - 1 Coat	SqFt	.30	.21
	2 Coat	SqFt	.40	.34
	Add for Scaffold to Above Sections	SqFt	.30	.14

0703.0	BUILDING INSULATION (S) (Carpenters)	UNIT	LABOR	MATERIAL
.1	FLEXIBLE (Batts and Rolls) - Friction			
	Fiberglass			
	2 1/4" R 7.4	SqFt	.30	.23
	3 1/2" R 11.0	SqFt	.30	.27
	3 5/8" R 13	SqFt.	.30	.36
	6" R 19.0	SqFt	.35	.42
	9" R 30.0	SqFt	.40	.68
	Add for Paper Faced Batts	SqFt	.02	.03
	Add for Polyethylene Barrier 2 Mil	SqFt	.04	.04
	Add for Staggered Stud Installation	SqFt	.10	.03

0703.0 BUILDING INSULATION, Cont'd...

		UNIT	LABOR	MATERIAL
.2	**RIGID**			
	Fiberglass			
	1" R 4.35 3# Density	SqFt	.35	.46
	1 1/2" R 6.52 3# Density	SqFt	.35	.84
	2" R 8.70 3# Density	SqFt	.40	1.05
	Add for 4.2# Density per Inch	SqFt	-	.11
	Add for 6.0# Density per Inch	SqFt	-	.35
	Add for Kraft Paper Backed	SqFt	-	.11
	Add for Aluminum Foil Backed	SqFt	-	.47
	Add for Fireproof Type	SqFt	-	10%
	Expanded Styrene			
	Molded, White (Bead Board)			
	1" x 16" x 8' R 5.40	SqFt	.35	.19
	1" x 24" x 8', T&G R 5.40	SqFt	.40	.26
	1 1/2" R 6.52	SqFt	.40	.29
	2" R 7.69	SqFt	.45	.38
	2" x 24" x 8', T&G R 7.69	SqFt	.45	.54
	Extruded, Blue			
	1" x 24" x 8' R 5.40	SqFt	.35	.44
	T&G	SqFt	.40	.55
	1 1/2" R 6.52	SqFt	.40	.55
	2" R 7.69	SqFt	.45	.57
	2" x 24" x 8', T&G R 7.69	SqFt	.45	.69
	Perlite			
	1" R 2.78	SqFt	.35	.43
	2" R 5.56	SqFt	.45	.87
	Urethane			
	1" R 6.67	SqFt	.40	.53
	2" R 13.34	SqFt	.45	.76
.3	**LOOSE**			
	Expanded Styrene 1" R 3.80	SqFt	.30	.24
	Fiberglass 1" R 2.20	SqFt	.30	.25
	Rockwool 1" R 2.90	SqFt	.30	.25
	Cellulose 1" R 3.70	SqFt	.30	.26
.4	**FOAMED**			
	Urethane per Inch or Bd.Ft.	SqFt	.50	.90
.5	**SPRAYED**			
	Fibered Cellulose per Inch or Bd.Ft.	SqFt	.50	.55
	Polystyrene per Inch or Bd.Ft.	SqFt	.60	.63
	Urethane per Inch or Bd.Ft.	SqFt	.65	1.13
.6	**ALUMINUM PAPER**	SqFt	.20	.20
.7	**VINYL FACED FIBERGLASS**			
	2 5/8" x 63 1/2" x 96" R 10.0	SqFt	.50	.98
	Add to All Above for Ceiling Work	SqFt	.10	-
	Add to All Above for Clip On	SqFt	.10	.02
	Add to All Above for Scaffold	SqFt	.25	.16

See Division 3 for Cementitious Poured and Rigid Insulation
See Division 4 for Core and Cavity Filled Masonry
See Division 7 for Roof Insulation
See Division 15 for Mechanical Insulations

0704.0 ROOF AND DECK INSULATION (L&M) (Roofers)	UNIT	COST
.1 RIGID - NON RATED		
Fiber Board 1/2" R 1.39	Sq	57.00
3/4" R 2.09	Sq	68.00
1" R 2.78	Sq	80.00
Fiberglass 1" R 3.70	Sq	93.00
1 1/2" R 2.09	Sq	122.00
Perlite 1/2" R 1.39	Sq	57.00
3/4" R 2.09	Sq	70.00
1" R 2.78	Sq	82.00
2" R 5.26	Sq	123.00
Expanded Polystrene 1" R 4.35	Sq	79.00
1 1/2" R 6.52	Sq	92.00
2" R 7.69	Sq	114.00
.2 RIGID - FIRE RATED		
Isocyanurate 1" R 6.30 Glass Faced	Sq	126.00
1 1/5" R 7.60	Sq	131.00
1 1/2" R 10.00	Sq	137.00
1 3/4" R 12.00	Sq	149.00
2" R 14.00	Sq	155.00
Phenolic Foam 1" R 7.60	Sq	103.00
1 1/2" R 12.50	Sq	118.00
2" R 16.60	Sq	144.00
Add for 5/8" Sheet Rock over Steel Deck	Sq	18.90
Add for Fiber or Mineral Cants	LnFt	2.10
Add for Felt Faces	Sq	12.60
Add for Composite Insulations	Sq	25%
.3 SPRAYED - 2" Polystyrene	Sq	290.00
0705.0 MEMBRANE ROOFING (L&M) (Roofers)		
.1 BUILT-UP ROOFING (50 SQUARES OR MORE)		
Asphalt & Gravel - 3-Ply	Sq	172.00
4 - Ply	Sq	185.50
5 - Ply	Sq	210.00
Add for Pitch and Gravel	Sq	53.00
Add for Curbed Openings	Each	155.00
Add for Round Vent Openings	Each	140.00
Add for Roof Skids	LnFt	35.00
Add for Sloped Roofs	Sq	41.00
Add for Applications on Wood	Sq	14.00
Add for Marble Chips	Sq	59.00
Add for Barriers - 15" Felt	Sq	12.00
Fire Resistant	Sq	28.00
Add for Walkways - 1"	SqFt	5.30
Add for Bond	Sq	13.00
Add for Roof Openings Cut in Existing	Each	490.00

See Quick Estimating 7A-10 for Combined Roofing, Insulation and Sheet Metal

0706.0 SINGLE-PLY ROOFING No Insulation or Flashing Included

	UNIT	Gravel Ballast	Application Mechanical Fastened	Adhesive Fastened
Butylene 100 mil	Sq	225.00	245.00	249.00
EPDM 50 mil	Sq	175.00	215.00	254.00
Neoprene 60 mil	Sq	330.00	390.00	273.00
P.V.C. 50 mil	Sq	165.00	240.00	262.00
Add per Opening	Opng	160.00	-	-

0707.0 TRAFFIC ROOF COATINGS (L&M)

		UNIT	LABOR	MATERIAL
.1	PEDESTRIAN TRAFFIC TYPE	SqFt	-	7.85
.2	VEHICULAR TRAFFIC TYPE			
	Rubberized Coating with 3/4" Asphalt Topping	SqFt	-	5.50
	Polyurethane with Non-Slip Aggregates on 20 mil silicone rubber	SqFt	-	5.10
	Elastomeric with Non-Skid - 2 Coat	SqFt	-	3.40
	3 Coat	SqFt	-	4.25

0708.0 SHINGLE, TILE and CORRUGATED ROOFING

		UNIT	LABOR	MATERIAL
.1	ASPHALT SHINGLES (S) (Carpenters) 4-12 Pitch			
	Square Butt 235#- Seal Down	SqFt	.50	.49
	300# - Laminated	SqFt	.55	.73
	325# - Fire Resistant	SqFt	.60	.73
	Timberline 300# - 25 Year	SqFt	.70	.64
	300# - 30 Year	SqFt	.70	.80
	Tab Lock 340#	SqFt	.70	1.09
	Roll 90# - 100 SqFt per Roll	SqFt	.30	.23
	55# - 100 SqFt per Roll	SqFt	.25	.20
	Base Starter - 240 SqFt per Roll	SqFt	.25	.28
	Ice & Water Starter - 100 SqFt per Roll	SqFt	.30	.51
	Add for Boston Ridge Shingle	LnFt	1.30	.58
	Add for 15# Felt Underlayment	SqFt	.06	.04
	Add for Pitches 6-12 & Up - Ea Pitch Increase	SqFt	.06	-
	Add for Removal and Haul - Away (2 Layers)	SqFt	.35	.17
	Add for Chimneys, Skylights & Bay Windows	Each	50.00	-
.2	FIBERGLASS SHINGLES - 215# - Seal Down	SqFt	.50	.49
	250# - Seal Down	SqFt	.55	.73
.3	WOOD			
	Sawed			
	Red Cedar - 16" x 5" to Weather - #1 Grade	SqFt	.90	2.01
	#2 Grade	SqFt	.90	1.54
	#3 Grade	SqFt	.80	1.01
	Hand Splits			
	Red Cedar - 1/2" x 3/4", 24" x 10" to Weather	SqFt	1.05	1.75
	3/4"x1 1/4", 24" x 10" to Weather	SqFt	1.15	2.12
	Fancy Butt - 7" to Weather	SqFt	1.30	4.03
	Add for Fire Retardant	SqFt	-	.48
	Add for Pitches over 5-12, Each Pitch Increase	SqFt	.08	-
.4	METAL			
	Aluminum - Mill .020	SqFt	.95	1.91
	.030	SqFt	.95	2.28
	Anodized .020	SqFt	.95	2.39
	.030	SqFt	.95	2.70
	Steel - Enameled - Colored	SqFt	1.00	3.23
	Galvanized - Colored	SqFt	1.00	2.49

0708.0 SHINGLE, TILE AND CORRUGATED ROOFING, Cont'd...

		UNIT	COST
.6	SLATE SHINGLES (Incl. Underlayment) (L&M) (Roofers)		
	Vermont and Pennsylvania		
	3/16" - 6 1/2" to 8 1/2" to Weather		
	Weathered Green or Black	Sq	1,200.00
	Gray	Sq	1,200.00
	Fading Purple	Sq	1,200.00
	Unfading Purple	Sq	1,600.00
	Add for Variegated Colors & Sizes - 1/4" to 1/2"	Sq	410.00
	3/8" to 1"	Sq	800.00
	Add for Hips and Valleys	LnFt	65.00
	Add for Pitches over 6-12	Sq	85.00
.7	TILE (L&M) (Roofers)		
.71	Clay, Interlocking Shingle Type - Designed	Sq	1,200.00
	Early American	Sq	1,200.00
	Williamsburg	Sq	1,300.00
	Mormon	Sq	1,900.00
	Architectural Pattern Shingle Type - Provincial	Sq	1,100.00
	Georgian	Sq	1,100.00
	Colonial	Sq	1,100.00
	Spanish, Red	Sq	820.00
	Mission	Sq	1,325.00
.72	Concrete - Plain - 10" to Weather - 9" Wide	Sq	730.00
	Colored	Sq	810.00
	Add for Staggered Installation	Sq	270.00
.73	Steel - 16 Ga - Ceramic Coated	Sq	490.00
.74	Aluminum .019	Sq	580.00
.8	CORRUGATED PANELS		
.81	Concrete - Plain	Sq	4.15
.82	Vinyl - 120	Sq	6.60
.83	Fiberglass - 8 oz	Sq	4.35
.84	Aluminum .024 - Plain	Sq	3.65
	.024 - Painted	Sq	4.45
	See Division 5 for Corrugated Metal Panels		

0709.0 SHEET METAL WORK (L&M)

			COST			
(Sheet Metal Workers)		UNIT	Galvanized 25 Ga	Aluminum .032"	Copper 16 oz	Enameled
.1	DOWNSPOUTS, GUTTERS AND FITTINGS					
	Downspouts - 3" x 2"	LnFt	2.90	3.00	8.25	3.70
	4" x 3"	LnFt	3.65	4.00	11.80	4.95
	5" x 4"	LnFt	5.00	5.20	13.00	6.25
	Round 3"	LnFt	2.80	3.50	7.60	3.60
	4"	LnFt	3.30	4.20	9.00	4.60
	5"	LnFt	4.15	5.10	10.00	5.55
	Chute Type 4" x 6"	LnFt	4.80	5.70	-	5.60
	5" x 7"	LnFt	5.50	6.45	-	7.65
	Gutters - Box or Half Round 4"	LnFt	3.90	5.10	8.25	5.85
	5"	LnFt	4.60	5.20	10.20	6.05
	6"	LnFt	5.50	6.00	10.45	6.30
	Add for Guards	LnFt	-	1.25	-	-
	Fittings (Elbows, Corners, etc.)	LnFt	11.70	11.10	14.10	13.70

See Quick Estimating 7A-10 for Combined Roofing, Insulation and Sheet Metal.

0709.0   SHEET METAL WORK, Cont'd...

			COST			
	UNIT	Galva-nized 25 Ga	Alum-inum .032"	Copper 16 oz	Enameled	PVC
.2 FASCIAS, GRAVEL STOPS & TRIM						
Fascias - 6"	LnFt	5.45	8.30	13.20	6.80	7.50
8"	LnFt	5.85	9.30	14.85	7.20	8.30
Copings - 12"	LnFt	7.05	10.95	15.75	8.40	-
Scuppers	Each	180.00	128.50	165.00	138.00	-
Gravel Stops - 4"	LnFt	5.35	7.70	10.10	6.80	-
6"	LnFt	5.00	8.70	12.55	7.20	7.70
8"	LnFt	6.50	9.20	14.10	7.85	8.20
Add for Durodonic Finish	LnFt		25%			

.3 FLASHINGS	UNIT	COST
Galvanized - 25 ga	SqFt	5.50
Aluminum - .019	SqFt	5.30
.032	SqFt	5.60
Copper - 16 oz	SqFt	9.10
20 oz	SqFt	9.40
Asphalted Fabric - Plain	SqFt	2.90
Copper Backed	SqFt	4.60
Aluminum Back	SqFt	4.10
Vinyl Fabric - .020	SqFt	1.40
.030	SqFt	1.60
Lead - 2.5#	SqFt	8.40
Rubber - 1/16"	SqFt	9.00
PVC - 24 mil	SqFt	3.70

.4 SHEET METAL ROOFING - Including Underlayment	UNIT	COST
Copper - Standing Seam - 16 oz	Sq	1,300.00
20 oz	Sq	1,350.00
Batten Seam 16 oz	Sq	1,200.00
20 oz	Sq	1,350.00
Flat Lock 16 oz	Sq	1,100.00
20 oz	Sq	1,300.00
Stainless Steel - Batten Seam 28 ga	Sq	1,170.00
Standing Seam 28 ga	Sq	1,300.00
Flat Seam 28 ga	Sq	1,120.00
Monel - Batten Seam .018"	Sq	1,360.00
Standing Seam .018"	Sq	1,390.00
Flat Seam .108"	Sq	1,280.00
Lead - Copper Coated - Batten Seam 3 lb	Sq	1,270.00
Flat Seam 3 lb	Sq	1,300.00
Aluminum - Clad	Sq	1,000.00
Galvanized - Colored .020"	Sq	1,000.00
See Division 5 for Corrugated Type		

.5 EXPANSION JOINTS - 2 1/2"	UNIT	COST
Polyethylene with galvanized	LnFt	7.95
Galvanized 25 ga	LnFt	9.30
Aluminum .032	LnFt	10.55
Copper 16 oz	LnFt	25.40
Stainless Steel	LnFt	14.00
Neoprene	LnFt	10.20
Butyl	LnFt	8.15
Add for 3 1/2"	LnFt	10%

0710.0 ROOF AND SOFFITT ACCESSORIES

(L&M) (Roofers)	UNIT	COST	or	UNIT	COST
.1 SKYLIGHTS					
Example: 4' - 0" x 4' - 0"	SqFt	42.00		Each	680.00
8' - 0" x 8' - 0"	SqFt	26.00		Each	1,700.00
.2 SKY DOMES (Plastic - Clear or White)					
20" x 20" Single				Each	189.00
Double				Each	220.00
24" x 24" Single				Each	225.00
Double				Each	270.00
48" x 48" Single				Each	550.00
Double				Each	625.00
72" x 72" Single				Each	925.00
Double				Each	1,100.00
96" x 96" Double				Each	1,750.00
Add for Bronze Top Colors				-	10%
Add for Electric Operated Type				Each	5.25
Add for Pyramid Type				Each	100%
Add for Hip Type				Each	50%
.3 GRAVITY VENTILATORS					
Diameter Aluminum or Galvanized 12"				Each	120.00
24"				Each	285.00
.4 SMOKE VENTILATORS					
Example: 48" x 96" - Aluminum				Each	2,400.00
48" x 48" - Steel				Each	2,300.00
.5 PREFAB CURBS & EXPANSION JOINTS - 3" Fibered				LnFt	1.95
4" Fibered				LnFt	2.00
.6 ROOF LINE LOUVRES				LnFt	1.90
.7 TURBINE VENTILATORS - 12"				Each	395.00
24"				Each	405.00
.8 CUPOLAS				Each	410.00
.9 ROOF VENTS - P.V.C.				Each	70.00
Aluminum				Each	63.00
See 1012 for Roof Hatches					

0711.0 SEALANTS (L&M) (Carpenters)

	UNIT	COST
.1 CAULKING - 1/2" x 1/2" Joints		
Windows and Doors - 2-Part Proprietary (Oil Base)	LnFt	2.25
Silicone Rubber	LnFt	2.60
Polysulfide (Thiakol)	LnFt	2.80
Acrylic	LnFt	2.70
Polyurethane	LnFt	2.70
Control Joints - 2 - Part Proprietary	LnFt	2.45
Silicone Rubber	LnFt	2.90
Polysulfide	LnFt	3.90
Acrylic	LnFt	2.90
Polyurethane	LnFt	2.90
Stone Pointing -Silicone Rubber	LnFt	3.30
Polysulfide	LnFt	3.40
Acrylic	LnFt	2.90
Add for Swing Stage Work	LnFt	.58
Add for 3/4" x 3/4" Joints	LnFt	1.05
Deduct for 1/4" x 1/4" Joints	LnFt	.32
.2 GASKETS AND JOINT FILLERS		
Gaskets - 1/4" Polyvinyl x 6"	LnFt	2.65
1/2" Polyvinyl x 6"	LnFt	3.30
1/4" Neoprene x 6"	LnFt	3.50
1/2" Neoprene x 6"	LnFt	4.45
Joint Fillers -1/2"	LnFt	.40
3/4"	LnFt	.46
1"	LnFt	.49

	SQ.FT. COST
0701.0 WATERPROOFING	
1-Ply Membrane Felt 15#	1.50
2-Ply Membrane Felt 15#	2.30
Hydrolithic	2.50
Elastomeric Rubberized Asphalt with Poly Sheet	2.30
Liquid	2.50
Metallic Oxide 3-Coat	3.95
Vinyl Plastic	2.75
Bentonite 3/8" - Trowel	1.85
5/8" - Panels	2.10
0702.0 DAMPPROOFING	
Asphalt Trowel Mastic 1/16"	.92
1/8"	1.10
Spray Liquid 1-Coat	.58
2-Coat	.80
Brush Liquid 2-Coat	.90
Hot Mop 1-Coat and Primer	1.50
1 Fibrous Asphalt	1.65
Cementitious Per Coat 1/2" Coat	.75
Silicone 1-Coat	.55
2-Coat	.85
Add for Scaffold and Lift Operations	.48
0703.0 BUILDING INSULATION	
FLEXIBLE	
Fiberglass 2 1/4" R 7.40	.70
3 1/2" R 11.00	.80
3 5/8" R 13.00	.90
6" R 19.00	1.00
9" R 30.00	1.30
12" R 38.00	1.40
Add for Ceiling Work	.09
Add for Paper Faced	.11
Add for Polystyrene Barrier (2m)	.11
Add for Scaffold Work	.57
RIGID	
Fiberglass 1" R 4.35 3# Density	1.05
1 1/2" R 6.52 3# Density	1.30
2" R 8.70 3# Density	1.60
Styrene, Molded 1" R 4.35	.80
1 1/2" R 6.52	.90
2" R 7.69	1.20
2" T&G R 7.69	1.55
Styrene, Extruded 1" R 5.40	1.10
1 1/2" R 6.52	1.30
2" R 7.69	1.40
2" T&G R 7.69	1.55
Perlite 1" R 2.78	1.10
2" R 5.56	1.75
Urethane 1" R 6.67	1.30
2" R 13.34	1.65
Add for Glued Applications	.09

	SQ.FT.COST
0703.0 BUILDING INSULATION, Cont'd...	
LOOSE 1" Styrene R 3.8	.77
1" Fiberglass R 2.2	.74
1" Rock Wool R 2.9	.76
1" Cellulose R 3.7	.72
FOAMED Urethane Per Inch	1.89
SPRAYED Cellulose Per Inch	1.37
Polystyrene	1.63
Urethane	2.31
ALUMINUM PAPER	.63
VINYL FACED FIBERGLASS	1.85

0704.0 ROOF & DECK INSULATION - COMBINED WITH 0709.0 BELOW

0705.0 MEMBRANE ROOFING - COMBINED WITH 0709.0 BELOW

0708.0 SHINGLE ROOFING

ASPHALT SHINGLES 235# Seal Down	1.50
300# Laminated	1.90
325" Fire Resistant	1.95
Timberline	1.90
340# Tab Lock	2.50
ASPHALT ROLL 90#	.85
55#	.80
FIBERGLASS SHINGLES 215#	1.40
250#	1.70
RED CEDAR 16" x 5" to Weather #1 Grade	3.55
#2 Grade	3.15
#3 Grade	2.25
24" x 10" to Weather - Hand Splits - 1/2" x 3/4" #2	3.30
3/4" x 1 1/4" #2	3.85
Add for Fire Retardant	.60
METAL Aluminum 020 Mill	3.80
020 Anodized	4.40
Steel, Enameled Colored	5.50
Galvanized Colored	4.75
Add to Above for 15# Felt Underlayment	
Add for Base Starter	.70
Add for Ice & Water Starter	1.15
Add for Boston Ridge	2.60
Add for Removal & Haul Away	1.00
Add for Pitches Over 5-12 each Pitch Increase	.06
Add for Chimneys, Skylights and Bay Windows - Each	75.00

0704.0/ 0705.0/ 0709.0 - COMBINED ROOFING INSULATION and SHEET METAL

	SQ. COST
MEMBRANE	
3-Ply Asphalt & Gravel - Fiberboard & Perlite - R 10.0	510.00
R 16.6	560.00
4-Ply - R 10.0	570.00
R 16.6	600.00
5-Ply - R 10.0	650.00
R 16.6	730.00
Add for Sheet Rock over Steel Deck - 5/8"	135.00
Add for Fiberglass Insulation	44.00
Add for Pitch and Gravel	70.00
Add for Sloped Roofs	55.00
Add for Thermal Barrier	44.00
Add for Upside Down Roofing System	127.00
SINGLE-PLY - 60M Butylene Roofing & Gravel Ballast - R 10.0	475.00
Mech. Fastened - R 10.0	490.00
PVC & EPDM Roofing & Gravel Ballast - R 10.0	460.00
Mech. Fastened - R 10.0	490.00
Blocking and Cants Not Included	

0801.0 HOLLOW METAL (M) (CARPENTERS)

	UNIT	LABOR	MATERIAL
.1 CUSTOM			
.11 Frames (16 Gauge)			
2'6" x 6'8" x 4 3/4"	Each	58	185
2'8" x 6'8" x 4 3/4"	Each	59	195
3'0" x 6'8" x 4 3/4"	Each	60	205
3'4" x 6'8" x 4 3/4"	Each	73	210
3'6" x 6'8" x 4 3/4"	Each	79	215
4'0" x 6'8" x 4 3/4"	Each	90	225
Deduct for 18 Gauge	Each	8	21.00
Add for 14 Gauge	Each	14	31
Add for A, B, or C Label	Each	8	15.50
Add for Transoms	Each	36	94
Add for Side Lights	Each	38	115
Add for Frames over 7'0" (Height)	Each	38	20.00
Add for Frames over 6 3/4" (Width)	Each	16	20.00
Add for Bolted Frame with Bolts	Each	27	42
.12 Doors (1 3/4" - 18 Gauge)			
2'6" x 6'8" x 1 3/4"	Each	61	223
2'8" x 6'8" x 1 3/4"	Each	62	233
3'0" x 6'8" x 1 3/4"	Each	64	245
3'4" x 6'8" x 1 3/4"	Each	74	256
3'6" x 6'8" x 1 3/4"	Each	83	278
4'0" x 6'8" x 1 3/4"	Each	96	315
Add for 16 Gauge	Each	14	47
Deduct for 20 Gauge	Each	9	20.00
Add for A Label	Each	10	20.00
Add for B or C Label	Each	9	20.00
Add for Vision Panels or Lights	Each	-	90
Add for Louvre Openings	Each	-	82
Add for Galvanizing	Each	-	52
.2 STOCK			
.21 Frames (4 3/4"-5 3/4"-6 3/4"-8 3/4"- 16 Ga)			
2'6" x 6'8" or 7'0"	Each	57	110
2'8" x 6'8" or 7'0"	Each	58	118
3'0" x 6'8" or 7'0"	Each	61	123
3'4" x 6'8" or 7'0"	Each	69	129
3'6" x 6'8" or 7'0"	Each	78	136
4'0" x 6'8" or 7'0"	Each	88	165
See above .11 for Size Change			
Add for Bolted Frame & Bolts	Each	23	42
Add for A, B, or C Label	Each	8	20.00
Deduct Non-Welded Frame (Knock Down)	Each	7	20.00
.22 Doors (1 3/8" or 1 3/4" - 18 Gauge)			
2'6" x 6'8" or 7'0"	Each	61	228
2'8" x 6'8" or 7'0"	Each	62	233
3'0" x 6'8" or 7'0"	Each	64	243
3'4" x 6'8" or 7'0"	Each	73	256
3'6" x 6'8" or 7'0"	Each	81	294
4'0" x 6'8" or 7'0"	Each	90	306
Add for A Label	Each	9	20.00
Add for B or C Label	Each	8	13.65
Add for Galvanizing	Each	-	52

Labor Above Includes Installation of Butts & Locksets

Add to All Above for:			
Door Closures - Surface Mounted	Each	56	120
Panic Bars (Exit Device)	Each	12	560
Kick, Push and Pull Plates	Each	24	42

See 8-13 for Other Hardware

0802.0 WOOD DOORS (M) (CARPENTERS)

See 0603.3 and 0802.5 for Custom Frames
Labor includes Installation of Butts and Locksets

.1 FLUSH DOORS - Pre-Machined

No Label - Standard - Birch - 7 Ply - Paint Grade

	UNIT	LABOR	Hollow Core	Solid Core
2'0" x 6'8" or 1 3/8"	Each	59	113	125
2'4" x 6'8" or 1 3/8"	Each	60	120	130
2'6" x 6'8" or 1 3/8"	Each	61	125	135
2'8" x 6'8" or 1 3/8"	Each	62	130	141
3'0" x 6'8" or 1 3/8"	Each	64	135	152
2'0" x 6'8" or 1 3/4"	Each	60	120	135
2'4" x 6'8" or 1 3/4"	Each	61	125	146
2'6" x 6'8" or 1 3/4"	Each	62	132	150
2'8" x 6'8" or 1 3/4"	Each	63	130	155
3'0" x 6'8" or 1 3/4"	Each	69	135	162
3'4" x 6'8" or 1 3/4"	Each	73	156	183
3'6" x 6'8" or 1 3/4"	Each	77	235	267
3'8" x 6'8" or 1 3/4"	Each	83	255	280
Add for Stain Grade	Each			43
Add for 5 Ply	Each			86
Add for Jamb & Trim - Solid - Knock Down	Each			86
Add for Jamb & Trim- Veneer- Knock Down	Each			75
Add for Red Oak - Rotary	Each			25
Add for Red Oak - Plain Sliced	Each			44
Add for Architectural Grade - 7 Ply	Each			92
Deduct for Lauan	Each			17
Add for Doors over 6'8" per Inch	Each			17
Add for Vinyl Overlay	Each			50
Add for Cutouts and Special Cuts	Each			59
Add for Lite Cutouts with Metal Frames	Each			85
Add for Private Door Eye	Each			24
Add for Wood Louvre	Each			120
Add for Transom Panels & Side Panels	Each	30		130
Add for Astragals	Each	31		55
Add for Trimming Door for Carpet	Each	26		-

Label - Birch - Paint Grade	UNIT	LABOR	MATERIAL 20-Min	45-Min	60-Min
2'0" x 6'8" x 1 3/4"	Each	59	150	182	195
2'4" x 6'8" x 1 3/4"	Each	60	161	193	210
2'6" x 6'8" x 1 3/4"	Each	61	166	204	215
2'8" x 6'8" x 1 3/4"	Each	62	172	251	267
3'0" x 6'8" x 1 3/4"	Each	63	177	294	300
3'4" x 6'8" x 1 3/4"	Each	73	193	315	312
3'6" x 6'8" x 1 3/4"	Each	78	276	331	332
3'8" x 6'8" x 1 3/4"	Each	86	303	340	352
See Above 0602.1 for Changes					

.2 PANEL DOORS

	UNIT	LABOR	MATERIAL Pine	Fir	Oak
Exterior Entranc					
2'8" x 6'8" x 1 3/4"	Each	92	378	390	603
3'0" x 6'8" x 1 3/4"	Each	97	398	410	627
Add for Sidelights	Each	46	222	245	390
Inter					
2'6" x 6'8" x 1 3/8"	Each	70	336	315	495
2'8" x 6'8" x 1 3/8"	Each	75	346	325	505
3'0" x 6'8" x 1 3/8"	Each	80	378	335	515

0802.0 WOOD DOORS (Cont'd...)

.3	LOUVERED DOORS	UNIT	LABOR	Birch/Oak	Pine	Lauan
					MATERIAL	
	1'0" x 6'8" x 1 3/8" Pine	Each	41	430	162	-
	1'3" x 6'8" x 1 3/8"	Each	44	462	167	-
	1'6" x 6'8" x 1 3/8"	Each	49	473	172	-
	2'0" x 6'8" x 1 3/8"	Each	58	558	198	-
	2'4" x 6'8" x 1 3/8"	Each	63	560	215	-
	2'6" x 6'8" x 1 3/8"	Each	63	570	270	-
	2'8" x 6'8" x 1 3/8"	Each	66	590	280	-
	3'0" x 6'8" x 1 3/8"	Each	80	60	-	
	Add for Half Louvered/Panel	Each				15%
	Add for Prehung	Each	-	100	100	0
.4	BI-FOLD - FLUSH					
	2'0" x 6'8" x 1 3/8" Pine	Each	58	-	-	95
	2'4" x 6'8" x 1 3/8"	Each	61	-	-	103
	2'6" x 6'8" x 1 3/8"	Each	66	-	-	104
	2'8" x 6'8" x 1 3/8"	Each	69	-	-	106
	3'0" x 6'8" x 1 3/8"	Each	75	-	-	116
	Add for Oak	Each	-	42	-	-
	Add for Birch	Each	-	37	-	-
	Add for Louvered Type	Each	12			92
	Add for Half Louvered/Panel	Each	12			93
	Add for Decorative Type	Each	12			189
	Add for Prefinished Type	Each	12			24
	Add for Heights over 6'8"	Each	12			5
	Add for Widths over 3'0"	Each	12			6

See 0803.2 for Closet Bi-fold Doors
  and Prehung Stock

.5	CAFE DOORS	UNIT	LABOR	Oak	Pine	Fir
	2'6" x 3'8" x 1 1/8"	Pair	78	-	270	284
	2'8" x 3'8" x 1 1/8"	Pair	86	-	290	295
	3'0" x 3'8" x 1 1/8"	Pair	92	-	302	305
.6	FRENCH - with Grille Patte					
	2'6" x 6'8" x 1 3/8"	Each	92	530	615	380
	2'8" x 6'8" x 1 3/8"	Each	94	550	625	412
	3'0" x 6'8" x 1 3/8"	Each	97	560	630	560
	Add for Prehung	Each	-	100	-	-
.7	DUTCH					
	2'6" x 6'8" x 1 3/4"	Each	115	-	755	-
	2'8" x 6'8" x 1 3/4"	Each	121	-	835	-
	3'0" x 6'8" x 1 3/4"	Each	127	-	860	-

.8	PREHUNG DOOR UNITS - Incl. Frame, Trim, Hardware and Jambs					
	Exterior	UNIT	LABOR	Birch	Pine	Fir
	2'8" x 6'8" x 1 3/4"	Each	77	-	348	-
	3'0" x 6'8" x 1 3/4"	Each	85	-	400	-
	3'4" x 6'8" x 1 3/4"	Each	90	-	510	-
	Add for Insulated	Each	12	-	-	150
	Add for Threshold	Each	12	-	-	20
	Add for Weatherstrip	Each	-	-	-	95
	Add - Sidelites 1'0" HC	Each	26	-	-	177
	Add - Sidelites 1'6" HC	Each	31	-	-	215
	Interior			Birch	Lauan	Oak
	2'6" x 6'8" x 1 3/8"	Each	73	231	162	238
	2'8" x 6'8" x 1 3/8"	Each	77	241	167	244
	3'0" x 6'8" x 1 3/8"	Each	83	252	172	255

0803.0	SPECIAL DOORS				MATERIAL			
.1	BLAST OR NUCLEAR RESISTANT							Pine & Fir
.2	CLOSET - BI-FOLDING (PREHUNG STOCK)			Oak	Birch	Lauan	Pine & Fir
.21	Wood - Units - 1 3/8"	UNIT	LABOR	Flush	Flush	Flush	Panel
	Incl. Jamb, Csg. Track & Hdwe.						
	2 Door - 2'0" x 6'8"	Each	53	190	205	135	450
	2'6" x 6'8"	Each	57	197	215	142	482
	3'0" x 6'8"	Each	61	205	226	148	540
	4 Door - 4'0" x 6'8"	Each	69	310	300	210	755
	5'0" x 6'8"	Each	76	320	320	215	865
	6'0" x 6'8"	Each	85	342	348	245	935
	Incl. Track & Hdwe (Unfinished)						
	2 Door - 2'0" x 6'8"	Each	45	110	103	103	-
	2'6" x 6'8"	Each	51	121	109	110	-
	3'0" x 6'8"	Each	53	131	121	121	-
	4 Door - 4'0" x 6'8"	Each	56	179	158	158	-
	5'0" x 6'8"	Each	59	192	188	173	-
	6'0" x 6'8"	Each	63	215	210	189	-
	Add for Louvered Type	Each					100%

		UNIT	LABOR	MATERIAL
.22	Metal			
	Flush 2 Door - 2'0" x 6'8"	Each	44	103
	2'6" x 6'8"	Each	46	109
	3'0" x 6'8"	Each	49	115
	Flush 4 Door - 4'0" x 6'8"	Each	53	142
	5'0" x 6'8"	Each	55	149
	6'0" x 6'8"	Each	61	161
	Add for Plastic Overlay	Each	-	37
	Add for Louvered or Decorative	Each	-	13
.23	Leaded Mirror			
	4 Panel Unit - 4'0" x 6'8"	Each	96	683
	5'0" x 6'8"	Each	102	740
	6'0" x 6'8"	Each	113	800
.3	FLEXIBLE DOORS (M) (CARPENTER)			
	(See 1020 - Retractable Partitions)			
	Wood Slat (Unfinished)	SqFt	2.30	13.15
	Fabric Accordion Fold	SqFt	2.30	10.90
	Vinyl Clad	SqFt	2.30	14.85

				COST
.4	GLASS-ALL (L&M) (GLAZIERS)			
	Manual (Including Hardware)	Each	-	2,550
	Add for Center Locking	Each	-	200
	Automatic (Including Hardware & Operator)			
	Mat or Floor Unit	Each	-	7,200
	Handle Unit	Each	-	7,800
.5	HANGAR (L&M) (IRONWORKERS)			
	Biparting or Sliding - Steel			
	Example: 100' x 20'	Each	-	63,600
	Add for Pass Doors	Each	-	1,550
	Add for Electric Operator	Each	-	2,000
	Add for Insulating	Each	-	2,250
	Tilt Up or Canopy	Each		Approx. Same
.6	METAL COVERED FIRE & INDUSTRIAL SLIDING DOORS			
	3'0" x 7'0" - Flush	Each	-	780
	4'0" x 7'0"	Each	-	2,250
	8'0" x 8'0" - U.L. Label	Each	-	3,010
	10'0" x 10'0"	Each	-	3,800
	10'0" x 12'0"	Each	-	4,150
	12'0" x 12'0"	Each	-	4,600

0803.0   SPECIAL DOORS, Cont'd...

.7   OVERHEAD DOORS (L&M) (CARPENTERS)

	UNIT	COST 1 3/4" Wood	2" 24-Ga Steel
Commercial			
8' x 8'	Each	940.00	985.00
8' x 10'	Each	1,100.00	1,170.00
8' x 12'	Each	1,200.00	1,320.00
10' x 10'	Each	1,380.00	1,550.00
10' x 12'	Each	1,490.00	1,630.00
12' x 12'	Each	1,650.00	1,780.00
14' x 10'	Each	1,700.00	1,830.00
14' x 12'	Each	2,650.00	2,250.00
Add for Panel Door	Each		5%
Add for Low Lift	Each		90.00
Add for High Lift	Each		151.00
Add for Electric Operator	Each		660.00
Add for Insulated Type	Each		10%
Residential			
8' x 7' x 1 3/4"	Each	520.00	550.00
9' x 7' x 1 3/4"	Each	550.00	570.00
16' x 7' x 1 3/4"	Each	1,140.00	1,240.00
Add for Wood Paneled Door	Each		10%
Add for Redwood	Each		250.00
Add for Electric Operator	Each		490.00
Add for Vision Lights	Each		26.50

.8   PLASTIC LAMINATE FACED (M) (CARPENTERS)

	UNIT	LABOR	MATERIAL
1 3/8"	SqFt	4.80	14.20
1 3/4"	SqFt	4.90	14.20
Add for Edge Strip - Vertical	Each		8.30
Add for Edge Strip - Horizontal	Each		7.30
Add for Cutouts	Each		68.70
Add for Metal Frame Cutout	Each		99.30
Add for Decorative Type	SqFt		22.00
Add for Solid Colors	SqFt		10%
Add for 1-hour B Label	SqFt		6.00
Add for 1 1/2-hour B Label	SqFt		6.00
Add for Color Core	-		50%
Add for Machining for Hardware	Each		57.00

.9   REVOLVING DOOR (L&M) (GLAZIERS)

	UNIT	COST
Aluminum		
3 Leaf - 6' - 6" x 6' - 6"	Each	25,900.00
4 Leaf - 6' - 6" x 6' - 6"	Each	27,600.00
6' - 0" x 7' - 0"	Each	20,000.00
Automatic - 6' - 6" x 10' - 0"	Each	39,000.00
Stainless	Each	35,000.00
Bronze	Each	37,800.00
Painted Steel - Dark Room 32"	Each	2,200.00
36"	Each	2,300.00

0803.0 SPECIAL DOORS, Cont'd...

		UNIT	LABOR	MATERIAL
.10	ROLLING DOORS & GRILLES (M) (IRONWORKERS)			
	Doors - Manual - 8' x 8'	Each	470.00	2,200.00
	10' x 10'	Each	486.00	2,300.00
	12' x 12'	Each	500.00	3,100.00
	14' x 14'	Each	530.00	4,700.00
	Add for Electric Controlled	Each	-	345.00
	Add for Fire Doors	Each	-	760.00
	Grilles - Manual -6'8" x 3'2"	Each	210.00	925.00
	6'8" x 4'2"	Each	820.00	1,020.00
	8'0" x 3'2"	Each	230.00	1,080.00
	8'0" x 4'2"	Each	240.00	1,200.00
	Add for Electric Controlled	Each	-	320.00
.11	SHOWER DOORS (M) (CARPENTERS)			
	28" x 66" Obscure Pattern Glass Wire	Each	64.00	170.00
	Tempered Glass	Each	64.00	180.00
.12	SLIDING OR PATIO DOORS (M) (CARPENTERS)			
	ONE SLIDING, ONE FIXED			
	Metal (Aluminum) (Including 5/8" Glass, Threshold, Hardware and Screen)			
	8'0" x 6'10"	Each	170.00	1,345.00
	8'0" x 8'0"	Each	190.00	1,520.00
	Wood (M) (Carpenters) Vinyl Sheathed (Including 5/8" Insulated Dbl. Temp. Glass, Weatherstripped, Hardware and Casing)			
	Vinyl Clad 6' 0" x 6' 8"	Each	170.00	1,830.00
	8' 0" x 6' 8"	Each	200.00	2,200.00
	Pine - Prefinished 6' 0" x 6' 8"	Each	170.00	1,800.00
	8' 0" x 6' 8"	Each	200.00	2,100.00
	Deduct for 3/16" Safety Glass/Insulated	Each	-	200.00
	Add for Tripe Glazing	Each	-	240.00
	Add for Screen	Each	19.00	165.00
	Add for Grilles	Each	23.00	250.00
.13	SOUND REDUCTION (M) (CARPENTERS)			
	Metal	Each	190.00	1,950.00
	Wood	Each	195.00	1,030.00
.14	TRAFFIC (M) (CARPENTERS)			
	Electric Powered			
	Hollow Metal - 8' x 8'	Each	470.00	5,280.00
	8' x 8' High Speed	Each	1,150.00	12,100.00
	Metal Clad (26 ga.) - 8' x 8'	Each	470.00	5,200.00
	Wood	Each	395.00	4,300.00
	Truck Impact - Double Acting (Including Bumpers and Vision Panels)			
	Metal Clad - 8' x 8' Openings	Each	340.00	3,000.00
	Rubber Plastic - 8' x 8' Openings 1/2"	Each	265.00	2,500.00
	Aluminum - 8' x 8' Openings 1 3/4"	Each	290.00	3,100.00
.15	SPECIAL MADE & ENGINEERED INDUSTRIAL DOORS (L&M) (CARPENTERS)			
	Four-Fold Garage Doors - Electric Operated	SqFt	-	120.00
.16	VAULT DOORS (M) (STEEL ERECTORS)			
	1 hour with Frame 6' 6" x 2' 8"	Each	390.00	2,550.00
	2 hour with Frame 6' 6" x 2' 8"	Each	390.00	3,300.00
	6' 6" x 3' 0"	Each	470.00	3,675.00
	6' 6" x 3' 4"	Each	520.00	4,100.00

0804.0 ENTRANCE DOORS, FRAMES & STORE FRONT CONSTRUCTION

Prices Include Hardware & Safety Plate Glazing

		UNIT	COST
.1	ALUMINUM		
.11	Stock		
	Door and Frame - 3' x 7'	Each	1,750.00
	6' x 7'	Each	3,130.00
	Window or Store Front Framing - 10'	SqFt	32.00
.12	Custom		
	Door and Frame - 3' x 7'	Each	2,100.00
	6' x 7'	Each	4,060.00
	Window or Store Front Framing - 10'	SqFt	39.00
	Add for Anodized Finish		15%
.2	BRONZE		
	Door and Frame - 3' x 7'	Each	4,400.00
	Window or Store Front Framing	SqFt	76.00
.3	STAINLESS STEEL		
	Door and Frame - 3' x 7'	Each	3,900.00
	Window or Store Front Framing	SqFt	78.50
	Add for Insulated Glass	SqFt	7.75
	Add for Exit Hardware	Each	390.00

See 0803.10 for Revolving Doors
See 0803.0 for Automatic Door Opening Assemblies

0805.0 METAL WINDOWS (M) (CARPENTERS OR STEEL ERECTORS) (SINGLE GLAZING INCLUDED)

All Example Sizes Below: 2'4" x 4'6"

		UNIT	LABOR	MATERIAL	or	UNIT	LABOR	MATERIAL
.1	ALUMINUM WINDOWS							
	Casement and Awning	Each	60.00	360.00		SqFt	5.70	25.80
	Sliding or Horizo Rolling	Each	60.00	206.00		SqFt	5.70	19.90
	Double and Single-Hung or Vertical Sliding	Each	61.00	206.00		SqFt	5.80	19.90
	Projected	Each	57.00	264.00		SqFt	5.50	25.70
	Add for Screens					SqFt	.80	4.50
	Add for Storms					SqFt	1.60	7.50
	Add for Insulated Glass					SqFt	-	7.80
	Add for Bronzed Finish					SqFt	-	10%
.2	ALUMINUM SASH							
	Casement	Each	49.00	264.00		SqFt	4.90	26.10
	Sliding	Each	49.00	184.00		SqFt	4.90	18.20
	Single-Hung	Each	49.00	184.00		SqFt	4.90	18.20
	Projected	Each	49.00	287.00		SqFt	4.90	28.40
	Fixed	Each	49.00	150.00		SqFt	4.90	15.00
.3	STEEL WINDOWS							
	Double-Hung	Each	56.00	420.00		SqFt	5.40	40.00
	Projected	Each	56.00	349.00		SqFt	5.40	34.50
	Add for Insulated Glass					SqFt	-	6.60
.4	STEEL SASH							
	Casement	Each	49.00	300.00		SqFt	4.90	29.70
	Double-Hung	Each	49.00	394.00		SqFt	4.90	40.30
	Projected	Each	49.00	336.00		SqFt	4.90	35.00
	Fixed	Each	49.00	195.00		SqFt	4.90	21.20

0806.0   WOOD WINDOWS (M) (Carpenters)

All Units Assembled, Kiln Dry Pine, Glazed, Vinyl Clad, Weather-stripped, and No Interior Trim. <u>Top Quality</u>. Other Sizes Available. Most commonly used listed below. Deduct 10% for Medium Quality and 25% for Low Quality Woods.

	UNIT	LABOR	MATERIAL
.1 BASEMENT OR UTILITY			
Prefinished 2'8" x 1'4"	Each	46.00	133.00
2'8" x 1'8"	Each	54.00	140.00
2'8" x 2'0"	Each	56.00	152.00
Add for Double Glazing	Each	-	43.00
Add for Storm	Each	21.00	30.60
Add for Screen	Each	16.00	20.40
.2 CASEMENT OR AWNING - Operable Units			
Single Clear Tempered Glass 1'8" x 3'0"	Each	58.00	331.50
1'8" x 3'6"	Each	59.00	342.00
2'4" x 3'6"	Each	69.00	362.00
2'4" x 4'0"	Each	71.00	440.00
2'4" x 5'0"	Each	78.00	485.00
Double (2 Units) 2'10" x 3'0"	Each	83.00	450.00
3'4" x 3'6"	Each	90.00	685.00
4'0" x 3'0"	Each	88.00	570.00
4'0" x 3'6"	Each	92.00	730.00
4'0" x 5'0"	Each	96.00	850.00
4'0" x 5'8"	Each	100.00	920.00
Triple (3 Units, 1 Fixed) 6'0" x 3'0"	Each	97.00	840.00
6'0" x 4'0"	Each	102.00	970.00
6'0" x 4'6"	Each	114.00	1,120.00
Add for Grille Patterns - Interior - Polycarbonate	Each	-	24.50
Add for Grille Patterns - Exterior - Prefinished	Each	-	65.30
Add for High Performance Glazing	Each	-	58.00
Add for Screen - per Unit	Each	-	20.40
Add for Extension Jambs	Each	-	30.60
Add for Blinds	Each	-	100.00
CASEMENT OR AWNING - Stationary & Fixed Units			
Single 1'8" x 3'0"	Each	58.00	280.00
1'8" x 3'6"	Each	59.00	310.00
2'4" x 3'6"	Each	68.00	320.00
2'4" x 4'0"	Each	71.00	390.00
2'4" x 5'0"	Each	78.00	430.00
2'4" x 6'0"	Each	83.00	495.00
Picture 4'0" x 4'0"	Each	51.00	510.00
4'0" x 4'6"	Each	55.00	545.00
4'0" x 6'0"	Each	57.00	725.00
6'0" x 4'0"	Each	59.00	715.00
6'0" x 6'0"	Each	64.00	845.00
Add for Grille Patterns - Wood - 2'4"	Each	26.00	92.00
Add for Grille Patterns - Wood - 4'6"	Each	31.00	148.00
.3 DOUBLE HUNG (Insulating Glass with Screen)			
2'6" x 3'0"	Each	49.00	360.00
2'6" x 3'6"	Each	52.00	370.00
2'6" x 4'2"	Each	55.00	390.00
3'2" x 3'0"	Each	62.00	380.00
3'2" x 3'6"	Each	64.00	410.00
3'2" x 4'2"	Each	69.00	425.00
Deduct for Primed Units	Each	6.00	31.00
Add for Grille Patterns	Each	9.00	31.00
Add for Triple Glazing	Each	-	69.00
Deduct for Screen Unit	Each	11.00	23.50

0806.0   WOOD WINDOWS, Cont'd...

		UNIT	LABOR	MATERIAL
.4	GLIDER WITH SCREEN & INSUL GLASS 4'0" x 3'6"	Each	61.00	1,025.00
	5'0" x 3'6"	Each	71.00	1,020.00
	4'0" x 4'0"	Each	83.00	1,035.00
	5'0" x 4'0"	Each	88.00	1,090.00
.5	PICTURE WINDOW WITH CASEMENTS (2)			
	& INSULATING GLASS 9'6" x 5'0"	Each	158.00	1,990.00
	10'1" x 5'0"	Each	164.00	2,100.00
	9'6" x 5'6"	Each	158.00	2,100.00
	SINGLE GLASS AND STORM 10'3" x 4'6"	Each	142.00	2,130.00
	10'3" x 5'6"	Each	158.00	2,180.00
	10'3" x 6'6"	Each	164.00	2,280.00
	Add for High Performance Glass	Each	-	175.00
.6	CASEMENT ANGLE BAY WINDOWS, INSULATING GLASS, VINYL SHEATHED			
	30° (3 units) 5'10" x 4'2" x 2 7/8"	Each	280.00	1,600.00
	(4 units) 7'10" x 4'2" x 2 7/8"	Each	290.00	1,930.00
	(3 units) 5'10" x 5'2" x 2 7/8"	Each	270.00	1,735.00
	(4 units) 7'10" x 5'2" x 2 7/8"	Each	280.00	1,930.00
	(5 units) 9'10" x 4'2" x 2 7/8"	Each	320.00	2,265.00
	(5 units) 9'10" x 5'2" x 2 7/8"	Each	320.00	2,480.00
	45° (3 units) 5'4" x 4'2" x 2 7/8"	Each	275.00	1,600.00
	(4 units) 7'4" x 4'2" x 2 7/8"	Each	280.00	1,750.00
	(3 units) 5'4" x 5'2" x 2 7/8"	Each	290.00	1,750.00
	(4 units) 7'4" x 5'2" x 2 7/8"	Each	300.00	1,930.00
	(5 units) 9'4" x 4'2" x 2 7/8"	Each	310.00	2,370.00
	(5 units) 9'4" x 5'2" x 2 7/8"	Each	330.00	2,590.00
	Add for Screens	Each	52.00	56.00
	Add for Combination Windows	Each	-	280.00
	Deduct for Triple Glazing	Each	-	285.00
	Add for High Performance Glazing	Each	-	75.00
	Add for Bronze Glazing	Each	-	165.00
	Add for Color	Each	-	76.50
	Add for Blinds	Each	-	400.00
	Add for Bottom or Roof Skirt - Plywood	Each	105.00	440.00
	Add for Bottom or Roof Skirt - Aluminum	Each	110.00	645.00
.7	CASEMENT BOW WINDOWS, INSULATING GLASS			
	(3 units) 6'2" x 4'2"	Each	340.00	1,400.00
	(4 units) 8'2" x 4'2"	Each	405.00	1,900.00
	(3 units) 6'2" x 5'2"	Each	350.00	1,750.00
	(4 units) 8'2" x 5'2"	Each	430.00	2,200.00
.8	90° CASEMENT BOX BAY WINDOWS, INSULATING GLASS			
	4'8" x 4'2"	Each	440.00	2,000.00
	6'8" x 4'2"	Each	530.00	3,530.00
	4'8" x 5'2"	Each	450.00	2,000.00
	6'8" x 5'2"	Each	590.00	2,600.00
	Add for Screens - per Unit	Each	52.00	76.50
	Deduct for Double Glazing - per Unit	Each	-	41.80
	Add for High Performance Glazing	Each	-	82.00

		UNIT	LABOR	STATIONARY	VENT
.9	ROOF WINDOWS - INSULATING GLASS	Each			
	1'10" x 3'10"	Each	200.00	465.00	770.00
	2'4" x 3'10"	Each	218.00	555.00	850.00
	3'8" x 3'10"	Each	240.00	682.00	1,050.00
	Add for Shingle Flashing	Each	46.80	90.00	85.00
	Add for High Performance Glass	Each	-	95.00	90.00

		UNIT	LABOR	MATERIAL
.10	CIRCLE TOPS - 2'4"	Each	121.50	600.00
	4'0"	Each	133.00	780.00
	4'8"	Each	140.00	925.00
	6'0"	Each	152.00	1,500.00

		UNIT	LABOR	MATERIAL
0807.0	**SPECIAL WINDOWS (M) (Carpenters/ Steel Workers)**			
.1	LIGHT-PROOF WINDOWS	SqFt	6.15	35.00
.2	PASS WINDOWS	SqFt	5.30	26.25
.3	DETENTION WINDOWS			
	Aluminum	SqFt	5.50	38.90
	Steel	SqFt	5.60	36.75
.4	VENETIAN BLIND WINDOWS (ALUMINUM)	SqFt	5.20	30.50
.5	SOUND-CONTROL WINDOWS	Each	4.80	24.15
0808.0	**DOOR AND WINDOW ACCESSORIES**			
.1	STORMS AND SCREENS (CARPENTERS)			
	Windows			
	Screen Only - Wood - 3' x 5'	Each	20.00	89.15
	Aluminum - 3' x 5'	Each	21.00	100.00
	Storm & Screen Combination - Aluminum	Each	24.00	122.00
	Doors			
	Screen Only - Wood - 3' x 6' - 8'	Each	34.00	215.00
	Aluminum	Each	32.00	225.00
	Storm & Screen Combination - Aluminum	Each	37.00	340.00
	Wood 1 1/8"	Each	39.00	325.00
.2	DETENTION SCREENS (M) (CARPENTERS)			
	4' 0" x 7' 0"	Each	96.00	605.00
.3	DOOR OPENING ASSEMBLIES (L&M) (GLAZIERS)			
	Floor or Overhead Electric Eye Units			
	Swing - Single 3' x 7' Door - Hydraulic	Each	-	4,500.00
	Double 6' x 7' Door - Hydraulic	Each	-	6,300.00
	Sliding - Single 3' x 7' Door - Hydraulic	Each	-	5,900.00
	Double 5' x 7' Door - Hydraulic	Each	-	7,960.00
	Industrial Door - 10' x 8	Each	-	7,730.00
.4	SHUTTERS - FOLDING (CARPENTERS)			
	16" x 1 1/8" x 48"	Pair	19.00	110.00
	x 60"	Pair	22.00	126.00
	x 72"	Pair	26.00	136.00

		UNIT	COST
0809.0	**CURTAIN WALL SYSTEMS (L&M) (IRONWORKERS)**		
.1	STRUCTURAL OR VERTICAL TYPE		
	Aluminum Tube Frame, Panel, Sills and Mullions - No glazing		
	Example: 4' Panel, 7' Fixed	SqFt	51.50 to 158.00
.2	PANEL WALL OR HORIZONTAL TYPE		
	Aluminum Tube Frame, Panel, Sills and Mullions - No glazing		
	Example: 1' Panel, 2' Oper., 4' Fixed	SqFt	46.00 to 128.00
.3	ARCHITECTURAL PANELS, INSULATED		
	Included in Above Prices		
	Metal		
	Baked Enamel on Steel - 24 ga	SqFt	16.80
	on Aluminum - 24 ga	SqFt	17.50
	Porcelain Enamel on Steel - 24 ga	SqFt	19.00
	on Aluminum - 24 ga	SqFt	19.50
	Exposed Aggregate - Resin	SqFt	15.00
	Fiberglass	SqFt	19.50
	Spandrel Glass	SqFt	17.50

See 0812 for Glazing Costs to be Added to Above

0810.0 FINISH HARDWARE (M) (CARPENTERS)

		EACH	LABOR	Painted	Bronze	Chrome
.1	BUTTS					
	3" x 3"	Pair	17.70	10.00	11.55	15.10
	3 1/2" x 3 1/2"	Pair	18.30	12.00	11.55	16.70
	4" x 4"	Pair	20.00	15.45	15.00	16.80
	4 1/2" x 4 1/2"	Pair	20.00	20.70	20.50	28.60
	4" x 4" Ball Bearing	Pair	21.50	38.85	38.85	49.10
	4 1/2" x 4 1/2" Ball Bearing	Pair	22.70	44.65	44.10	51.15

		UNIT	LABOR	MATERIAL
.2	CATCHES - ROLLER	Each	17.70	18.50
.3	CLOSURES - SURFACE MOUNTED - 3' - 0" Door	Each	54.00	120.00
	3' - 4"	Each	55.00	123.00
	3' - 8"	Each	56.00	126.00
	4' - 0"	Each	62.00	136.00
	CLOSURES - CONCEALED OVERHEAD - Interior	Each	90.00	188.00
	Exterior	Each	96.00	317.00
	Add for Fusible Link - Electric	Each	24.00	195.00
	CLOSURES - FLOOR HINGES - Interior	Each	130.00	600.00
	Exterior	Each	130.00	635.00
	Add for Hold Open Feature	Each	-	87.00
	Add for Double Acting Feature	Each	-	285.00
.4	DEAD BOLT LOCK - Cylinder - Outside Key	Each	42.00	149.00
	Cylinder - Double Key	Each	48.00	165.00
	Flush - Push/ Pull	Each	26.00	26.00
.5	EXIT DEVICES (PANIC) - Surface	Each	116.00	595.00
	Mortise Lock	Each	121.00	710.00
	Concealed	Each	170.00	2,200.00
	(Hand drop) Automatic	Each	132.00	1,600.00
.6	HINGES, SPRING (PAINTED) - 6" Single Acting	Each	31.00	75.00
	6" Double Acting	Each	31.00	95.00
.7	LATCHSETS - Bronze or Chrome	Each	42.00	155.00
	Stainless Steel	Each	42.00	176.00
.8	LOCKSETS - Mortise - Bronze or Chrome - H.D.	Each	40.00	228.00
	S.D.	Each	37.00	165.00
	Stainless Steel	Each	37.00	310.00
	Cylindrical - Bronze or Chrome	Each	42.00	185.00
	Stainless Steel	Each	42.00	235.00
.9	LEVER HANDICAP - Latch Set	Each	40.00	195.00
	Lock Set	Each	40.00	240.00
.10	PLATES - Kick - 8" x 34" - Aluminum	Each	24.00	24.00
	Bronze	Each	25.00	50.00
	Push - 6" x 15"- Aluminum	Each	23.00	25.00
	Bronze	Each	24.00	41.00
	Push & Pull Combination - Aluminum	Each	26.00	58.00
	Bronze	Each	26.00	95.00
.11	STOPS AND HOLDERS			
	Holder - Magnetic (No Electric)	Each	51.00	145.00
	Bumper	Each	30.00	21.00
	Overhead - Bronze, Chrome or Aluminum	Each	30.00	78.00
	Wall Stops	Each	24.00	18.00
	Floor Stops	Each	24.00	19.00
	See 0808.3 for Automatic Openers & Operators			

0811.0 WEATHERSTRIPPING (L&M) (CARPENTERS)

		UNIT	LABOR	MATERIAL
.1	ASTRAGALS - Aluminum - 1/8" x 2"	Each	24.00	17.00
	Painted Steel	Each	24.00	17.00
.2	DOORS (WOOD) - Interlocking	Each	40.00	37.00
	Spring Bronze	Each	34.00	60.00
	Add for Metal Doors	Each	34.00	11.00
.3	SWEEPS - 36" WOOD DOORS - Aluminum	Each	19.00	18.00
	Vinyl	Each	19.00	13.00
.4	THRESHOLDS - Aluminum - 4" x 1/2"	Each	23.00	20.00
	Bronze - 4" x 1/2"	Each	24.00	37.00
	5 1/2" x 1/2"	Each	25.00	42.00
.5	WINDOWS (WOOD) - Interlocking	Each	44.00	32.00
	Spring Bronze	Each	37.00	53.00

0812.0	**GLASS AND GLAZING (L&M) (Glaziers)**	UNIT	COST
.1	BEVELED GLASS - 1/4" x 1/2" Bevel	SqFt	135.00
.2	COATED - Used with Insulated Glass and Heat		
	Absorber and Light Reflector	SqFt	31.00
.3	HEAT ABSORBING AND SOLAR REJECTING COMBINATIONS of Tinted, Coated and Clear Glass in Insulated Glass Form with 1/4" or 1/2" Air Space. Usual thickness with 1/4" air space, 9/16", 11/16" and 1 3/16". With 1/2" air space, 13/16", 15/16" and 1 /16". Factory priced. Greatly variable.	SqFt	24.00
.4	INSULATED GLASS		
	1/2" and 5/8" Welded	SqFt	17.30
	1" Clear	SqFt	19.25
	Tempered Insulated	SqFt	31.00
	Triple Insulated	SqFt	27.00
	Add for Tinting	SqFt	10%
.5	LAMINATED (SAFETY AND SOUND)		
	7/32"	SqFt	16.65
	1/4"	SqFt	19.55
	3/8"	SqFt	20.80
	1/2"	SqFt	30.00
	1 3/16", 1 1/2", 1 3/4" and 2" Bulletproof	SqFt	62.00
.6	MIRROR GLASS		
	Copper Plated Back and Polished Edges	SqFt	15.00
	Unfinished	SqFt	9.50
.7	PATTERNED OR ROUGH (OBSCURE)		
	1/8"	SqFt	7.60
	7/32"	SqFt	7.90
.8	PLASTIC GLASS (SAFETY)		
	Acrylic - 1/8" .125"	SqFt	13.10
	3/16" .187"	SqFt	15.90
	1/4" .250"	SqFt	16.65
	5/16" .312"	SqFt	19.25
	3/8" .375"	SqFt	23.90
	Polycarbonates - Add to Above	SqFt	50%
.9	PLATE - CLEAR		
	1/4" (See .4 for Tinted)	SqFt	8.30
	3/8"	SqFt	11.65
	1/2"	SqFt	18.20
	5/8"	SqFt	21.50
	3/4"	SqFt	25.00
.10	SANDBLASTED - 3/16"	SqFt	10.50
.11	SHEET GLASS		
	Light Sheet or Window Glass - Double Strength	SqFt	5.25
	Heavy Sheet or Crystal	SqFt	7.20
.12	STAINED GLASS - Abstract	SqFt	93.60
	Symbolism	SqFt	135.00
	Figures	SqFt	320.00
.13	STRUCTURAL GLASS - 1/4"	SqFt	13.50
.14	TEMPERED (SAFETY PLATE)		
	1/4"	SqFt	9.90
	3/8"	SqFt	12.80
	1/2"	SqFt	27.00
	5/8"	SqFt	31.50
.15	TINTED PLATE - LIGHT REFLECTIVE		
	1/4"	SqFt	10.40
	3/8"	SqFt	14.30
	1/2"	SqFt	24.50
.16	WIRED (SAFETY)		
	1/4" - Clear	SqFt	15.60
	Obscure	SqFt	11.50

The costs below are average, priced as total contractor / subcontractor costs with an overhead and fee of 10% included. Units include fasteners, tools and equipment, fringe benefits, 30% taxes and insurance on labor, and 5% General Conditions.

0801.0 HOLLOW METAL (Installation of Butts and Locksets included but no hardware material)

		UNIT	COST
.1	CUSTOM FRAMES (16 ga)		
	2'6" x 6'8" x 4 3/4"	Each	288
	2'8" x 6'8" x 4 3/4"	Each	311
	3'0" x 6'8" x 4 3/4"	Each	328
	3'4" x 6'8" x 4 3/4"	Each	347
	Add for A, B or C Label	Each	37
	Add for Side Lights	Each	167
	Add for Frames over 7'0" - Height	Each	69
	Add for Frames over 6 3/4" - Width	Each	60
	CUSTOM DOORS (1 3/8" or 1 3/4") (18 ga)		
	2'6" x 6'8" x 1 3/4"	Each	347
	2'8" x 6'8" x 1 3/4"	Each	360
	3'0" x 6'8" x 1 3/4"	Each	381
	3'4" x 6'8" x 1 3/4"	Each	386
	Add for 16 ga	Each	68
	Add for B and C Label	Each	37
	Add for Vision Panels or Lights	Each	84
.2	STOCK FRAMES (16 ga)		
	2'6" x 6'8" or 7'0" x 4 3/4"	Each	208
	2'8" x 6'8" or 7'0" x 4 3/4"	Each	214
	3'0" x 6'8" or 7'0" x 4 3/4"	Each	225
	3'4" x 6'8" or 7'0" x 4 3/4"	Each	243
	Add for A, B or C Label	Each	37
	STOCK DOORS (1 3/8" or 1 3/4" - 18 ga)		
	2'6" x 6'8" or 7'0"	Each	330
	2'8" x 6'8" or 7'0"	Each	344
	3'0" x 6'8" or 7'0"	Each	365
	3'4" x 6'8" or 7'0"	Each	386
	Add for B or C Label	Each	31

0802.0 WOOD DOORS (Installation of Butts and Locksets included but no hardware material)

		UNIT	Hollow Core	Solid Core
.1	FLUSH DOORS - No Label - Paint Grade			
	Birch - 7 Ply 2'4" x 6'8" x 1 3/8"	Each	198	219
	2'6" x 6'8" x 1 3/8"	Each	204	224
	2'8" x 6'8" x 1 3/8"	Each	209	234
	3'0" x 6'8" x 1 3/8"	Each	214	255
	2'4" x 6'8" x 1 3/4"	Each	209	240
	2'6" x 6'8" x 1 3/4"	Each	214	246
	2'8" x 6'8" x 1 3/4"	Each	219	268
	3'0" x 6'8" x 1 3/4"	Each	230	269
	3'4" x 6'8" x 1 3/4"	Each	235	293
	3'6" x 6'8" x 1 3/4"	Each	240	408
	Add for Stain Grade	Each		38
	Add for 5 Ply	Each		81
	Add for Jamb & Trim - Solid - Knock Down	Each		83
	Add for Jamb & Trim - Veneer - Knock Down	Each		55
	Add for Red Oak - Rotary Cut	Each		34
	Add for Red Oak - Plain Sliced	Each		44
	Deduct for Lauan	Each		26
	Add for Architectural Grade - 7 Ply	Each		81
	Add for Vinyl Overlay	Each		61
	Add for 7' - 0" Doors	Each		26
	Add for Lite Cutouts with Metal Frame	Each		91
	Add for Wood Louvres	Each		137
	Add for Transom Panels & Side Panels	Each		175

0802.0   WOOD DOORS, Cont'd...

			MATERIAL		
.1	FLUSH DOORS, Cont'd...	UNIT	20-Min	45-Min	60-Min
	Label - 1 3/4" - Paint Grade				
	2'6" x 6'8" - Birch	Each	275	306	306
	2'8" x 6'8"	Each	285	321	331
	3'0" x 6'8"	Each	295	341	341
	3'4" x 6'8"	Each	318	369	369
	3'6" x 6'8"	Each	387	379	277

		UNIT	Pine	Fir	Birch/ Oak	Lauan
.2	PANEL DOORS					
	Exterior - 1 3/4"					
	2'8" x 6'8"	Each	560	580	820	-
	3'0" x 6'8"	Each	505	618	850	-
	Interior - 1 3/8"					
	2'6" x 6'8"	Each	497	440	640	-
	2'8" x 6'8"	Each	507	450	670	-
	3'0" x 6'8"	Each	540	460	695	-
	Add for Sidelights	Each	320	460	535	
.3	LOUVERED DOORS - 1 3/8"					
	2'0" x 6'8"	Each	335	330	685	-
	2'6" x 6'8"	Each	395	390	710	-
	2'8" x 6'8"	Each	400	400	730	-
	3'0" x 6'8"	Each	415	410	750	-
.4	BI-FOLD - 2 DOOR WITH HDWE - 1 3/8"					
	2'0" x 6'8" - Flush	Each	-	-	250	210
	2'4" x 6'8"	Each	-	-	260	220
	2'6" x 6'8"	Each	-	-	270	230
	Add for Prefinished	Each				26
	See 0804.22 for 1 1/8" Closet Bi-folds					
.5	CAFE DOORS - 1 1/8" - Pair					
	2'6" x 3'8"	Each	450	-	-	-
	2'8" x 3'8"	Each	465	-	-	-
	3'0" x 3'8"	Each	485	-	-	-
.6	FRENCH DOORS - 1 3/8"					
	2'6" x 3'8"	Each	760	605	820	-
	2'8" x 3'8"	Each	770	620	850	-
	3'0" x 3'8"	Each	790	630	860	-
.7	DUTCH DOORS					
	2'6" x 3'8"	Each	970	-	-	-
	2'8" x 3'8"	Each	1,035	-	-	-
	3'0" x 3'8"	Each	1,100	-	-	-
.8	PREHUNG DOOR UNITS (INCL. FRAME, TRIM, HARDWARE, and SPLIT JAMBS)					
	Exterior Entrance - 1 3/4"					
	Panel - 2'8" x 6'8"	Each	530	-	-	-
	3'0" x 6'8"	Each	560	-	-	-
	3'0" x 7'0"	Each	605	-	-	-
	Add for Insulation	Each	220			
	Add for Side Lights	Each	230			
	Interior - 1 3/8"					
	Flush, H.C. - 2'6" x 6'8"	Each	-	-	380	298
	2'8" x 6'8"	Each	-	-	390	304
	3'0" x 6'8"	Each	-	-	415	306
	Add for Int. Panel Door	Each				267

0803.0 SPECIAL DOORS

		UNIT	Oak Flush	Birch Flush	Lauan Flush	Pine Panel
.2	CLOSET BI-FOLDING - PREHUNG STOCK AND UNFINISHED					
	Wood - 2 Door - 2'0" x 6'8" x 1 3/8"	Each	300	345	265	560
	2'6" x 6'8" x 1 3/8"	Each	320	370	275	580
	3'0" x 6'8" x 1 3/8"	Each	340	425	285	670
	4 Door - 4'0" x 6'8" x 1 3/8"	Each	385	435	335	915
	5'0" x 6'8" x 1 3/8"	Each	395	455	390	1,025
	6'0" x 6'8" x 1 3/8"	Each	445	465	400	1,110

	UNIT	COST
Add for Prefinished -	Each	$35.70
Add for Jambs and Casings -	Each	$85.70

	UNIT	COST
Metal - 2 Door - 2'0" x 6'8"	Each	180
2'6" x 6'8"	Each	185
3'0" x 6'8"	Each	220
4 Door - 4'0" x 6'8"	Each	248
5'0" x 6'8"	Each	259
6'0" x 6'8"	Each	288
Add for Plastic Overlay	Each	43
Add for Louvre or Decorative Type	Each	21
Leaded Mirror (Based on 2-Panel Unit)		
4'0" x 6'8"	Each	880
5'0" x 6'8"	Each	945
6'0" x 6'8"	Each	945

		UNIT	COST
.3	FLEXIBLE DOORS (M) (CARPENTERS)		
	Wood Slat (Unfinished)	SqFt	1,800
	Fabric Accordion Fold	SqFt	1,680
	Vinyl Clad	SqFt	2,120
.8	PLASTIC LAMINATE FACED (M) (CARPENTERS) - 1 3/8"	SqFt	2,245
	1 3/4"	SqFt	2,245
	Add for Decorative Type	SqFt	2,360
	Add for Label Doors	SqFt	6.20
	Add for Edge Strip - Vertical and Horizontal	Each	11.50
	Add for Machining for Hardware	Each	56.70
.10	ROLLING - DOORS & GRILLES		
	Doors - 8' x 8'	Each	3,250
	10' x 10'	Each	3,470
	Grilles - 6'-8" x 3'-2"	Each	1,155
	6'-8" x 4'-2"	Each	1,270
.11	SHOWER DOORS - 28" x 66" (CARPENTERS)	Each	320
.12	SLIDING OR PATIO DOORS (M) (CARPENTERS)		
	Metal (Aluminum) - Including Glass Thresholds & Screen		
	Opening 8'0" x 6'8"	Each	1,880
	8'0" x 8'0"	Each	1,990
	Wood		
	Vinyl Clad 6'0" x 6'10"	Each	2,290
	8'0" x 6'10"	Each	2,600
	Pine - Prefinished 6'0" x 6'10"	Each	2,260
	8'0" x 6'10"	Each	2,615
	Add for Grilles	Each	375
	Add for Triple Glazing	Each	250
	Add for Screen	Each	170
.13	SOUND REDUCTION - Metal	Each	2,165
	Wood	Each	1,470
.14	TRAFFIC DOORS (CARPENTERS)		
	Electric Powered - Hollow Metal - 8' x 8' Opening	Each	6,625
	Wood - 8' x 8' Opening	Each	6,520
	Truck Impact - Metal Clad - 8' x 8' Opening	Each	3,885
	(Double Acting) - Rubber - 8' x 8' Opening	Each	3,165
	Add for Frames	Each	945
.16	VAULT DOORS - 6'6" x 2'2" with Frame - 2 hour	Each	3,895

0805.0 METAL WINDOWS (M) (CARPENTERS OR STEEL ERECTORS) (SINGLE GLAZING INCLUDED)

All Example Sizes Below: 2'4" x 4'6"

		UNIT	COST	UNIT	COST
.1	ALUMINUM WINDOWS				
	Casement and Awning	Each	400.00	SqFt	38.00
	Sliding or Horizontal	Each	325.00	SqFt	30.00
	Double and Single-Hung or Vertical Sliding	Each	355.00	SqFt	33.70
	Projected	Each	400.00	SqFt	37.95
	Add for Screens	Each	58.00	SqFt	5.40
	Add for Storms	Each	105.00	SqFt	9.85
	Add for Insulated Glass	Each	88.00	SqFt	8.20
.2	ALUMINUM SASH				
	Casement	Each	375.00	SqFt	35.70
	Sliding	Each	325.00	SqFt	30.10
	Single-Hung	Each	325.00	SqFt	30.10
	Projected	Each	270.00	SqFt	25.65
	Fixed	Each	280.00	SqFt	26.50
.3	STEEL WINDOWS				
	Double-Hung	Each	585.00	SqFt	54.90
	Projected	Each	560.00	SqFt	52.50
.4	STEEL SASH				
	Casement	Each	460.00	SqFt	42.30
	Double-Hung	Each	515.00	SqFt	52.50
	Projected	Each	390.00	SqFt	36.25
	Fixed	Each	400.00	SqFt	37.40

0806.0 WOOD WINDOWS (M) (Carpenters) - All Units Assembled, Kiln Dry Pine, Glazed, Vinyl Clad, Weatherstripped, and Top Quality. Many Other Sizes Available.

		UNIT	COST
.1	BASEMENT OR UTILITY		
	Prefinished with Screen 2'8" x 1'4"	Each	220
	2'8" x 2'0"	Each	260
	Add for Double Glazing or Storm	Each	56
.2	CASEMENT OR AWNING		
	Operating Units - Insulating Glass		
	Single 2'4" x 4'0"	Each	497
	2'4" x 5'0"	Each	550
	Double with Screen 4'0" x 4'0" (2 units)	Each	795
	4'0" x 5'0" (2 units)	Each	1,030
	Triple with Screen 6'0" x 4'0" (3 units)	Each	1,270
	6'0" x 5'0" (3 units)	Each	1,370
	Fixed Units - Insulating Glass		
	Single 2'4" x 4'0"	Each	475
	2'4" x 5'0"	Each	550
	Picture 4'0" x 4'6"	Each	675
	4'0" x 6'0"	Each	850
.3	DOUBLE HUNG - & Insul. Glass with Screen - 2'6" x 3'6"	Each	475
	2'6" x 4'2"	Each	485
	3'2" x 3'6"	Each	495
	3'2" x 4'2"	Each	550
	Add for Triple Glazing	Each	71
.4	GLIDER - & Insul. Glass with Screen - 4'0" x 3'6"	Each	1,160
	5'0" x 4'0"	Each	1,370
.5	PICTURE WINDOWS with CASEMENTS - & Insul. Glass with Screen		
	9'6" x 4'10"	Each	2,420
	9'6" x 5'6"	Each	2,640

0806.0	**WOOD WINDOWS Cont'd...**			
.6	CASEMENT ANGLE BAY WINDOWS-Insulating Glass with Screens			
	30° - 5'10" x 4'2" - (3 units)	Each		1,870
	7'10" x 4'2" - (4 units)	Each		2,370
	5'10" x 5'2" - (3 units)	Each		1,980
	7'10" x 5'2" - (4 units)	Each		2,315
	45° - 5'4" x 4'2" - (3 units)	Each		1,860
	7'4" x 4'2" - (4 units)	Each		2,090
	5'4" x 5'2" - (3 units)	Each		2,255
	7'4" x 5'2" - (4 units)	Each		2,480
.7	CASEMENT BOW WINDOWS - Insulating Glass			
	6'2" x 4'2" - (3 units)	Each		1,870
	8'2" x 4'2" - (4 units)	Each		2,640
	6'2" x 5'2" - (3 units)	Each		2,150
	8'2" x 5'2" - (4 units)	Each		2,960
	Add for Triple Glazing - per unit	Each		71
	Add for Bronze Glazing - per unit	Each		71
	Deduct for Primed Only - per unit	Each		18
	Add for Screens - per unit	Each		22
.8	90° CASEMENT BOX BAY WINDOWS - Insulating Glass 4'8" x 4'2"	Each		2,640
	6'8" x 4'2"	Each		3,480
	6'8" x 5'2"	Each		3,640

		UNIT	STATIONARY	MOVABLE
.9	SKY OR ROOF WINDOWS 1'10" x 3'10"	Each	755	975
	2'4" x 3'10"	Each	880	1,260
	3'8" x 3'10"	Each	1,045	1,490
.10	CIRCULAR TOPS & ROUNDS - 4'0"	Each	-	820
	6'0"	Each	-	1,770

0807.0	**SPECIAL WINDOWS (M) (CARPENTERS/ STEEL WORKERS)**		
.1	LIGHT-PROOF WINDOWS	SqFt	47
.2	PASS WINDOWS	SqFt	36
.3	DETENTION WINDOWS	SqFt	49
.4	VENETIAN BLIND WINDOWS (ALUMINUM)	SqFt	41
.5	SOUND-CONTROL WINDOWS	SqFt	40
0808.0	**DOOR AND WINDOW ACCESSORIES**		
.1	STORMS AND SCREENS (CARPENTERS)		
	Windows		
	Screen Only - Wood - 3' x 5'	Each	126
	Aluminum - 3' x 5'	Each	145
	Storm & Screen Combination - Aluminum	Each	163
	Doors		
	Screen Only - Wood	Each	305
	Aluminum - 3' x 6' - 8'	Each	300
	Storm & Screen Combination - Aluminum	Each	360
	Wood 1 1/8"	Each	400
.2	DETENTION SCREENS (M) (CARPENTERS)		
	Example: 4' 0" x 7' 0"	Each	850
.3	DOOR OPENING ASSEMBLIES (L&M) (GLAZIERS)		
	Floor or Overhead Electric Eye Units		
	Swing - Single 3' x 7' Door - Hydraulic	Each	4,930
	Double 6' x 7' Door - Hydraulic	Each	7,310
	Sliding - Single 3' x 7' Door - Hydraulic	Each	6,310
	Double 5' x 7' Doors- Hydraulic	Each	7,270
	Industrial Doors - 10' x 8'	Each	8,490
.4	SHUTTERS (CARPENTERS)		
	16" x 1 1/8" x 48"	Pair	139
	16" x 1 1/8" x 60"	Pair	155
	16" x 1 1/8" x 72"	Pair	160

0810.0 FINISH HARDWARE (M) (CARPENTERS)

		UNIT	Painted	Bronze	Chrome
.1	BUTTS				
	3" x 3"	Pair	40	42	45
	3 1/2" x 3 1/2"	Pair	42	43	48
	4" x 4"	Pair	45	45	50
	4 1/2" x 4 1/2"	Pair	49	52	60
	4" x 4" Ball Bearing	Pair	74	76	86
	4 1/2" x 4 1/2" Ball Bearing	Pair	79	86	91

		UNIT	COST
.2	CATCHES - ROLLER	Each	45
.3	CLOSURES - SURFACE MOUNTED - 3' - 0" Door	Each	228
	3' - 4"	Each	234
	3' - 8"	Each	240
	4' - 0"	Each	295
	CLOSURES - CONCEALED OVERHEAD - Interior	Each	370
	Exterior	Each	515
	Add for Fusible Link - Electric	Each	260
	CLOSURES - FLOOR HINGES - Interior	Each	880
	Exterior	Each	915
	Add for Hold Open Feature	Each	105
	Add for Double Acting Feature	Each	345
.4	DEAD BOLT LOCK - Cylinder - Outside Key	Each	230
	Cylinder - Double Key	Each	275
	Flush - Push/ Pull	Each	73
.5	EXIT DEVICES (PANIC) - Surface	Each	880
	Mortise Lock	Each	925
	Concealed	Each	2,520
	Handicap (ADA) Automatic	Each	1,950
.6	HINGES, SPRING (PAINTED) - 6" Single Acting	Each	132
	6" Double Acting	Each	165
.7	LATCHSETS - Bronze or Chrome	Each	228
	Stainless Steel	Each	285
.8	LOCKSETS - Mortise - Bronze or Chrome - H.D.	Each	295
	Mortise - Bronze or Chrome - S.D.	Each	258
	Stainless Steel	Each	420
	Cylindrical - Bronze or Chrome	Each	270
	Stainless Steel	Each	345
.9	LEVER HANDICAP - Latch Set	Each	285
	Lock Set	Each	360
.10	PLATES - Kick - 8" x 34" - Aluminum	Each	105
	Bronze	Each	93
	Push - 6" x 15" - Aluminum	Each	59
	Bronze	Each	88
	Push & Pull Combination - Aluminum	Each	107
	Bronze	Each	155
.11	STOPS AND HOLDERS		
	Holder - Magnetic (No Electric)	Each	245
	Bumper	Each	57
	Overhead - Bronze, Chrome or Aluminum	Each	126
	Wall Stops	Each	39
	Floor Stops	Each	52
	See 0808.3 for Automatic Openers & Operators		

0811.0 WEATHERSTRIPPING (L&M) (CARPENTERS)

		UNIT	COST
.1	ASTRAGALS - Aluminum - 1/8" x 2"	Each	52
	Painted Steel	Each	52
.2	DOORS (WOOD) - Interlocking	Each	97
	Spring Bronze	Each	112
	Add for Metal Doors	Each	52
.3	SWEEPS - 36" WOOD DOORS - Aluminum	Each	45
	Vinyl	Each	34
.4	THRESHOLDS - Aluminum - 4" x 1/2"	Each	52
	Bronze 4" x 1/2"	Each	79
	5 1/2" x 1/2"	Each	87
.5	WINDOWS (WOOD) - Interlocking	Each	89
	Spring Bronze	Each	110

All items in this division are subcontractors' costs and include all labor, materials, equipment and fees.

0901.0   LATH & PLASTER (L&M) (Latherers and Plaster)

		UNIT	COST
.1	LATHING		
.11	Metal Lath	SqYd	18.10
.12	Gypsum Lath	SqYd	16.00
.13	Metal Studs	SqYd	19.90
.14	Channels - Studs - 16" O.C.	SqYd	19.35
	Furring - Beams & Columns - 16" O.C.	SqYd	23.20
	Ceilings (including hangers) - 16" O.C.	SqYd	26.40
.15	Metal Trim - Base Bead and Corner Bead	LnFt	4.50
	Picture Mould	LnFt	5.60
.2	PLASTERING		
.21	Gypsum (Putty Coat, Sand Float Textured),Walls - 1 Coat	SqYd	20.00
	3 Coat	SqYd	56.00
	Add for Ceiling, Column and Beam Applications	SqYd	5.50
.22	Acoustical	SqYd	32.00
.23	Vermiculite	SqYd	29.00
.24	Stucco or Cement Plaster		
	On Masonry - Large Areas - Float Finish - 1 Coat	SqYd	34.00
	3 Coat	SqYd	44.00
	Panels, Facias, Soffits - 3 Coat	SqYd	52.20
	On Metal Lath - Large Areas - 3 Coat	SqYd	64.00
	Panels, Facias, Soffits, Columns	SqYd	70.00
	On Metal Studs - 4" - 16 ga	SqYd	38.50
	6" - 16 ga	SqYd	55.00
	Deduct for 18 ga Studs	SqYd	10%
	Add for Trowel Finish	SqYd	5.00
.25	Fireproofing (Sprayed On) - Mineral Fiber		
	Steel and Decks - 1 Hour	SqYd	11.90
	2 Hour	SqYd	20.30
	Beams and Columns - Not Wrapped - 2 Hour	LnFt	21.30
	3 Hour	LnFt	23.50
.26	Thin Coat or Veneer Plaster - Walls - 1 Coat	SqYd	18.00
	2 Coat	SqYd	26.80
	Ceilings - 2 Coat	SqYd	33.50
	Add for Patching	SqYd	50%
	Add Color to Plaster and Stucco	SqYd	6.10
	Add for Scaffold - Average	SqYd	10.00
.27	Exterior Wall System - Stucco or Synthetic Plaster		
	Includes Structural Board and 2" Insulation	SqYd	118.00
	Add for Esthetic Grooving	LnFt	6.00

LATH AND GYPSUM PLASTER IN COMBINATION UNITS:		FINISHED	
WALLS	UNIT	1 Side	2 Side
1 Coat Plaster on Waterproofed Found. Walls	SqYd	19.80	-
2 Coat Plaster on Masonry and Concrete	SqYd	39.30	76.60
on Gypsum Lath	SqYd	49.00	110.00
3 Coat Plaster on Metal Lath	SqYd	61.00	122.00
2 Coat Plaster on Metal Studs & Gypsum Lath	SqYd	80.00	130.50
CEILINGS			
3 Coat Plaster on Metal Lath and Channel for Suspended Ceiling (including hangers)	SqYd	114.00	-
3 Coat Plaster and Metal Lath attached to joists, beams, etc.	SqYd	96.00	-
FURRED			
Beam - 3 Coat Plaster, Metal Lath, Channel	SqYd	115.00	-
Column & Pipe - 3 Coat Plaster - Metal Lath	SqYd	108.00	-
Cabinet - 3 Coat Plaster, Metal Lath, Chnl.	SqYd	74.00	-
2 Coat Plaster on Gypsum Lath	SqYd	68.00	-

0902.0 GYPSUM DRYWALL (L&M) (Carpenters)
Based on 8' Ceiling Heights & Screwed-on Application

		UNIT	COST
.1	BACKER BOARD		
	3/8"	SqFt	1.22
	1/2"	SqFt	1.25
	5/8" Fire Rated	SqFt	1.26
	Deduct for Nailed-on	SqFt	.08
.2	FINISH BOARD - Walls		
	1/2" - Standard	SqFt	1.93
	Fire Rated	SqFt	1.96
	Moisture Resistant	SqFt	2.08
	Insulating (Foil Backed)	SqFt	2.13
	Combined Fire Rated and Insulating	SqFt	2.18
	5/8" - Standard	SqFt	1.95
	Fire Rated	SqFt	1.97
	Moisture Resistant	SqFt	1.97
	Insulating (Foil Backed)	SqFt	2.11
	Combined Fire Rated and Insulating	SqFt	2.20
	Lead Lined with #4 Lead - 1/16"	SqFt	9.65
	#2 Lead - 1/16"	SqFt	7.60
	Add for Ceiling Work - to Wood	SqFt	.20
	Add for Ceiling Work - to Steel	SqFt	.46
	Add for Adhesive Method	SqFt	.20
	Deduct for Nailed On	SqFt	.10
	Add for Beam and Column Work	SqFt	.80
	Add for Resilient Clip Application	SqFt	.95
	Add for Small Cut Up Areas	SqFt	.70
	Add for Each Floor Added	SqFt	.10
	Add for Work Above 10'	SqFt	.28
	Add for Filling Hollow Metal Frames	Each	95.00
.3	VINYL COATED BOARD - 1/2"	SqFt	2.40
	5/8"	SqFt	2.50
.4	LINER PANELS - 1"	SqFt	3.30

		UNIT	COST 25 ga	COST 20 ga
.5	STEEL STUDS (Incl. Top & Bottom Plates)			
	16" O.C. - 1 5/8"	SqFt	1.70	1.90
	2 1/2"	SqFt	1.72	1.92
	3 5/8"	SqFt	1.70	1.90
	6"	SqFt	1.74	1.92
	24" O.C. - 1 5/8"	SqFt	1.33	1.52
	2 1/2"	SqFt	1.37	1.58
	3 5/8"	SqFt	1.38	1.62
	6"	SqFt	1.36	1.72
	Add for Work Over 10' Heights	SqFt	.20	.20
	Add for 16 Ga 6" Galvanized	SqFt	1.98	1.50
.6	FURRING CHANNELS			
	16" O.C. 3/4" x 1 3/8" walls	SqFt	-	1.40
	24" O.C. 3/4" x 1 3/8" walls	SqFt	-	1.40
	Resilient Channels - 16" O.C.	SqFt	-	1.40
	Add for Ceiling Work	SqFt	-	.20
	Add for Beam and Column Work	SqFt	-	1.40
.7	METAL TRIM - Casing Bead	LnFt	-	1.40
	Corner Bead	LnFt	-	1.20
.8	TAPING AND SANDING	SqFt	-	.60
.9	TEXTURING	SqFt	-	.70
.10	SKIM COATING	SqFt	-	1.00

0902.0 GYPSUM DRYWALL, Cont'd...
      COMBINATION UNITS - METAL FRAMING & BOARD

	UNIT	COST
PARTITIONS 3 5/8" - 25 ga Studs - 24" O.C.		
1/2" Board One Side	SqFt	3.60
Two Sides	SqFt	4.90
1/2" Fire Rated Board Two Sides	SqFt	4.95
1/2" Fire Rated Board One Side - 2 Layers 2nd Side (1 Hr.)	SqFt	6.00
2 Layers Each Side (2 Hr.)	SqFt	7.02
5/8" Board One Side	SqFt	3.55
Two Sides	SqFt	5.10
5/8" Fire Rated Board Each Side (1 Hr.)	SqFt	5.15
5/8" Fire Rated Board - 2 Layers Each Side (2 Hr.)	SqFt	7.40
3 Layers to Columns & Beams (2 Hr.)	SqFt	11.00
Add for Studs 16" O.C. - 25 Ga	SqFt	.34
Deduct for 1 5/8" Studs - 25 Ga	SqFt	.30
Deduct for 2 5/8" Studs - 25 Ga	SqFt	.16
Add for Studs - 20 Ga and 16" O.C.	SqFt	.38
Add for Studs - 20 Ga and 24" O.C.	SqFt	.36
Add for 6" Studs - 25 Ga and 16" O.C.	SqFt	.16
Add for 6" Studs - 20 Ga and 16" O.C.	SqFt	.28
Add for Sound Deadening	SqFt	1.05
PARTITIONS - CAVITY SHAFT WALL -		
25 Ga Studs - 24" O.C. - All Board Fire Code C		
1" Liner Board One Side - 5/8" Board 2nd Side (1 Hr.)	SqFt	6.45
2 Layers - 1/2" Board 2nd Side (2 Hr.)	SqFt	5.85
3 Layers - 5/8" Board 2nd Side (3 Hr.)	SqFt	8.50
1" Liner Board and 5/8" Board One Side		
2 Layers 1" Liner Board 2nd Side	SqFt	11.90
PARTITIONS - DEMOUNTABLE		
2 1/2" Studs 24" O.C.-1/2" Vinyl Coated Bd. 2 Sides	SqFt	5.90
3 5/8" Studs 24" O.C.-1/2" Vinyl Coated Bd. 2 Sides	SqFt	6.40
Add for 16" O.C.	SqFt	.40
Add for 5/8" Vinyl Coated Board 2 Sides	SqFt	.43
Add for Special Colors Baked On	SqFt	25%
FURRED WALLS		
16" O.C. 1/2" Board	SqFt	3.20
24" O.C. 1/2" Board	SqFt	3.30
Resilient Channels and 1/2" Board	SqFt	3.25
CEILINGS		
To Wood Joists - 1/2" Fire Rated Board (1 Hr.)	SqFt	2.10
To Steel Joists with Furring Channels		
24" O.C. - 1/2" F.R. Board (2 Hr. with 2 1/2" Conc.)	SqFt	3.10
5/8" F.R. Board (1 Hr. with 2" Conc.)	SqFt	3.15
12" O.C. - 5/8" F.R. Board (2 Hr. with 2 1/2" Conc.)	SqFt	3.85
COLUMNS - 14 WF and Up		
1/2" F.R. Board with Screw Studs at Corners (1 Hr.)	SqFt	4.10
2 Layers - 1/2" F.R. Bd. with Screw Studs @ Corners (2 Hr.)	SqFt	4.45
Add for Corner Bead	LnFt	1.55

See 0703.0 for Insulation Work

		UNIT	COST
0903.0	**TILEWORK (L&M) (Tile Setters)**		
.1	CERAMIC TILE		
	Floors - 1" Square - Thin Set (Unglazed)	SqFt	9.60
	- 1" Hex - Thin Set	SqFt	10.30
	1" x 2"	SqFt	10.40
	2" Square	SqFt	9.75
	16" Square	SqFt	10.40
	Add for Mortar Setting Bed	SqFt	5.50
	Add for Random Colors	SqFt	1.30
	Add for Epoxy Joints	SqFt	2.85
	Conductive - In Mortar Setting Bed	SqFt	14.60
	Walls - 2" x 2" - Thin Set	SqFt	11.70
	4 1/4" x 4 1/4"	SqFt	8.85
	4 1/4" x 6"	SqFt	9.00
	4 1/4" x 8"	SqFt	9.30
	6" x 6"	SqFt	9.80
	Add for Plaster Setting Bed	SqFt	5.35
	Add for Decorator Type	SqFt	7.71
	Base - 4 1/4"	LnFt	9.20
	6"	LnFt	9.25
	Add for Coved Base	LnFt	1.05
	Accessories - Toilet and Bath Embedded	Each	68.15
.2	QUARRY TILE		
	Floors - 4" x 4" - Thin Set	SqFt	9.50
	6" x 6"	SqFt	9.38
	4" x 8"	SqFt	9.38
	Hexagon, Valencas, etc.	SqFt	10.80
	Walls - 4" x 4" - Thin Set	SqFt	10.38
	6" x 6"	SqFt	10.20
	Stairs	SqFt	13.42
	Base - 4" x 4" x 1/2"	LnFt	9.55
	6" x 6" x 1/2"	LnFt	10.95
	Add for Hydroment Joints	SqFt	1.05
	Add for Epoxy Joints	SqFt	2.80
	Add for Non-Slip Tile	SqFt	.60
	Add for Mortar Setting Bed	SqFt	5.30
0904.0	**TERRAZZO (L&M) (Terrazzo Workers) - Based on Gray Cement, 4' Panel, and White Dividing Strips**		
.1	CEMENT TERRAZZO		
	Floors - 2" Bonded	SqFt	15.05
	2 1/2" Not Bonded	SqFt	12.95
	Base - 6" without Grounds or Base Bead	LnFt	23.20
	6" with Grounds and Base Bead	LnFt	29.60
	Stairs - Treads and Risers - Tread Length	LnFt	59.80
	Stringers without Base Bead	LnFt	52.75
	Pan Filled Treads and Landings	LnFt	25.60
	Add for White Cement	SqFt	.90
	Add for Brass Dividing Strips	SqFt	1.32
	Add for Large Chips (Venetian) - 3"	SqFt	7.16
	Add for 2-Color Panels	SqFt	4.25
	Add for 3-Color Panels	SqFt	5.00
	Add for Non-Slip Abrasives	SqFt	1.20
	Add for Small or Scattered Areas	SqFt	15%
.2	CONDUCTIVE TERRAZZO - 2" Bonded	SqFt	16.65
	1/4" Thin Set Epoxy	SqFt	14.52
.3	EPOXY TERRAZZO - 1/4" Thin Set	SqFt	11.80
.4	RUSTIC TERRAZZO (WASHED AGGREGATE) - Marble	SqFt	8.33
	Quartz	SqFt	9.05
	See 0907 for Precast Terrazzo Tiles		

0905.0 ACOUSTICAL TREATMENT (L&M) (Carpenters)

		UNIT	COST
.1	MINERAL TILE (No Backing or Supports)		
	Fissured or Perforated - 1/2" x 12" x 12" or 12" x 24"	SqFt	2.50
	5/8" x 12" x 12" or 12" x 24"	SqFt	2.80
	3/4" x 12" x 12" or 12" x 24"	SqFt	2.90
	Add to all above for Backing or Supports if needed:		
	Ceramic Faces	SqFt	.58
	Concealed Z Spline Application	SqFt	.72
	Wood Furring Strips	SqFt	.80
	Rock Lath	SqFt	1.10
	1 1/2" Channel Suspension	SqFt	1.50
	Resilient Furring Channels	SqFt	1.15
.2	PLASTIC COVERED TILE (No Backing or Supports)		
	3/4" x 12" x 12"	SqFt	2.85
	5/8" x 12" x 12"	SqFt	2.38
.3	METAL PAN TILE (Supports Included)		
	12" x 24" or 12" x 36" or 12" x 48" - Steel (24 Ga)	SqFt	8.60
	Aluminum (.025)	SqFt	10.55
	Aluminum (.032)	SqFt	12.00
	Stainless Steel	SqFt	14.65
	Add for Color	SqFt	.60
.4	CLASS A MINERAL TILE		
	(Grid System with Suspension incl. & Partitions to Clg.)		
	5/8" x 24" x 24" or 24" x 48" - Perforated	SqFt	2.00
	Fissured	SqFt	2.00
	Add for Partitions thru Ceilings	SqFt	.30
	Add for Translucent Panels for Lights	SqFt	1.65
.5	FIRE RATED DESIGN MINERAL TILE		
	(Grid System with Suspension incl. & Partitions to Clg.)		
	5/8" x 24" x 24" or 24" x 48" - Perforated (2-hour rating)	SqFt	2.14
	Fissured (2-hour rating)	SqFt	2.18
	3/4" x 24" x 24" or 24" x 48" - Perforated (3-4 Hr rating)	SqFt	2.35
	Fissured (3-4 Hr rating)	SqFt	2.37
	Add for Partitions thru Ceilings	SqFt	.30
	Add for Reveal Edge or Shadow Line (24" x 24" only)	SqFt	.40
	Add for Nubby Tile	SqFt	1.50
	Add for Ceramic Faces (5/8")	SqFt	.90
	Add for Colored Tile	SqFt	.33
	Add for Fixture Fire Protection - Fixtures only	SqFt	1.27
.6	GLASS FIBRE BOARD (Grid System with Suspension included)		
	5/8" x 24" x 24"	SqFt	2.15
	3/4" x 24" x 48"	SqFt	2.20
	1" x 48" x 48"	SqFt	2.15
	1-1/2" x 60" x 60"	SqFt	3.75
	Add for Three-Dimensional	SqFt	3.65
.7	SOUND CONTROL PANELS AND BAFFLES	SqFt	14.60

		UNIT	COST		
.8	ACOUSTICAL WALL PANELS - Special				
	Fiberglass with Cloth Face - 3/4"	SqFt	4.85	to	11.30
	1"	SqFt	6.20	to	14.05
	1-1/2"	SqFt	9.60	to	16.25
	3/4" Mineral	SqFt	1.55	to	4.30
	1/2" Fibre Board	SqFt	1.00	to	1.48
.9	LINEAR METAL CEILINGS				
	4" Wide - Painted	SqFt	7.00	to	9.20
	Chrome or Brass	SqFt	10.15	to	12.95

See 0307 for Fibre Cementitious Acoustical Plank

0906.0 VENEER STONE (Floors, Walls, Stools, Stairs, Partitions)
(2" and Under) (L&M) (Marble Setters)

		UNIT	COST
.1	LIMESTONE		
.11	Cut Stone - Floors 7/8" Interior	SqFt	35.00
	Floors 2" Exterior	SqFt	39.50
	Walls 1"	SqFt	38.50
	Stools 1" x 8"	LnFt	46.10
.12	Flagstone Floors 1"	SqFt	42.50
.2	MARBLE Floors 5/8"	SqFt	36.50
	Floor Tiles 3/8" x 12" x 12"	SqFt	38.80
	Walls 3/8" x 12" x 12"	SqFt	42.60
	Base 1" x 6"	LnFt	30.75
	Stool 1" x 8"	LnFt	43.50
	Stairs - Treaded Risers	SqFt	84.40
.3	SLATE Floors 3/8" Package	SqFt	24.00
	Floors 3/4" Random or Flagstone	SqFt	25.20
	Walls 3/4" Random	SqFt	31.20
	Stools 1" x 8"	LnFt	44.50
.4	SANDSTONE Floors 2"	SqFt	40.10
.5	GRANITE Floors 5/6" Interior	SqFt	45.00
	Walls - 2" Exterior	SqFt	56.80
	1 1/2" Interior	SqFt	51.50
	Counter Tops 1 1/4"	SqFt	76.25
.6	SYNTHETIC MARBLE Floors 5/8"	SqFt	21.00
	Walls 5/8"	SqFt	24.40
	Add for Leveling Old Floors, per Square Foot		3.00

0907.0 SPECIAL FLOORING (L&M)

		UNIT	COST
.1	MAGNESIUM OXYCHLORIDE (Seamless)	SqFt	10.75
.2	ELASTOMERIC	SqFt	12.50
.3	SYNTHETIC		
	Epoxy with Granules 1/16" Single Speed	SqFt	6.25
	3/32" Double Speed	SqFt	7.50
	Epoxy with Aggregates 1/4" Industrial	SqFt	10.00
	Polyester with Granules 3/32"	SqFt	8.25
	1/4"	SqFt	10.30
	See 0904.3 for Epoxy Terrazzo and 0603.2 for Counter Tops		
.4	ASPHALTIC MASTIC	SqFt	9.90
	Add for Acid Proof	SqFt	1.80
.5	BRICK PAVERS - Mortar Setting Bed Application		
	3 7/8" x 8" x 1 1/4" - Red	SqFt	11.40
	Iron Spot	SqFt	13.60
	Acid Proof	SqFt	24.50
	See 0206.3 for Patios and Walks on Sand Cushion		
.6	PRECAST PANELS		
	12" x 12" x 1" Precast Terrazzo	SqFt	31.20
	12" x 12" x 1" Precast Exposed Aggregate	SqFt	31.60
	12" x 12" x 1" Ceramic (Terra Cotta)	SqFt	38.00
	6" Precast Terrazzo Base	LnFt	24.50
.7	NEOPRENE 1/4"	SqFt	16.00

0908.0	**RESILIENT FLOORING (L&M)**		
	(Carpet and Resilient Floor Layers)	UNIT	COST
.1	ASPHALT - Tile 9" x 9" x 1/8"	SqFt	4.15
.2	CORK - Tile 1/8" - Many Sizes	SqFt	4.95
	3/16" - Many Sizes	SqFt	5.35
.3	RUBBER		
	Tile 12" x 12" x 3/32"	SqFt	6.56
	12" x 12" x 3/32" Conductive	SqFt	7.70
	Base 2 1/2"	LnFt	1.90
	4"	LnFt	2.18
	6"	LnFt	2.45
	Treads, Stringers and Risers		
	Treads 3/16" Gauge Pre-formed	LnFt	15.57
	1/4" Gauge Pre-formed	LnFt	17.90
	5/16" Gauge Pre-formed	LnFt	23.00
	Stringers 10" x 1/8"	LnFt	11.95
	Risers	LnFt	6.56
.4	VINYL COMPOSITION TILE 12" x 12" x 3/32"	SqFt	1.90
	12" x 12" x 1/8"	SqFt	2.08
	Conductive	SqFt	7.15
	Treads 1/8"	LnFt	7.60
	3/16"	LnFt	9.57
	1/4"	LnFt	11.95
	Stringers 10" x 1/8"	LnFt	12.05
	Risers 7" x 1/8"	LnFt	5.40
	Add for Marbleized or Patterns	SqFt	1.65
.5	VINYL TILE 9" x 9" x 1/8" Solid	SqFt	8.14
	12" x 12" x 1/8"	SqFt	9.35
	Base 2 1/2"	LnFt	1.95
	4"	LnFt	2.00
	6"	LnFt	1.15
.6	VINYL SHEET 1/8" Inlaid	SqFt	3.45 – 8.75
	1/8" Homogenous	SqFt	5.30 – 9.57
	Acoustic Cushioned	SqFt	5.75 – 13.85
	Coving	LnFt	7.65
.7	VINYL CORNER GUARDS	LnFt	6.92
	Add Plywood or Masonite Underlayment	SqFt	2.00
	Add Diagonal Cuttings	SqFt	.68
	Add Clean and Wax	SqFt	.50
	Add Skim Coat Leveling	SqFt	2.35 – 4.44

0909.0	**CARPETING (L&M) (Carpet Layers)**	UNIT	CUT PILE	LOOP PILE
.1	NYLON - 20 oz	SqYd		16.40 - 28.00
	22 oz	SqYd		17.50 - 29.25
	24 oz	SqYd	14.70 – 21.60	18.90 - 34.40
	26 oz	SqYd		20.45 - 34.40
	28 oz	SqYd		20.50 - 36.50
	30 oz	SqYd	17.62 – 26.00	22.10 - 39.40
	32 oz	SqYd	19.10 – 27.00	24.00 - 42.00
.2	WOOL - 36 oz	SqYd		31.80 - 76.50
	42 oz	SqYd		40.60 - 90.10
.3	OLEFIN - 20 oz	SqYd		14.55 - 25.20
	22 oz	SqYd		16.15 - 26.10
	24 oz	SqYd		17.52 - 28.50
	26 oz	SqYd		18.90 - 32.00
	28 oz	SqYd		20.95 - 35.00
.4	CARPET TILE, MODULAR-Tension Bonded	SqYd		40.10 - 77.65
	Tufted	SqYd	28.00 – 43.00	27.50 - 55.50
.5	INDOOR-OUTDOOR	SqYd		10.80 - 25.95

Installation included in above prices

0909.0	CARPETING, Cont'd...	UNIT	COST
	Add to Section 0909.0 above:		
	Add for Custom Carpet	SqYd	11.30 - 26.00
	Add for Cushion (Urethane, Rubber, Synthetic)	SqYd	4.70 - 7.90
	Add Bonded Cushion (Urethane Backed)	SqYd	1.65 - 2.20
	Add for Carpet Base, Top Edge Bound	LnFt	2.45 - 4.00
	Add for Skim Coat Leveling, Latex	SqFt	1.33 - 1.95
	Add for Border and Inset Work	LnFt	2.90 - 5.10
	Add for Reduction Strips	LnFt	2.15 - 3.40

0910.0 WOOD FLOORING (L&M) (Carpenters)

.1 STRIP AND PLANK FLOORING

Oak Floors (based on Standard Grade)		UNIT	COST
White Oak 25/32 1 1/2" Select Job Finished		SqFt	11.80
2 1/4" Select Job Finished		SqFt	12.00
3 1/4" Select Job Finished		SqFt	12.30
Add for Clear Grade		SqFt	.45
Deduct for Antique or Rustic Floors		SqFt	.55
Maple Floors - Iron Bound (Edge Grain)			
3/4" x 1 1/2" #2 & Better Gr	Job Finished	SqFt	12.50
3/4" x 2 1/4" #2 & Better Gr	Job Finished	SqFt	13.20
33/32 x 2 1/4" #2 & Better Gr	Job Finished	SqFt	12.50
33/32 x 2 1/4" #3 Grade	Job Finished	SqFt	11.80
Add for #1 Grade		SqFt	1.35
Add to above for Cork Underlayment		SqFt	1.45
Fir Floors			
1" x 4" Vertical Grain B&B Job Finished		SqFt	6.20
Flat Grain B&B Job Finished		SqFt	5.95

.2	WOOD PARQUET Pre Finished 5/16" Oak or Maple	SqFt	9.60
	FLOORING Pre Finished 3/4 " Oak or Maple	SqFt	11.80
	Pre Finished 5/16" Teak	SqFt	13.00
	5/16" Walnut	SqFt	13.30
.3	RADIANT TREATED (Plastic and Wood) 5/16" x 12" x 12"	SqFt	14.50

.4 RESILIENT WOOD FLOOR SYSTEMS

Cushion Sleeper Floors (Maple)		
33/32 2 1/4" #1 Grade Pre-Finished	SqFt	10.65
#2 Grade Pre-Finished	SqFt	10.20
#3 Grade Pre-Finished	SqFt	9.50
Cork Underlayment included	SqFt	1.50
Add for Plywood Underlayment (2 layers)	SqFt	2.45
Fixed Sleeper Floors (Oak)		
33/32 2 1/4" #1 Grade Pre-Finished	SqFt	10.60
#2 Grade Pre-Finished	SqFt	10.50
1/4" #3 Grade Pre-Finished	SqFt	10.40

.5	WOOD BLOCK INDUSTRIAL FLOORS (Creosoted) 2"	SqFt	5.60
	2 1/2"	SqFt	6.50
	3"	SqFt	6.70

.6 FINISHING (Sanding, Sealing and Waxing)

Included in Job Finished Prices Above for New House	SqFt	2.20
for New Gym	SqFt	2.15
for Old Gym	SqFt	3.60
Add to Section 0910.0 above:		
Small Cut-up Areas	SqFt	30%
Trim and Irregular Areas	SqFt	15%
Polyurethane Finish with Stain	SqFt	20%
Deduct for Residential Work	SqFt	10%

0911.0 SPECIAL COATINGS

		UNIT	COST		
.1	CEMENTITIOUS (Glazed Cement)	SqFt	3.10	-	5.15
.2	EPOXIES	SqFt	1.90	-	3.70
.3	POLYESTERS	SqFt	1.95	-	3.80
.4	VINYL CHLORIDE	SqFt	2.20	-	4.10
.5	AGGREGATE TO EPOXY - Blown on Quartz	SqFt	9.60		
	Troweled on Quartz	SqFt	10.00		

		UNIT	COST
.6	SPRAYED FIREPROOFING (with Perlite)		
	Column - 1" 2 Hour	LnFt	2.10
	1 3/8" 3 Hour	LnFt	2.40
	1 3/4" 4 Hour	LnFt	3.30
	Beams - 1 1/8" 2 Hour	LnFt	2.30
	1 1/4" 3 Hour	LnFt	2.40
	1 1/2" 4 Hour	LnFt	2.62
	Ceilings - 1/2" 1 Hour	SqFt	1.68
	5/8" 2 Hour	SqFt	1.73
	1" 3 Hour	SqFt	2.20

See 0901.25 for Other Fireproofing

0912.0 PAINTING (L&M) (Painters)

WALLS AND CEILINGS - BRUSH

	UNIT	COST
Brick 2 Coats	SqFt	.84
Concrete 2 Coats	SqFt	.75
Concrete Block - Interior 2 Coats	SqFt	.78
Exterior 2 Coats	SqFt	.80
Light Weight 2 Coats	SqFt	.84
2 Coats/Filler	SqFt	1.03
Plaster 2 Coats	SqFt	.79
Sheet Rock 2 Coats	SqFt	.67
Steel Decking & Sidings 1 Coat	SqFt	.57
Stucco 2 Coats	SqFt	.96
Wood Siding & Shingles 2 Coats	SqFt	.93
Wood Paneling - Stain, Seal and Varnish	SqFt	1.71
Deduct for Roller Application	SqFt	.14
Deduct for Spray Application	SqFt	.19
Add for Scaffold Work	SqFt	.28
Add for Epoxy Paint	SqFt	.26

DOORS AND WINDOWS

	UNIT	COST
Door, Wood - 2 Coats	Each	50.00
Stain, Seal and Varnish	Each	72.00
Bi-fold Door - Stain, Seal and Varnish 48"	Each	73.00
60"	Each	82.00
72"	Each	98.00
Door Frame, Wood (incl. Trim) - 2 Coats	Each	46.00
Stain, Seal & Varnish	Each	56.00
Door, Metal (Factory Primed) - 1 Coat	Each	42.00
2 Coats	Each	54.00
Door Frame, Metal (Factory Primed) - 1 Coat	Each	38.00
2 Coats	Each	42.00
Window, Wood (including Frame & Trim) - 2 Coats	Each	55.00
Add for Storm Windows or Screens	Each	29.00
Add for Shutters - Pair	Pair	77.00
Window, Steel	Each	49.00

	UNIT	COST
FLOORS, EPOXY	SqFt	2.50

0912.0   PAINTING (L&M) (Painters) — UNIT — COST

MISCELLANEOUS WOOD

	UNIT	COST
Cabinets - Enamel 2 Coats	SqFt	1.03
Stain and Varnish	SqFt	1.24
Enamel 3 Coats	SqFt	1.55
Stain, Seal and Varnish	SqFt	1.96
Wood Trim - Stain, Seal and Varnish - Large	LnFt	1.96
Small or Decorative	LnFt	2.30

MISCELLANEOUS METAL - 1 Coat Sprayed

	UNIT	COST
Miscellaneous Iron and Small Steel	Ton	1.24
Structural Steel	Ton	.81
Structural Steel - 2 Sq.Ft. per Ln.Ft.	LnFt	.63
3 Sq.Ft. per Ln.Ft.	LnFt	.76
4 Sq.Ft. per Ln.Ft.	LnFt	1.08
5 Sq.Ft. per Ln.Ft.	LnFt	1.28
Add for Brush	LnFt	40%
Add for 2 Coats	LnFt	75%
Gutters, Down Spouts and Flashings - 4"	LnFt	1.66
5"	LnFt	1.70
6"	LnFt	1.92
Piping - Prime and 1 Coat - 4"	LnFt	.81
6"	LnFt	1.19
8"	LnFt	1.34
10"	LnFt	1.62
Radiators	SqFt	3.50

MISCELLANEOUS

	UNIT	COST
Gold and Silver Leaf	SqFt	52.00
Parking Lines - Striping	LnFt	.37
Wood Preservatives	SqFt	.62
Waterproof Paints - 2 Coats	SqFt	1.06
Clear - 1 Coat	SqFt	.56
2 Coat	SqFt	.84
Taping and Sanding	SqFt	.56
Texturing	SqFt	.62

See 0910 for Wood Floor Finishing

0913.0   WALL COVERINGS (L&M) (Painters)

		UNIT	COST	
.1	VINYL PLASTICS (54" Roll)			
	Light Weight	SqFt	1.85 -	2.40
	Medium Weight	SqFt	1.90 -	3.00
	Heavy Weight	SqFt	2.00 -	5.40
	Add for Sizing	SqFt	.25 -	.47
	Add for 27" and 36" Rolls	SqFt	.20 -	.49
.2	PLASTIC WALL TILE	SqFt	3.75 -	5.35
.3	WALLPAPER ($10.00-40.00 Roll, 36 S.F. to Roll)	SqFt	1.70 -	4.50
	Add or Deduct per Roll - $1.00	SqFt	.22 -	.90
.4	FABRICS (Canvas, etc.)	SqFt	1.80 -	3.95
.5	LEATHER	SqFt	2.50 -	4.15
.6	WOOD VENEERS	SqFt	6.25 -	11.80
.7	FIBERGLASS	SqFt	2.60 -	4.60
.8	CORK - 3/16"	SqFt	2.10 -	5.10
.9	GLASS - 5/16"	SqFt	1.45 -	2.85
.10	GRASS CLOTH	SqFt	2.00 -	3.70

1001.0 ACCESS PANELS (M)
(Lathers, Carpenters)

	UNIT	LABOR	MATERIAL		
			Flush Flange	Drywall	UL Label
10" x 10"	Each	17.00	39.00	43.00	122.00
12" x 12"	Each	18.00	45.00	-	127.00
14" x 14"	Each	19.00	49.00	53.00	150.00
16" x 16"	Each	21.00	51.00	-	168.00
18" x 18"	Each	23.00	60.00	-	172.00
22" x 22"	Each	25.00	78.00	88.00	205.00
24" x 24"	Each	30.00	91.00	-	227.00
24" x 36"	Each	34.00	105.00	-	288.00
32" x 32"	Each	39.00	122.00	-	315.00
Add for Plaster Type					15%
Add for Locks					10.50

1002.0 CHALKBOARDS AND TACKBOARDS (Carpenters)

	UNIT	LABOR	MATERIAL
Chalkboards			
Slate - Natural 3/8" - New	SqFt	4.50	18.50
Resurfaced	SqFt	4.50	9.50
Porcelain Enameled Steel			
1/2" Foil Backed Gypsum and 24 Ga	SqFt	4.30	9.10
28 Ga	SqFt	4.30	8.60
Marker (White) Board	SqFt	4.30	12.40
Tackboard			
Cork - 1/4" on 1/4" Gypsum Backing - Washable	SqFt	2.00	7.35
Add for Colored Cork	SqFt	-	3.25
Deduct for Natural Style - Not Washable	SqFt	-	3.15
Trim (Aluminum)			
Trim-Slip & Snap (incl. Metal Grounds) 1/4#	LnFt	2.70	2.20
1/2#	LnFt	3.30	4.40
Map Rail - 3/4 lb/ft	LnFt	3.50	6.20
1/4 lb/ft	LnFt	3.25	3.40
Chalk Tray	LnFt	4.30	7.35
Average Trim Cost	SqFt	3.30	6.55
Combination Unit Costs (Average)			
Slate - 3/8" - with Tackboard and Trim	SqFt	4.45	15.90
Enameled Steel (24 Ga) with Tackbd. & Trim, 8' x 4'	SqFt	4.20	9.50
Marker (White) Board	SqFt	4.30	9.90
Tackboard with Trim	SqFt	4.40	12.50
Add Vertical and Horizontal Sliding Units	SqFt	-	6.00
Portable Chalkboard Tackboard - 4' x 6'	Each	70.00	980.00
Add for Revolving Type		-	335.00

1003.0 CHUTES (Laundry & Rubbish)(M)(Sheet Metal Workers)

	UNIT	LABOR	MATERIAL
Laundry or Linen			
(16 Ga Aluminized Steel and 10' Floor Height)			
1 Floor Opening - 24" Dia - per Opening	Opng	245.00	1,060.00
2 Floors or Openings	Opng	225.00	870.00
6 Floors or Openings	Opng	215.00	820.00
Average	LnFt	25.00	90.00
Rubbish			
(16 Ga Aluminized Steel)			
1 Floor Opening - 24" Dia - per Opening	Opng	240.00	1,050.00
2 Floors or Openings	Opng	225.00	895.00
6 Floors or Openings	Opng	215.00	785.00
Add for Explosion Vent - per Opening	Opng	-	530.00
Add for Stainless Steel	Opng	-	450.00
Add for 30" Diameter	Opng	23.00	210.00
Deduct for Galvanized	Opng	-	90.00

1004.0 COAT/ HAT RACKS & CLOSET ACCESS. (M) (Carpenters)

	UNIT	LABOR	MATERIAL
ALUMINUM	LnFt	15.00	84.00
STAINLESS STEEL	LnFt	15.00	104.00

1005.0 CUBICLE CURTAIN TRACK & CURTAINS (M) (Carpenters)

	UNIT	LABOR	MATERIAL
	LnFt	9.50	18.00

1006.0 DIRECTORIES & BULLETIN BOARDS (M) (Carpenters)
(Directories For Changeable Letters)

	UNIT	LABOR	MATERIAL
Interior - 48" x 36" Aluminum	Each	166.00	1,120.00
Stainless Steel	Each	165.00	1,292.00
Bronze	Each	165.00	1,790.00
60" x 36" Aluminum	Each	187.00	1,280.00
Stainless Steel	Each	192.00	1,900.00
Bronze	Each	192.00	2,862.00
Exterior - 48" x 36" Aluminum	Each	225.00	1,550.00
Stainless Steel	Each	235.00	2,242.00
Bronze	Each	235.00	2,950.00
60" x 36" Aluminum	Each	245.00	2,120.00
Stainless Steel	Each	245.00	2,835.00
Bronze	Each	245.00	3,850.00
Illuminated - 72" x 48" Aluminum	Each	345.00	6,650.00
Stainless Steel	Each	345.00	10,600.00
Bronze	Each	345.00	12,900.00

1007.0 DISPLAY & TROPHY CASES (M) (Carpenters)

	UNIT	LABOR	MATERIAL
Aluminum Frame 8' x 6' x 1'6"	Each	375.00	3,980.00
4' x 6' x 1'6"	Each	220.20	2,160.00

1008.0 FLOORS - ACCESS OR PEDESTAL (L&M) (Carpenters)
(Includes Laminate Topping)

	UNIT	LABOR	MATERIAL
Aluminum	SqFt		23.25
Steel - Galvanized	SqFt		16.00
Plywood - Metal Covered	SqFt		14.70
Add for Carpeting	SqFt		3.25

1009.0 FIREPLACE AND STOVES

1010.0 FIRE FIGHTING DEVICES (M) (Carpenters)

	UNIT	LABOR	MATERIAL
Extinguishers - 2½ Gal - Water Pressure	Each	28.00	90.00
Carbon Dioxide - 5 Lb	Each	28.00	216.00
10 Lb	Each	30.00	304.00
5 Lb	Each	29.00	66.00
Dry Chemical - 10 Lb	Each	29.00	80.10
20 Lb	Each	31.00	134.20
Halon - 2 1/2 Lb	Each	28.00	147.00
5 Lb	Each	24.00	176.00
Cabinets - Enameled Steel - 18 Ga			
12" x 27" x 8" - Recessed - Portable Ext	Each	50.00	82.00
24" x 40" x 8" - Recessed - Hose Rack with Nozzle	Each	96.00	168.00
Deduct for Surface Plastic	Each	-	24.00
Add for Aluminum	Each	-	74.00
Blanket & Cabinet - Enameled and Roll Type	Each	50.00	92.00

1011.0 FLAG POLES (M) (Carpenters)

	UNIT	LABOR	MATERIAL
Aluminum Tapered - Ground 20' - 5" Butt		208.00	1,220.00
25' - 5 1/2" Butt		220.00	1,720.00
30' - 6" Butt		285.00	1,872.00
35' - 7" Butt		380.00	2,580.00
40' - 8" Butt		515.00	3,880.00
50' - 10" Butt		640.00	5,240.50
60' - 12" Butt		845.00	9,125.00
Wall 15' - 4" Butt		212.00	108.00
Add for Architectural Grade			25%
Fiberglass Tapered - Deduct from Above Prices			20%
Steel Tapered - Deduct from Above Prices			20%
Steel Tube - Deduct from Above Prices			40%
Add for Concrete Bases		385.00	275.00

1012.0 FLOOR & ROOF ACCESS DOORS (M) (Carpenters)

	UNIT	LABOR	MATERIAL
Floor - Single Leaf 1/4" Steel			
24" x 24"	Each	108.00	690.00
30" x 30"	Each	136.00	740.00
30" x 36"	Each	164.00	852.00
36" x 36"	Each	170.00	890.00
Deduct for Recess Type	Each		38.00
Add for Aluminum	Each		70.00
Roof - Steel			
30" x 36"	Each	171.00	640.00
30" x 54"	Each	180.00	904.00
30" x 96"	Each	286.00	1,640.00
Add for Disappearing Stairs	Each	830.80	5,610.00
Add for Fixed stairs	Each	230.00	1,524.00

1013.0 FLOOR MATS & FRAMES (M) (Carpenters)

Mats - Vinyl Link 4' x 5' x 1/2"	Each	47.00	420.00
4' x 7' x 1/2"	Each	50.00	635.00
Add for Color	SqFt		4.30
Frames - Aluminum 4' x 5'	Each	85.00	258.00
4' x 7'	Each	92.00	315.00

1014.0 FOLDING GATES (M) (Carpenters)

8' x 8' - with Lock Cylinder	Each	330.00	1,590.00
	or SqFt	5.50	26.00

1015.0 LOCKERS (Incl. Benches) (M) (Sheet Metal Workers)

	UNIT	LABOR	MATERIAL 60"	MATERIAL 72"
Single - Open Type with 6" Legs				
9" x 12" x 72"	Each	23.40	135.00	142.00
9" x 15" x 72"	Each	23.40	140.40	149.00
12" x 12" x 72"	Each	26.80	151.20	161.00
12" x 15" x 72"	Each	28.00	156.60	163.00
12" x 18" x 72"	Each	29.00	158.76	164.00
15" x 15" x 72"	Each	30.00	160.92	167.00
15" x 18" x 72"	Each	31.00	169.56	169.00
15" x 21" x 72"	Each	32.00	174.96	184.00
Double Tier				
12" x 12" x 36"	Each	18.50	80.00	
12" x 15" x 36"	Each	19.00	83.60	
12" x 18" x 36"	Each	19.20	85.20	
15" x 15" x 36"	Each	19.20	89.00	
15" x 18" x 36"	Each	19.90	96.50	
15" x 21" x 36"	Each	20.10	102.00	
Box Lockers				
12" x 12" x 12"	Each	17.10	50.50	
15" x 15" x 12"	Each	17.70	52.80	
18" x 18" x 12"	Each	18.40	57.20	
12" x 12" x 24"	Each	18.40	67.80	
15" x 15" x 24"	Each	19.00	76.10	
18" x 18" x 24"	Each	19.50	79.10	
Add Flat Key Locks (Master Keyed)	Each	-	11.00	
Add for Combination Locks	Each	-	13.00	
Add for Sloped Tops	Each	8.60	13.00	
Add for Closed Base	Each	8.60	10.00	
Add for Other than Standard Colors	Each	-	15%	
Add for Benches	LnFt	9.70	32.20	
Add for Less than Banks of 4	Each	5%	10%	
Add for Recessed Latch (Quiet)	Each	-	3.90	

1016.0 LOUVERS AND VENTS (M) (Carpenters or Sheet Metal Workers)

LOUVRES	UNIT	LABOR	MATERIAL
Exterior			
Galvanized - 16 Ga	SqFt	15.90	50.00
Aluminum - 14 Ga	SqFt	16.40	59.50
Extruded 12 Ga	SqFt	16.40	68.30
Add for Brass, Bronze or Stainless	SqFt	-	56.10
Add for Insect Screen	SqFt	-	5.00
Interior Door or Partition - Steel	SqFt	15.00	61.40
Aluminum	SqFt	15.00	65.00
VENTS - Brick - Aluminum	Each	30.00	80.50
Block - Aluminum	Each	30.00	124.00
See Div. 15 for Mechanically Connected			

1017.0 PARTITIONS - WIRE MESH (M) (Carpenters)

PARTITIONS	UNIT	LABOR	MATERIAL
6 Ga - 2" Mesh & Channel Frame	SqFt	5.70	12.50
10 Ga - 1 1/2" Mesh - 8'	SqFt	4.60	9.80
Add for Door	Each	113.00	455.00
WINDOW GUARDS - 10 Ga with Frame	SqFt	6.70	20.00
Add for Galvanized	-	-	15%

1018.0 PARTITIONS AND CUBICLES - DEMOUNTABLE (L&M) (Carpenters)

PARTITIONS - DEMOUNTABLE - 1 9/16" x 10'		COST
Aluminum or Enameled Steel Extrusions (Acoustical)		
Gypsum Panels (Unpainted)	SqFt	16.00
Vinyl Laminated Gypsum Panels	SqFt	17.20
Steel Panels	SqFt	17.20
Wood Panels - Hard Wood	SqFt	11.60
Add for 2 3/4"	SqFt	2.20
Add per Door	Each	606.00
CUBICLES - DEMOUNTABLE (Includes Glass)		
Steel Frame and Panels (Acoustical) Burlap		
3' - 6" High	SqFt	27.00
4' - 8" High	SqFt	24.10
5' - 8" High	SqFt	20.40
7' - 0" High	SqFt	21.00
Aluminum Frame and Panels (Acoustical) Burlap		
3' - 6" High	SqFt	22.30
4' - 8" High	SqFt	19.60
5' - 8" High	SqFt	19.45
7' - 0" High	SqFt	19.35
Deduct for Non-Acoustical Type	SqFt	2.30
Add for Vinyl Laminated	SqFt	2.10
Add for Carpeted	SqFt	4.70
Add for Curved Panels	SqFt	8.40
Add per Door	Each	494.00
Add per Gate	Each	312.00

1019.0 PARTITIONS - OPERABLE (Including Moving Dividers and Operable Walls) (L&M) (Carpenters)

	UNIT	LABOR	MATERIAL
ACCORDION FOLD (Fabric)	SqFt	5.80	17.50
Add for Acoustical Type	SqFt	-	6.40
Add for Metal & Wood Supports	LnFt	5.30	7.70
FOLDING (Wood, Plastic Lam., Fabric Cover)	SqFt	7.05	36.60
Add for Acoustical Type	SqFt	-	6.80

	UNIT	LABOR	MATERIAL
1019.0 PARTITIONS - OPERABLE, Cont'd...			
OPERABLE WALLS (Electrically Operated)			
Folding - Plastic Laminated	SqFt	8.25	46.70
Vinyl Overlaid	SqFt	8.25	44.20
Wood (Prefinished)	SqFt	8.25	44.20
Side Coiling - Wood	SqFt	-	61.50
Metal	SqFt	-	67.00
REMOVABLE OR PORTABLE WALLS (Acoustical)			
4"	SqFt	-	62.60
2 1/4"	SqFt	-	49.90
1020.0 PEDESTRIAN CONTROLS - GATES & TURNSTILES	-	-	-
1021.0 POSTAL SPECIALTIES (M) (Carpenters)			
CHUTES - Aluminum	Per Floor	268.00	1,165.00
Bronze	Per Floor	268.00	1,662.00
RECEIVING BOX - Aluminum	Each	155.00	1,100.00
Bronze	Each	155.00	1,850.00
LETTER BOXES			
3" x 5" Alum. with Cam Locks Front Load	Each	12.60	74.20
Rear Load	Each	12.60	90.20
1022.0 SHOWER & TUB RECEPTORS & DOORS (M) (Cement Finishers)			
PRECAST TERRAZZO WITH STAINLESS STEEL CAP			
32" x 32" x 6"	Each	118.00	377.00
36" x 36" x 6"	Each	130.00	464.00
36" x 24" x 12"	Each	135.00	660.00
1023.0 SIGNS, LETTERS & PLAQUES (M) (Carpenters)			
LETTERS			
Cast Aluminum, Baked Enamel, Anodized Finish			
6" x 1/2" x 2"	Each	13.60	33.50
8" x 1/2" x 2"	Each	15.00	40.20
12" x 1/2" x 2"	Each	16.20	74.30
Plastic - Character	Each	3.20	4.70
PLAQUES - 24" x 24" Cast Aluminum	Each	122.00	1,092.00
24" x 24" Bronze	Each	123.50	1,270.00
SIGNS - HANDICAP (Metal)	Each	16.00	43.00
1024.0 STORAGE SHELVING (L&M) (Sheet Metal Workers)			
METAL - 18 Ga - 36" Sections 7'1" High			
12" Deep, 6 Shelves	LnFt	17.00	47.60
18" Deep, 6 Shelves	LnFt	18.25	56.20
24" Deep, 6 Shelves	LnFt	20.50	66.60
Add or Deduct per Shelf	LnFt	3.30	5.85
Add for Closed Back and Ends	LnFt	5.50	5.85
Add for 48' Sections	LnFt	5.50	4.20
Deduct for 22 Ga	LnFt	.65	4.20
PALLET RACKS - 6' x 36" - 4 Shelves	LnFt	34.80	127.00
1025.0 SUN CONTROL & PROTECTIVE COVERS (L&M)	SqFt	6.30	23.00
1026.0 TELEPHONE AND SOUND BOOTHS (M) (Carpenters)	Each	260.00	4,036.00
1027.0 TOILET & BATH ACCESSORIES (L&M) (Plumbers)			
BASED ON STAINLESS STEEL	UNIT	LABOR	MATERIAL
Curtain Rods - 60"	Each	22.40	39.00
Medicine Cabinets - 14" x 24"	Each	37.60	92.80
18" x 24"	Each	39.60	138.20
Mirrors - 16" x 10"	Each	24.00	85.20
18" x 24"	Each	25.00	106.00
24" x 30"	Each	38.50	127.50
Add for Shelves	-	-	33.40
Mop Holders	Each	33.00	88.00
Paper Dispenser - Surface Mounted	Each	25.20	40.80
Recessed	Each	32.20	77.30
Toilet Seat Covers - Recessed	Each	32.20	90.30

1027.0 TOILET & BATH ACCESSORIES, Cont'd...

	UNIT	LABOR	MATERIAL
Purse Shelf	Each	26.50	77.00
Robe Hooks	Each	19.70	19.30
Handicap Grab Bar - 18"	Each	26.20	44.90
36"	Each	30.00	52.40
42"	Each	37.00	57.80
Set of Three	Each	80.00	118.00
Soap Dispenser - Wall Mount	Each	25.20	56.90
- with Lather Shelf	Each	26.00	116.50
Soap and Grab Bar	Each	25.20	64.20
Toilet Seat Cover Dispenser	Each	29.60	90.00
Towel Bars - 24"	Each	25.30	38.60
Towel Dispenser - Recessed	Each	54.80	573.00
- Surface Mounted	Each	50.20	165.00
and Disposal - Recessed	Each	50.20	573.00
Sanitary Napkin Disposal - Recessed	Each	29.00	77.20
Electric Hand Dryer	Each	75.00	421.10

1028.0 TOILET COMPARTMENTS (Incl. Shower & Dressing Rooms) (L&M) (Sheet Metal Workers & Plumbers)

	UNIT	LABOR	MATERIAL
PARTITIONS - FLOOR BRACED			
(Door & 1 Side Panel) Baked Enameled	Each	142.00	490.00
Stainless Steel	Each	147.00	1,200.00
Plastic Laminate	Each	152.00	547.00
Marble	Each	240.00	902.00
Add for Extra Side Panel - Baked Enameled	Each	85.30	245.00
Plastic Laminate	Each	85.30	272.00
Marble	Each	172.40	352.00
Add for Ceiling Hung	Each	85.00	118.00
Add for Reinforcing for Handicap Bars (ADA)	Each	-	88.00
Add for Paper Holders	Each	18.25	42.00
Urinal Screens - Baked Enameled	Each	103.00	245.00
Plastic Laminate	Each	104.00	288.00
Marble	Each	151.00	448.00
Shower Partitions (No Plumbing)			
Baked Enameled (with Curtain & Terrazzo Base)			
32" x 32"	Each	183.00	768.00
36" x 36"	Each	183.00	705.00
Fiberglass & Fiberglass Base - 32" x 32"	Each	115.00	321.00
36" x 36"	Each	115.00	363.00
Add for Doors	Each	48.50	246.00
Tub Enclosures			
Aluminum Frame and Tempered Glass Door	Each	85.00	230.00
Chrome Frame and Tempered Glass Door	Each	85.00	300.00

1029.0 URNS AND TRAYS

	UNIT	LABOR	MATERIAL
CIGARETTE URNS - SS Rectangular or Round	Each	48.00	118.00

1030.0 WALL AND CORNER GUARDS

	UNIT	LABOR	MATERIAL
CORNER GUARDS			
Stainless Steel			
16 Ga 4" x 4" with Anchor	LnFt	7.50	25.00
18 Ga 4" x 4" with Anchor	LnFt	6.85	25.00
22 Ga 3½" x 3½" with Anchor	LnFt	7.50	21.00
22 Ga 3½" x 3½" with Tape	LnFt	6.95	20.00
Aluminum - Anodic with Tape	LnFt	6.95	17.50
Vinyl	LnFt	6.45	11.00

See 0502.3 for Steel

1101.0   MEDICAL CASEWORK (L&M) (Carpenters)
INCLUDING PLASTIC LAMINATE TOP, HARDWARE & FINISH

		UNIT	LABOR	MATERIAL
.1	METAL			
	Base Cabinets - 35" High x 24" Deep	LnFt	37.20	255.00
	Wall Cabinets - 24" High x 12" Deep	LnFt	35.30	205.00
	High Wall (Utility) - 84" High x 12" Deep	LnFt	37.50	208.00
.2	PLASTIC LAMINATE (Including Plastic Laminator)			
	Base Cabinets - 35" High x 24" Deep	LnFt	37.50	255.00
	Wall Cabinets - 24" High x 12" Deep	LnFt	35.30	194.00
	High Wall (Utility) - 84" High x 12" Deep	LnFt	38.80	215.00
.3	WOOD			
	Base Cabinets - 35" High x 24" Deep	LnFt	37.50	230.00
	Wall Cabinets - 24" High x 12" Deep	LnFt	35.30	185.00
	High Wall (Utility) - 84" High x 12" Deep	LnFt	38.30	210.00
.4	STAINLESS STEEL			
	Base - 35" High x 24" Deep	LnFt	38.50	300.00
	Wall - 24" High x 12" Deep	LnFt	35.30	280.00

1102.0   EDUCATIONAL CASEWORK (L&M) (Carpenters)
Same as 1101.0 Medical Casework above.

1103.0   KITCHEN AND BATH CASEWORK (M) (Carpenters)

.1	PREFINISHED WOOD - NO TOPS			
	Base Cabinets - 35" High x 18" Deep	LnFt	37.20	187.00
	Front Only	LnFt	35.30	107.00
	with 1 Drawer	LnFt	37.50	225.00
	with 4 Drawers	LnFt	38.50	298.00
	with Lazy Susan	LnFt	38.00	235.00
	Upper Cabinets - 30" High x 12" Deep	LnFt	36.30	150.00
	18" High x 12" Deep	LnFt	35.30	119.00
	with Lazy Susan	LnFt	36.85	198.00
	High Cabinets - 84" High x 18" Deep	LnFt	38.40	300.00
	Add for Counter Tops - See 0603.2			
.2	PLASTIC LAMINATE			Add 10%

1104.0   MEDICAL EQUIPMENT (M) (Carpenters)

.1	STATION AND SERVICE CENTER EQUIPMENT			
.11	Kitchen - Example: 4'6" x 4'2" Base & 30" Upper	Each	280.00	2,480.00
.12	Medical Preparation - Example: 4'0" x 6'8" x 1'8" (also 5' and 6' wide)	Each	344.00	4,860.00
.13	Nourishment and Ice Stations - Example: 6'0" x 6'8" x 2'8"	Each	374.00	12,800.00
.14	Lavatory Unit - Example: 4'7" x 1'8" x 4'0"	Each	168.00	1,255.00
.15	Janitor's Closet - Example: 2'0" x 5'4" x 6'8"	Each	322.00	4,820.00
.16	Glove Packaging - Example	Each	170.00	1,365.00
.17	Linen Inspection - Example	Each	190.00	1,850.00
.2	LAB TABLES AND DEMONSTRATION DESKS	Each	182.00	2,720.00

1104.0   MEDICAL EQUIPMENT, Cont'd...

	UNIT	LABOR	MATERIAL
.3 TOPS AND BOWLS (M) (Carpenter or Plumber)			
Calcium Aluminum Silicate	SqFt	8.00	29.00
Corian	SqFt	8.00	56.00
Epoxy Resins (Kemstone)	SqFt	8.00	27.00
Marble - Artificial	SqFt	6.50	29.00
Plastic Laminate - 25" - 1 1/2"	SqFt	5.00	27.00
Add for Backsplash	LnFt	2.00	6.00
Soapstone	SqFt	5.50	40.00
Stainless Steel - Bowl	Each	80.00	225.00
Tops	SqFt	7.50	74.00
Add for Backsplash	LnFt	3.00	10.00
Vinyl Sheet - 25" - 1 1/2"	SqFt	4.00	17.00
Add for Backsplash	LnFt	2.50	6.00
.4 FUME HOODS (INCLUDING DUCT WORK)			
Stock - 4"	Each	480.00	6,200.00
Custom	Each	480.00	6,600.00
.5 KEY CABINETS (100 KEY)	Each	95.00	360.00
.6 BLANKET AND SOLUTION WARMERS (NO MECHANICAL OR ELECTRICAL) Example: 27 x 11 x 30" x 74			
Free Standing - Steam	Each	440.00	5,750.00
Electric	Each	440.00	5,950.00
Recessed - Steam	Each	500.00	5,840.00
Electric	Each	500.00	5,950.00
.7 ENVIRONMENTAL GROWTH CHAMBERS & LABS	Each	1,420.00	5,140.00
.8 CHART RACKS AND CHART RACK DESKS			
Racks	Each	85.00	390.00
Desks	Each	128.00	1,920.00

		ELECTRIC		STEAM	
.9 STERILIZING EQUIPMENT (NO MECHANICAL/ ELECTRICAL)	UNIT	Re-cessed	Open Mtd or Mobile	Re-cessed	Open Mtd or Mobile
Dressing and Instrument -					
Example: 16" x 26"	Each	15,250	-	1,610.00	-
Dressing -					
Example: 20" x 20" x 38"	Each	32,000	-	26,400	2,800
Solution Warming/ Storage Cab.	Each	-	-	-	-
Bedpan -					
Example: 16" x 16" x 27"					
Non Pressure	Each	-	3,700	-	-
Pressure	Each	-	3,600	-	-
Laboratory (Painted)	Each	17,600	19,700	12,200	19,850
Add for Stainless Steel					
Autoclave (All Purpose)					
Portable Inst. - Non Pressure					
6" x 6" x 13"	Each	-	1,490.00	-	-
8" x 8" x 16"	Each	-	2,200	-	-
10" x 10" x 22"	Each	-	7,660	-	-
Hot Air -					
Example: 39" x 14" x 19"					
Gravity	Each	4,130	4,030	-	-
Convection	Each	5,710	7,700	-	-

1104.0 MEDICAL EQUIPMENT, Cont'd...

.10   X-RAY AND DARK ROOM EQUIPMENT
     Lead Protection - See 0801 for Doors & View Window Frames
     Lead Protection - See 0902 for Lead Lined Sheetrock
     Manual Dark Room

Item	UNIT	LABOR	MATERIAL
Example: Room including Cassette Pass Box, Cassette Storage Cabinet, Film Identifier Cabinet, Film Illuminator and Dryer, Development Tank including Tops and Splashes	Each	1,720.00	17,480.00
Automatic			
Processor with Solution Storage Tank	Each	930.00	13,200.00
Film Loader	Each	327.00	6,560.00
.11 AUTOPSY AND MORTUARY EQUIPMENT			
Refrigerators	Each	530.00	11,100.00
Tables	Each	337.00	6,800.00
Carts	Each	95.00	1,840.00
.12 NARCOTIC SAFES	Each	108.00	720.00
.13 REFRIGERATORS (OTHER THAN MORTUARY)			
Under Counter	Each	270.00	3,600.00
.14 TOTE TRAYS AND UTILITY CARTS	Each	92.00	580.00
.15 GAS TRACKS - Example: Operating Room	Each	580.00	3,880.00
Straight	LnFt	52.00	330.00
Curved	LnFt	63.00	316.00
.16 ANIMAL FENCING AND CAGING	SqFt	4.00	7.20
.17 DENTAL	-	-	-
.18 SURGICAL	-	-	-
.19 INCUBATORS	Each	-	5,220.00
.20 THERAPY-HEAT	Each	-	2,580.00
.21 OVERHEAD HOISTS	Each	-	2,530.00

1105.0 EDUCATIONAL EQUIPMENT

1106.0 RESIDENTIAL EQUIPMENT (NO MECH. OR ELEC.)
     See 1504 for Supply, Waste and Vent
     See 1611 for Electric Power

.1   FREE STANDING

Item	UNIT	LABOR	MATERIAL
Clothes Dryer - Gas	Each	96.00	510.00
Electric	Each	96.00	480.00
Clothes Washers	Each	96.00	500.00
Compactors - 15"	Each	92.00	560.00
Disposals	Each	91.00	180.00
Dishwasher	Each	95.00	620.00
Freezers - Upright - 16 CuFt	Each	95.00	500.00
19 CuFt	Each	104.00	570.00
21 CuFt	Each	118.00	660.00
Freezers - Upright - Frost Proof			
15 CuFt	Each	96.00	610.00
18 CuFt	Each	96.00	700.00
Freezers - Chest - 15 CuFt	Each	96.00	610.00
20 CuFt	Each	102.00	700.00
25 CuFt	Each	116.00	830.00
Dehumidifier - 40 Pint	Each	96.00	200.00
Humidifier - 10 Gals/Day	Each	96.00	285.00
Range Hood	Each	81.00	200.00
Water Heater - 30 Gal. & 40 Gal.	Each	145.00	265.00
Water Softener - 30 Grains	Each	172.00	880.00

1106.0 RESIDENTIAL EQUIPMENT, Cont'd...

	UNIT	LABOR	MATERIAL
.1 FREE STANDING, Cont'd.			
Refrigerators			
Compact - 11 CuFt	Each	96.00	445.00
Conventional- 14 CuFt	Each	104.00	550.00
With Freezer- 15 CuFt (Also 17 & 19)	Each	107.00	660.00
21 CuFt	Each	112.00	825.00
Frostproof- 12 CuFt	Each	107.00	715.00
15 CuFt	Each	117.00	910.00
Side-by-Side- 22 CuFt	Each	117.00	1,235.00
25 CuFt	Each	120.00	1,410.00
Ranges - Electric - 30"	Each	96.00	715.00
40"	Each	104.00	1,510.00
Gas - 20"	Each	92.00	380.00
30"	Each	96.00	735.00
Microwave Ovens - Counter	Each	96.00	235.00
Over-counter	Each	133.00	400.00
.2 BUILT-IN			
Air Conditioners - 110 Volt	Each	91.00	410.00
220 Volt	Each	91.00	605.00
Dishwashers	Each	91.00	585.00
Disposals	Each	91.00	180.00
Hoods	Each	91.00	190.00
Ranges - Surface - 30" Gas	Each	91.00	660.00
42" Gas with Broiler	Each	94.00	1,440.00
30" Electric	Each	91.00	715.00
42" Elec. with Broiler	Each	94.00	1,440.00
Ovens - Single - Gas	Each	101.00	760.00
Double	Each	112.00	1,000.00
Single - Electric	Each	112.00	710.00
Double	Each	116.00	1,130.00

1107.0 ATHLETIC EQUIPMENT (M) (Carpenters)

	UNIT	LABOR	MATERIAL
.1 BASKETBALL BACKSTOPS			
Stationary	Each	415.00	790.00
Retractable	Each	580.00	1,950.00
Suspended	Each	750.00	3,900.00
Add for Electric Operated	Each	-	1,160.00
.2 GYM SEATING - See Div. 1306.0			
.3 SCOREBOARDS (Great Variable)	Each	1,180.00	6,920.00
.4 BOWLING AND BILLIARDS - See Div. 1302.0			
.5 SWIMMING POOL EQUIPMENT- See Div. 1318.0			
.6 OUTSIDE RECREATIONAL EQ.- See Div. 0208.2			
.7 GYMNASTIC EQUIPMENT - See Div. 0208.2			
.8 SHOOTING RANGE EQUIPMENT	Point	860.00	7,400.00
.9 HEALTH CLUB EQUIPMENT	-	-	-

1108.0 FOOD SERVICE EQUIPMENT (L&M) (Sheet Metal and Plumbing)

			COST
Broilers - 36" Electric	Each	-	3,250.00
Can Washers	Each	-	4,000.00
Coffee Stand and Urn	Each	-	4,320.00
Hot Food Carts	Each	-	4,140.50
Conveyors - 12'	Each	-	6,920.00
Cutter - Mixer	Each	-	13,000.00
Dishtables - Clean	Each	-	4,300.00
Soiled	Each	-	5,200.00

1108.0	**FOOD SERVICE EQUIPMENT, Cont'd...**	UNIT	COST
	Disposer - Garbage - 3 H.P.	Each	3,250.00
	1 1/2 H.P.	Each	2,740.00
	Dishwasher- Automatic – Conveyor Type	Each	15,100.00
	Door Type	Each	9,620.00
	Fryers - Double	Each	5,300.00
	Hot Food Carts	Each	4,040.00
	Ice Cream Dispenser	Each	1,730.00
	Ice Machine with Bin	Each	4,875.00
	Juice and Beverage Dispenser	Each	4,625.00
	Meat Saw and Grinder	Each	4,000.00
	Microwave	Each	425.00
	Oven - Double Convector - Electric	Each	9,100.00
	Single	Each	4,825.00
	Portable Sink	Each	1,130.00
	Range - Oven- Four Burner	Each	1,480.00
	Range Hoods – Per Foot	Per Foot	430.00
	Refrigerators – Reach In	Each	3,150.00
	Silverware Dispensers	Each	330.00
	Sinks - Utility	Each	970.00
	Soiled Dish	Each	3,780.00
	Slicer	Each	3,575.00
	Steamers	Each	11,850.00
	Tray Dispensers	Each	1,080.00
	Setup Unit	Each	1,720.00
	Utility Carts	Each	450.00
	Water Stations	Each	755.00
	Work Tables –30"	Each	865.00
	Fire Protection	SqFt	40.00
1109.0	**LAUNDRY EQUIPMENT (L&M)**		
	Dryer - 50 Lb.	Each	2,370.00
	Ironer, Air	Each	8,140.00
	Hand	Each	5,520.00
	Washer Tumbler - 135 Lb.	Each	41,110.00
	50 Lb.	Each	22,650.00

1110.0	**LIBRARY EQUIPMENT (M) (Carpenters)**		LABOR	MATERIAL
	Book Trucks	Each	135.00	1,410.00
	Card Catalog Index - 30 drawer	Each	139.00	2,420.00
	Chairs	Each	19.80	130.00
	Charging Desks - Card File	Each	107.00	1,240.00
	Charging Unit	Each	106.50	1,320.00
	Open Shelf	Each	107.00	880.05
	Newspaper Rack	Each	104.00	850.00
	Shelving (Maple) - Example: 36" x 60" x 8"	LnFt	20.60	124.00
	Tables	Each	80.00	858.00

1111.0	**ECCLESIASTICAL EQUIPMENT (M) (Carpenters)**		LABOR	MATERIAL
.1	CROSSES, SPIRES AND STEEPLES	-	-	-
.2	CONFESSIONALS - Two Person	Each	700.00	6,600.00
	One Person	Each	535.00	4,580.00
.3	PEWS (OAK) (With Kneelers)	LnFt	17.10	130.00
	Add for Frontals	LnFt	17.50	65.00
	Add for Padded Kneelers	LnFt	4.70	3.70
	Add for Birch	LnFt	-	13.00
.4	BAPTISMAL FONTS	Each	75.15	895.00
.5	MISCELLANEOUS (WOOD ONLY)			
	Main Altars	Each	520.00	6,400.00
	Side Altars	Each	300.00	2,450.00
	Lecterns	Each	171.00	1,460.00
	Credence Table	Each	145.00	995.00

1112.0 STAGE AND THEATRICAL EQUIPMENT (L&M) (Carpenters)

		UNIT	LABOR	MATERIAL
.1 STAGE DRAPERIES, HARDWARE, CONTROLS AND OTHER EQUIPMENT				
Motorized Rolling Curtain - 38' x 16'		Each	-	7,020.00
Stage Equipment Sets		Each	-	2,500.00
Light Bridge		Each	-	24,800.00
.2 FOLDING STAGES - Portable Thrust		Each	-	16,240.00
.3 REVOLVING STAGES - 32' Dia x 12" High		Each	-	150,000.00
.4 FIXED AUDITORIUM SEATING - Cushioned		Each	-	225.00
.5 PROJECTION SCREENS				
Motor Oper. - 8' x 8'		Each	160.00	1,780.00
10' x 10'		Each	170.00	2,120.00
Stationary - 20' x 20'		Each	210.00	3,410.00

1113.0 BANK EQUIPMENT (M) (Carpenters)

		UNIT	LABOR	MATERIAL
.1 SAFES		Each	185.00	1,410.00
.2 DRIVE-UP WINDOW UNIT - Including Cash Drawers, Counter, Window, Depository and Lock Box		Each	1,130.00	10,300.00
.3 TELLER UNIT		Each	385.00	2,820.00
Cash Dispensing		Each	3,400.00	46,500.00
.4 NIGHT DEPOSITORY - Envelope		Each	255.00	1,260.00
Incl. Head & Chest		Each	1,120.00	10,950.00
.5 SURVEILLANCE SYSTEMS				
Receiver and Transmitter		Each	-	850.00
Cameras		Each	-	1,235.00
Time Lapse Recorder		Each	-	3,920.00
.6 SAFE DEPOSIT BOX		Each	8.50	86.00
Vault Doors - See Div. 0803.16				
Pneumatic Tube System - See Div. 14				

1114.0 DETENTION EQUIPMENT

1115.0 PARKING EQUIPMENT

		UNIT	LABOR	MATERIAL
.1 AUTOMATIC DEVICES				
Cash Registers		Each	640.00	13,450.00
Clocks - Rate Computing		Each	102.00	1,025.00
Standards		Each	80.00	790.00
Gate		Each	473.00	3,760.00
Loop Sensor		Each	255.00	1,160.00
Treadle		Each	192.00	478.00
Operator Station - Coin		Each	595.00	5,770.00
Key		Each	604.00	1,250.00
Radio Control - Transmitter		Each	-	2,200.00
Ticket Spitter Station		Each	288.00	7,025.00
.2 BOOTHS - Example: 4' x 6'		Each	355.00	6,820.00
.3 METERS AND POSTS		Each	95.00	380.00

1116.0 LOADING DOCK EQUIPMENT

		UNIT	LABOR	MATERIAL
.1 DOCK BUMPERS				
16" x 12" x 4"		Each	28.00	60.00
24" x 6" x 4"		Each	29.00	63.00
24" x 10" x 4"		Each	30.00	70.00
24" x 12" x 4"		Each	31.00	92.00
36" x 6" x 4"		Each	32.00	82.00
36" x 10" x 4"		Each	34.00	100.00
36" x 12" x 4"		Each	40.00	120.00
Add for Galvanized Angles		Each	-	10.00

		UNIT	LABOR	MATERIAL
1116.0	**LOADING DOCK EQUIPMENT, Cont'd...**			
.2	DOCK BOARDS -			
	5,000# 3' - 6" x 6' - 0"	Each	130.00	1,100.00
	10,000# 4' - 0" x 6' - 0"	Each	147.00	1,420.00
	15,000# 4' - 0" x 6' - 0"	Each	158.00	1,870.00
.3	LEVELERS & ADJUSTABLE RAMPS			
	8' - 0" x 8' (Add Concrete)	Each	260.00	3,800.00
.4	SHELTERS - 10' x 10' with Dock Pad	Each	375.00	2,150.00
	Strip Curtain - 10' x 10' x 8"	Each	105.00	280.00
	Dock Pad - 10' x 10'	Each	206.00	770.00
1117.0	**SERVICE STATION EQUIPMENT**			
.1	REELS - Chassis (No Mech. or Electric)	Each	145.00	760.00
	Air	Each	145.00	635.00
	Water	Each	145.00	660.00
	Motor Oil	Each	145.00	750.00
	A.T.F.	Each	145.00	815.00
	Gear Lube	Each	145.00	750.00
	Combination of Above - 3 Hose	Each	590.00	5,700.00
	Combination of Above - 5 Hose	Each	970.00	7,200.00
.2	PUMPS - Chassis	Each	170.00	675.00
	Gear Oil	Each	170.00	735.00
	A.T.F.	Each	170.00	735.00
	Oil - Motor	Each	127.00	785.00
	Gasoline	Each	380.00	2,360.00
.3	COMPRESSORS - 5 H.P.	Each	380.00	4,920.00
	3 H.P.	Each	370.00	2,410.00
	1 1/2 H.P.	Each	370.00	2,285.00
.4	TIRE CHANGERS - AUTO	Each	500.00	3,420.00
	Exhaust Systems - See Div. 15			
	Hoisting Equipment - See Div. 14			
	Tanks/Air/Water Connections - See Div. 15			
1118.0	**MUSICAL EQUIPMENT**			
1119.0	**CHECKROOM EQUIPMENT**			
	MOTORIZED, 1-Shelf, 16 ft	LnFt	24.00	135.00
	2-Shelf, 16 ft	LnFt	33.00	270.00
1120.0	**AUDIO VISUAL EQUIPMENT**			
	PROJECTION SCREEN	Each	-	144.00
	ELECTRIC CONTROLLED	Each	-	572.00
	TELEVISION CAMERA	Each	-	1,115.00
	MONITOR	Each	-	800.00
	VIDEO TAPE RECORDER	Each	-	1,160.00
1121.0	**INCINERATORS**			
	SMALL - 18" x 18"	Each	265.00	2,330.00
	MEDIUM - 22" x 22"	Each	288.00	3,400.00
	LARGE	Each	430.00	4,760.00
1122.0	**PHOTO AND GRAPHIC ART EQUIPMENT**			
1123.0	**WASTE HANDLING EQUIPMENT**			
	COMPACTORS - Bag - 3 CuYd Hopper	Each	1,050.00	12,800.00
	Cart	Each	1,050.00	11,750.00

1201.0 MANUFACTURED CASEWORK (L&M) (Carpenters)
(Including Plastic Laminate Top & Hardware)

		UNIT	LABOR	MATERIAL
.1	MEDICAL CASEWORK			
.11	Metal			
	Base Cabinets - 35" High x 24" Deep	LnFt	38.50	252.00
	Upper Cabinets - 24" High x 12" Deep	LnFt	37.50	198.00
	High Wall - 84" High x 12" Deep	LnFt	38.10	204.00
.12	Plastic Laminate			
	Base Cabinets - 35" High x 24" Deep	LnFt	38.10	270.00
	Upper Cabinets - 24" High x 12" Deep	LnFt	37.50	200.00
	High Wall - 84" High x 12" Deep	LnFt	38.10	315.00
.13	Wood - Prefinished			
	Base Cabinets - 35" High x 24" Deep	LnFt	38.10	240.00
	Upper Cabinets - 24" High x 12" Deep	LnFt	37.50	180.00
	High Wall - 84" High x 12" Deep	LnFt	38.10	295.00
.14	Stainless Steel			
	Base - 35" High x 24" Deep	LnFt	39.50	305.00
	Wall - 24" High x 12" Deep	LnFt	38.50	274.00
.2	EDUCATIONAL CASEWORK			

1202.0	BLINDS, SHADES AND SHUTTERS (L&M) (Carpenters)	UNIT	COST
.1	BLINDS - Horizontal		
	Wood 1"	SqFt	7.10
	Aluminum 1"	SqFt	6.70
	1"	SqFt	5.30
	Steel 2"	SqFt	4.90
	Cloth 1"	SqFt	7.90
	Vertical		
	Cloth or PVC 3"	SqFt	6.50
	Aluminum 3"	SqFt	8.20
.2	SHADES - Cotton	SqFt	2.35
	Vinyl Coated	SqFt	2.65
	Lightproof	SqFt	3.45
	Slat	SqFt	2.80
	Woven Aluminum	SqFt	4.80
	Fibre Glass	SqFt	3.40
	X-ray and Dark Room	SqFt	11.70
.3	SHUTTERS		
	16" x 1 1/8" x 48"	Pair	126.00
	16" x 1 1/8" x 60"	Pair	147.00
	16" x 1 1/8" x 72"	Pair	154.00

1203.0	DRAPERIES AND CURTAIN HARDWARE (L&M) (Carpenters)		
	TRACK	LnFt	5.75
	DRAPERIES	SqYd	10.30
	Add for Lined	SqYd	2.60
	Add for Rods	SqYd	2.60
	Add for Motorized	SqYd	7.70

1204.0 OPEN OFFICE FURNITURE

1205.0	FLOOR MATS AND FRAMES (M) (Carpenters)	UNIT	LABOR	MATERIAL
	MATS - Vinyl Link - 4' x 5' x 1/2"	Each	36.80	382.00
	4' x 7' x 1/2"	Each	36.80	540.00
	Add for Color	SqFt	-	19.00
	FRAMES - Aluminum - 4' x 5'	Each	74.90	238.00
	4' x 7'	Each	86.30	302.00

1206.0	AUDITORIUM AND THEATRE SEATING (L&M) (Carpenters)	UNIT	COST
	WOOD AND PLYWOOD	Each	178.00
	CUSHIONED	Each	210.00
	ROCKING	Each	296.00

1207.0	MULTIPLE-USE SEATING		
	MOVABLE - Chrome and Solid Plastic	Each	85.00
	Wood and Plywood	Each	75.50

1208.0	BUILT-IN FOLDING TABLES AND SEATING (M) (Carpenters)		
.1	TABLES - 3' x 8' - Tempered Hardboard Top	Each	230.00
	Vinyl Laminate Top	Each	260.00
	Folding Table & Bench-Pocket Unit	Each	1,900.00
.2	CHAIRS - Metal	Each	32.00

1301.0 AIR SUPPORTED STRUCTURES

		UNIT	COST
.1	TENNIS COURTS - 2 LAYER THERMAL DOMES (Includes Doors, Heating, Equipment, Lights & Power)		
	1 Court - 58' x 118'	SqFt	21.50
	2 Courts - 106' x 118'	SqFt	20.50
	3 Courts - 156' x 118'	SqFt	19.30
	4 Courts - 201' x 118'	SqFt	18.00
	Deduct for Non Thermal Type	SqFt	2.50
.2	CONSTRUCTION DOMES, WAREHOUSES, ETC.	SqFt	9.75
	Add for Heating	SqFt	4.10
	Add for Light and Power	SqFt	2.15
	Add for Air Lock Doors	Each	16,000.00
	Add for Revolving Doors	Each	8,300.00

1302.0 BOWLING ALLEYS (L&M) (Carpenters)

	UNIT	COST
BOWLING ALLEYS (L&M) (Carpenters)	Lane	43,000.00
Add for Automatic Scorers	Lane	17,000.00

1303.0 CHIMNEYS - SPECIAL (Foundations Not Included)

.1 JOB CONSTRUCTED (L&M) (Bricklayers)

Inside Diam.	Height		UNIT	COST
5'	100'	Radial Brick	Each	142,000.00
6'	150'	Radial Brick	Each	174,000.00
7'	200'	Radial Brick	Each	230,000.00
8'	250'	Reinforced Concrete	Each	584,000.00
9'	200'	Reinforced Concrete	Each	710,000.00
10'	250'	Reinforced Concrete	Each	970,000.00
12'	300'	Reinforced Concrete	Each	1,700,000.00

.2 PREFABRICATED (METAL REFRACTORY LINED)
1800° - 2000° (L&M) (Sheet Metal & Iron Workers)

	UNIT	COST
10"	LnFt	71.00
12"	LnFt	75.00
15"	LnFt	89.00
18"	LnFt	107.00
21"	LnFt	130.00
24"	LnFt	155.00
30"	LnFt	278.00
36"	LnFt	396.00
Add for Cleanouts or T's	Each	406.00
Add for V.L. Label	Each	10%
Deduct for 800° Chimney	Each	5%

1304.0 CLEAN ROOMS

	UNIT	COST
CLEAN ROOMS	SqFt	225.00 – 500.00

1305.0 FLOORS - ACCESS OR PEDESTAL (L&M) (Carpenters)
(Includes Laminate Topping)

	UNIT	COST
Aluminum	SqFt	23.50
Steel - Galvanized	SqFt	15.50
Plywood - Metal Covered	SqFt	14.40
Add for Carpeting	SqFt	3.70
Add for Stairs and Ramps	SqFt	50%

1306.0   GRANDSTANDS, BLEACHERS AND GYM SEATING

		UNIT	COST
.1	GRANDSTANDS AND BLEACHERS		
	Not Permanent	Each Seat	30.00
	Permanent - Aluminum	Each Seat	116.00
	Steel	Each Seat	75.00
	Concrete	Each Seat	278.00
.2	GYM SEATING - FOLDING	Each Seat	84.00

1307.0   GREENHOUSE (L&M) (Glaziers)

	UNIT	COST
SINGLE ROOM TYPE - Commercial	SqFt	26.00
Educational	SqFt	35.00
Residential	SqFt	39.00
Add for Heating, Lighting and Benches	SqFt	29.00
Add for Cooling	SqFt	9.00

1308.0   INCINERATORS (L&M) (Ironworkers and Bricklayers)

Stack and Breaching Not Included
Pounds/Hour

	UNIT	COST
100	Each	10,100.00
200	Each	10,200.00
300	Each	11,460.00
400	Each	13,000.00
500	Each	14,380.00
600	Each	18,100.00
800	Each	29,800.00
Add for Gas Burner	Each	2,000.00
Add for Controls	Each	1,070.00
Add for Piping	Each	1,160.00

1309.0   INSULATED ROOMS (L&M) (Carpenters)

		UNIT	COST
.1	CUSTOM - Cooler	SqFt	202.00
	Freezer	SqFt	235.00
.2	PREFABRICATED (SELF-CONTAINED)		
	Cooler Example: Room 7'6" x 9'6"		
	Wood (Plywood)	Each	7,700.00
	Metal Covered 20 ga Galvanized #3 SS	Each	9,500.00
	Add for 3/4 HP Compressor	Each	1,260.00
	Add for 3/4 HP Compressor Starter & Coils	Each	5,600.00
	Add for Electrical	Each	1,000.00
	Cooler - Total Cost - Wood	SqFt	215.00
	Metal Covered	SqFt	236.00
	Freezer Example: Room 7'6" x 9'6"		
	Wood (Plywood)	Each	8,040.00
	Metal Covered 20 ga Galvanized #3 SS	Each	9,820.00
	Add for 3/4 HP Compressor	Each	1,660.00
	Add for 3/4 HP Compressor Starter & Coils	Each	5,100.00
	Add for Electrical	Each	1,050.00
	Freezer - Total Cost - Wood	SqFt	235.00
	Metal Covered	SqFt	267.00
	Add for Shelving	SqFt	10.50

		UNIT	COST
1310.0	**METAL BUILDINGS**		
.1	SHELL - FLOOR AREA (NO FOUNDATION)	SqFt	17.50
	24 ga. 12' Sidewalls and 60' Span (Galvanized)		
	Add per foot above 12' - Floor Area	SqFt	.48
	Add per foot of Span above or below 60'	SqFt	.30
	Add for 2' Overhand - Overhang Area	SqFt	7.00
	Add for Aluminum	SqFt	.80
	Add for Liner Panels - Wall Area	SqFt	2.50
	Add for Insulation 3 1/2" - Wall Area	SqFt	.95
	Add for Insulation 6" - Ceiling Area	SqFt	1.30
	Add for Door Openings - Including Hardware	Each	850.00
	Add for Window Openings	Each	440.00
	Add for Insulated Glass Area	SqFt	12.25
	Add for Overhead Door Area	SqFt	11.80
	See 0803.4 for Door Cost		
	Add for Gutter	LnFt	6.00
	FOUNDATION & GROUND SLAB COST AVG (3-Foot Frost)	SqFt	9.80
1311.0	**RADIATION PROTECTION (L&M) (Carpenters)**		
.1	ELECTROSTATIC SHIELDING		
	Custom - Vinyl Sandwiched Copper Mesh for Floors, Walls & Ceilings (including Copper Foil Tabs & Plastic Tape)	SqFt	31.75
	Add per door and Frame with RF Shielded Glass (including Grounding Wires)	Each	4,620.00
	Add per Borrowed Light RF Shielded Glass	Each	1,955.00
	Example: Room 10' x 8' (Prefab)	Room	36,800.00
		or SqFt	460.00
.2	ELECTROMAGNETIC SHIELDING		
	Example: Room 10' x 8' (Prefab)	Room	15,600.00
		or SqFt	195.00
	Add for Finish, Electricity and Erection	Room	13,000.00
.3	X-RAY		
	Deep Therapy		
	Example: Room 10' x 15'	Room	15,560.00
	Radiography or Fluoroscopy		
	Example: Room 10' x 15'	Room	6,720.00
.4	RADIO FREQUENCY SHIELDING		
	Example: Room 10' x 10'	Room	38,300.00
	See 1104.10 for X-Ray Equipment		
1312.0	**SAUNAS (M) (Carpenters)**		
	Examples (includes Heaters):		
	Room 5' x 6' Cedar (5 K.W. Unit)	Room	5,580.00
		or SqFt	186.00
	Room 6' x 6' Cedar (6 K.W. Unit)	Room	6,750.00
		or SqFt	190.00
	Room 6' x 7' Cedar (7.5 K.W. Unit)	Room	6,840.00
		or SqFt	168.00
	Add for Electrical Connections and Ventilating		1,000.00

1313.0 SCALES (NO PORTABLE) (Ironworkers)

.1 FLOOR SCALES (HEAVY DUTY INDUSTRIAL)

Size	Capacity	Labor	Material	Concrete Work
46" x 38"	800 lb.	520.00	5,450.00	-
48" x 48"	1,350 lb.	550.00	5,770.00	-
60" x 48"	1,600 lb.	780.00	6,200.00	-
72" x 48"	2,600 lb.	810.00	7,200.00	-
76" x 54"	6,000 lb.	1,400.00	7,600.00	-
84" x 60"	10,000 lb.	2,320.00	9,900.00	-

.2 TRUCK SCALES - FULL WITH WEIGH BEAM

Truck (4-Section) -

Size	Capacity	Labor	Material	Concrete Work
45" x 10"	50 Ton	3,320.00	26,500.00	24,700.00
50" x 10"	50 Ton	3,500.00	27,200.00	25,300.00
60" x 10"	50 Ton	4,140.00	28,800.00	25,900.00
70" x 10"	50 Ton	4,820.00	30,000.00	27,700.00
Add for 60-Ton Capacity			4,300.00	

Axle Load -

Size	Capacity	Labor	Material	Concrete Work
8" x 10"	20 Ton	2,300.00	11,200.00	8,300.00
8" x 10"	30 Ton	3,000.00	13,540.00	8,400.00
10" x 10"	20 Ton	3,230.00	14,050.00	8,900.00
10" x 10"	30 Ton	3,750.00	15,820.00	9,000.00
Add to Above for Printer and Dial			3,300.00	

.3 CRANE SCALES -

	Capacity	Labor	Material	Concrete Work
	1 Ton	173.00	3,230.00	-
	5 Ton	340.00	3,440.00	-

1314.0 SIGNS (Special Exterior) (L&M) (Sheet Metal Workers)

1315.0 SKYDOMES (L&M) (Carpenters)

EXTRUDED ALUMINUM FRAME, WIRE GLASS
EXTERIOR AND FIBERGLASS SUB CEILING

	UNIT	COST
12' x 18' Ridge Type	Each	10,720.00
	or SqFt	45.00
18' x 18' Pyramid Type	Each	19,400.00
	or SqFt	60.00
36' Diameter Geometric Domes	Each	75,600.00
	or SqFt	72.45
18' Diameter Revolving Domes	Each	20,000.00
	or SqFt	70.00

1316.0 SOUND INSULATED ROOMS (Including Vibration Control) (M) (Carpenters)

	UNIT	COST
.1 ANECHOIC ROOMS (ISOLATORS, PANELS AND WEDGES)	Room	142,500.00
Example: Room 30' x 30'	or SqFt	158.00
.2 AUDIOMETRIC ROOM (PREFABRICATED PANELS)		
Example: Research Room - 5' x 8'	Room	13,000.00
	or SqFt	325.00
Example: Medical Practice Room - 5' x 8'	Room	29,200.00
	or SqFt	730.00

1318.0   SWIMMING POOLS

.1   POOLS

Deep Pools - 3 to 9 feet
(Incl. Filters, Skimmers, Lights, Clng. Equip.)

Rectangular or L Shape:	UNIT	COST
Residential - 1,000 SqFt	Each	46,000.00
	or SqFt	46.00
Motels and Apartments - 2,000 SqFt	Each	108,000.00
	or SqFt	54.00
Municipal - 5,000 SqFt	Each	310,000.00
	or SqFt	62.00
Add for Diving Stand - Steel - 1 Meter	Each	3,850.00
Steel - 3 Meter	Each	5,700.00
Add for Diving Boards - 12' Fiberglass	Each	1,000.00
16' Aluminum	Each	1,840.00
Add for Slides - 6' Fiberglass	Each	970.00
12' Fiberglass	Each	1,500.00
Add for Ladders - 10'	Each	375.00
Add for Lifeguard Chairs	Each	1,250.00
Add for Covers	Each	900.00

Shallow Pools - 3 to 5 feet -
Gunite with Plaster Finish

Residential - 1,000 SqFt	Each	34,500.00
	or SqFt	34.50
Motels and Apartments - 2,000 SqFt	Each	90,100.00
	or SqFt	45.50
Deduct for Vinyl Lined Pools	SqFt	11.00
Add for Free Form Pools	Each	5%
Add for Heaters	Each	4,600.00
Add for Automatic Cleaners	Each	4,400.00
Wading Pools - 12' x 12' or 9' Round	Each	5,580.00
	or SqFt	40.00

.2 DECKS - CONCRETE - Average 10' around Pool	Each	4,300.00
and Average 1,000 SqFt	or SqFt	4.30
Add for Tile	SqFt	9.70
Add for Brick	SqFt	8.30
.3 FENCES - 4' ALUMINUM OR GALVANIZED	LnFt	1,300.00

1319.0   TANKS

.1   STEEL - GROUND LEVEL (NO FOUNDATION)

150,000 Gals	Each	160,100.00
500,000 Gals	Each	280,000.00
1,000,000 Gals	Each	460,000.00
2,000,000 Gals	Each	735,000.00

.2   STEEL - ELEVATED

100,000 Gals	Each	370,000.00
250,000 Gals	Each	485,000.00
500,000 Gals	Each	780,000.00
1,000,000 Gals	Each	1,800,000.00

1320.0   WOOD DECKS - WITH RAILS

CEDAR	SqFt	17.75
TREATED FIR	SqFt	16.00
Add for Seats	LnFt	4.40
Add for Stairs	Riser	60.00

1401.0 ELEVATORS (L&M) (Elevator Constructors & Ironworkers)

.1 ELECTRIC (CABLE/ TRACTION)

.11 Passenger - Std Specifications

	Speed to F.P.M.	2,000#	3,000#	4,000#	10,000#
Geared A.C. Rheostatic:					
Selective Collective Operation					
3 Openings	125	85,700	-	-	-
4 Openings	125	88,000	-	-	-
5 Openings	125	92,400	-	-	-
Add per Floor	-	6,300	-	-	-
Geared Variable Voltage:					
Selective Collective Operation					
8 Openings	250	153,500	162,000	166,000	-
	350	158,000	163,500	169,000	-
10 Openings	250	156,500	162,000	172,000	-
	350	171,500	164,000	175,000	-
Add per Floor	-	8,200	8,500	9,500	-
Group Supervisory					
8 Openings	250	-	172,000	175,000	-
	350	-	180,000	188,800	-
10 Openings	250	-	176,000	178,500	-
	350	-	180,000	183,000	-
Add per Floor	-	-	8,800	9,200	-
Gearless Variable Voltage:					
Group Supervisory					
8 Openings	500	-	201,000	206,000	-
	800	-	211,000	223,000	-
	1000	-	218,000	242,000	-
10 Openings	500	-	213,000	218,500	-
	800	-	231,000	237,000	-
	1000	-	235,000	240,000	-
Add per Floor	-	-	8,500	8,700	-
Add per Fl. of Express Zone	-	8,700	7,980	8,800	

.12 Freight

	Speed to F.P.M.	2,000#	3,000#	4,000#	10,000#
3 Openings	100	-	-	113,000	118,000
4 Openings	100	-	-	116,000	124,000
Add per Floor	-	-	-	26,000	15,400
Add per Power Operated Door	-	-	-	-	8,600

.2 OIL HYDRAULIC

.21 Passenger

	Speed to F.P.M.	2,000#	3,000#	4,000#	10,000#
Passenger - 2 Openings	100	60,000	-	-	-
3 Openings	100	64,000	-	-	-
4 Openings	100	74,200	-	-	-
5 Openings	100	76,600	-	-	-
6 Openings	100	90,000	-	-	-

Deduct for Limited Use Elevator, non-Commercial 8,000# - $5,000

.22 Freight

	Speed to F.P.M.	2,000#	3,000#	4,000#	10,000#
Freight - 2 Openings	100	-	-	71,000	85,000
3 Openings	100	-	-	83,000	91,000
4 Openings	100	-	-	86,000	94,200

Add per Power Operated Door - $12,100

.3 RESIDENTIAL (WINDING DRUM)

2 Openings - Speed to 36 F.P.M., 700# Capacity - $25,000
Speed to 30 F.P.M., 410# Capacity - $19,400
Add for 3 Openings - $4,500

Add for ADA Updating -$15,400
Add for Updating Generators, Controllers & Operating Equipment -$65,000
Add to 1401.1 and 1401.2 Above for Custom Specifications - 10%
Add to 1401.2 for Shaft Work, Electric Power & Mechanical - approx. $66,000
Add for Demolition – Electric (5 openings) $19,500
Add for Demolition – Hydraulic (5 openings) $12,000

1402.0 MOVING STAIRS & WALKS (L&M) (Elevator Constructors & Ironworkers)

.1   MOVING STAIRS (Escalators)

	UNIT	CAPACITY	COST
16' Floor Height			
Metal Balustrade 32" Wide			147,000
48"			158,000
Glass Balustrade 32" Wide			157,000
48"			172,000
Add or Deduct per Foot Floor Height			4,000
Add for Over 20 Feet Floor Height			25%

.2   MOVING WALKS - Belt Type 32"

	UNIT	CAPACITY	COST
MOVING WALKS - Belt Type 32"	LnFt		920
48"	LnFt		1,035.00
Pallet Type 32"	LnFt		1,140
48"	LnFt		1,200.00

1403.0 DUMBWAITERS (L&M) (Elevator Constructors)

.1   ELECTRIC

	Speed F.P.M.		COST
Drum Type			
2 Openings - 1 Stop	25 to 75	50# to 500#	18,000
3 Openings - 2 Stops	25 to 75	50# to 500#	21,300
Add per Floor			4,800
Traction Type			
3 Openings - 2 Stops	50 to 300	50# to 500#	23,200
4 Openings - 3 Stops	50 to 300	50# to 500#	26,800
5 Openings - 4 Stops	50 to 300	50# to 500#	32,000
6 Openings - 5 Stops	50 to 300	50# to 500#	35,300
Add per Floor			5,100

.2   HAND OPERATED

	COST
2 Openings - 1 Stop	7,800
3 Openings - 2 Stops	8,800
Add per Floor	1,180.00
Add for all Stainless Steel	25%

1404.0 LIFTS (L&M) (Ironworkers & Elevator Constructors)

		UNIT	CAPACITY	COST
.1	WHEELCHAIR LIFTS - 42"	Each	1,050#	21,600
	96"	Each	1,400#	26,200
.2	STAIR LIFTS (CLIMBERS)	Each		7,400
.3	VEHICLE - SEMI HYDRAULIC LIFTS - 1 Post	Each	8,000#	9,100
	2 Post	Each	10,000#	14,150
	2 Post	Each	15,000#	21,500
	Add for Fully Hydraulic - 2 Post	Each	10,000#	5,000.00
.4	MATERIAL HANDLING LIFTS	Each		-
.5	STAGE LIFTS - 12' x 30'	Each		105,000
	Add for Permits, Inspections & Elec Hookups			2,000

See 1116 for Loading Dock Lift Equipment

1405.0 PNEUMATIC TUBE SYSTEMS (L&M) (Sheet Metal Workers)

	UNIT	COST
3" ROUND - Single Tube	LnFt	37.70
Twin Tube	LnFt	47.50
4" ROUND - Single Tube	LnFt	38.10
Twin Tube	LnFt	50.50
4" x 7" OVAL - Single Tube	LnFt	45.00
Twin Tube	LnFt	63.20

1406.0 MATERIAL HANDLING (L&M) (Ironworkers & Millwrights)   -
1407.0 TURNTABLES (L&M) (Ironworkers & Millwrights)   -
1408.0 POWERED SCAFFOLDING (L&M) (Ironworkers)   -

Costs of mechanical work are priced as total contractor's costs with an overhead and fee of 20% included. Not included are scaffold, hoisting, temporary heat, enclosures and bonding. Included are 35% taxes and insurance on labor, equipment, tools and 5% sales tax.

1501.0   BASE MATERIALS AND METHODS

.1   PIPE AND PIPE FITTINGS (Including Fittings)

	UNIT	COST
Steel - Black - Threaded 3/4"	LnFt	3.90
1"	LnFt	4.35
1-1/2"	LnFt	6.45
2"	LnFt	12.20
2-1/2"	LnFt	17.12
3"	LnFt	23.50
4"	LnFt	29.45
5"	LnFt	100.00
6"	LnFt	43.30
8"	LnFt	63.60
Steel - Galvanized Schedule 40 3/4"	LnFt	8.12
1"	LnFt	10.40
1-1/4"	LnFt	11.75
1-1/2"	LnFt	13.60
2"	LnFt	18.00
3"	LnFt	30.05
4"	LnFt	38.50
5"	LnFt	49.18
6"	LnFt	65.70
8"	LnFt	71.70
Deduct for Black Iron	LnFt	5%
Deduct for Underground	LnFt	10%
Cast Iron - Hub and Heavy Duty 2"	LnFt	19.82
3"	LnFt	19.89
4"	LnFt	27.65
5"	LnFt	32.92
6"	LnFt	45.20
8"	LnFt	53.40
Add for Line Pipe	LnFt	5.40
Deduct for Hubless Type	LnFt	10%
Deduct for Standard	LnFt	15%
P.V.C. - Schedule 40 1/2"	LnFt	6.05
3/4"	LnFt	6.60
1"	LnFt	7.35
1-1/4"	LnFt	8.10
1-1/2"	LnFt	8.95
2"	LnFt	9.65
3"	LnFt	10.90
4"	LnFt	18.66
6"	LnFt	32.00
Deduct for Underground	LnFt	10%
P.V.C. - Type L 3/8"	LnFt	4.48
1/2"	LnFt	5.88
3/4"	LnFt	6.95
1"	LnFt	7.96
1-1/4"	LnFt	8.88
1-1/2"	LnFt	9.85
2"	LnFt	11.05
3"	LnFt	12.80
4"	LnFt	19.15
6"	LnFt	36.40
Add for Type K (Underground)	LnFt	20%
Deduct for Type M (Residential)	LnFt	5%

1501.0   BASE MATERIALS AND METHODS (Cont'd...)

.1 PIPE AND PIPE FITTINGS (Cont'd...)	UNIT	COST
Brass - Threadless 1/2"	LnFt	11.50
3/4"	LnFt	13.05
1"	LnFt	16.03
1-1/4"	LnFt	19.80
1-1/2"	LnFt	23.40
2"	LnFt	29.10
3"	LnFt	40.65
4"	LnFt	52.90
Add for Threaded	LnFt	30%
Stainless Steel Schedule 40 1/4"	LnFt	9.90
1/2"	LnFt	14.80
3/4"	LnFt	18.90
1"	LnFt	22.20
2"	LnFt	30.36
4"	LnFt	73.85
Add for Type 316	LnFt	20%
Fibre Glass - 1"	LnFt	19.05
1-1/2"	LnFt	29.96
2"	LnFt	24.88
3"	LnFt	28.90
4"	LnFt	33.00
5"	LnFt	41.60
6"	LnFt	62.12
8"	LnFt	72.50

Utility Piping -

	UNIT	Reinforced Concrete	Vitrified Clay	Bituminous Coated Corrugated	Smooth Paved Corrugated	Ductile Iron
6"	LnFt	$8.23	$7.84	$10.70	$11.00	$18.42
8"	LnFt	8.85	10.65	11.00	12.05	24.95
1"	LnFt	11.35	14.05	12.95	14.48	29.10
12"	LnFt	15.30	16.60	16.50	17.62	44.30
15"	LnFt	17.85	25.05	19.10	20.35	53.50
18"	LnFt	24.13	38.25	23.00	35.25	71.10
21"	LnFt	29.60	44.90	27.75	30.66	86.30
24"	LnFt	33.40	63.75	30.42	35.90	105.50
27"	LnFt	45.12	87.50	37.00	41.75	-
30"	LnFt	55.45	116.60	38.20	48.50	-
36"	LnFt	66.60	161.20	42.15	60.25	-
42"	LnFt	86.10	-	49.50	70.30	-
48"	LnFt	112.00	-	67.80	78.60	-
54"	LnFt	128.75	-	89.10	106.80	-
60"	LnFt	152.50	-	108.90	130.35	-

Add for Trenching and Backfill - See Division 0202.0
See 0205 for Site Drainage Items

1501.0 BASE MATERIALS AND METHODS, Cont'd...

		UNIT	COST
.2	PIPING SPECIALTIES		
.21	Expansion Joints - Copper 1/2"	Each	$83.80
	3/4"	Each	139.50
	1"	Each	196.00
	1-1/2"	Each	420.00
	2"	Each	672.00
	3"	Each	1,200.00
	4"	Each	1,300.00
.22	Vacuum Breakers - 1/2"	Each	50.50
	3/4"	Each	57.80
	1"	Each	78.00
	1-1/2"	Each	106.00

		UNIT	IRON BODY	BRONZE BODY
.23	Strainers - Screwed Ends - 1/2"	Each	37.90	52.80
	3/4"	Each	43.90	60.40
	1"	Each	50.25	81.60
	1-1/2"	Each	69.60	128.20
	2"	Each	113.00	213.00
	3"	Each	200.00	408.00
	4"	Each	533.00	1,560.00
	Strainers - Flanged Ends - 2"	Each	180.00	547.00
	3"	Each	320.00	1,122.00
	4"	Each	523.00	2,370.00
	5"	Each	790.00	3,195.00
	6"	Each	1,090.00	3,730.00

.3 MECHANICAL - SUPPORTING ANCHORS & SEALS

.4 VALVES

Bronze	UNIT	150 psi Gate	150 psi Check	150 psi Globe	Relief	310 psi Reducing
Body - 1/2"	Each	$34.00	$31.00	$41.00	$61.00	$83.00
3/4"	Each	42.00	35.00	53.00	71.00	99.00
1"	Each	50.00	41.00	71.00	105.00	144.00
1-1/2"	Each	81.00	66.00	113.00	370.00	327.00
2"	Each	105.00	100.00	164.00	400.00	485.00
2-1/2"	Each	188.00	176.00	282.00	-	-
3"	Each	256.00	219.00	422.00	-	-

Iron	UNIT	125 psi Gate	125 psi Check	125 psi Globe
Body - 2"	Each	$303.00	$240.00	$433.00
2-1/2"	Each	304.00	245.00	483.00
3"	Each	346.00	250.00	564.05
4"	Each	535.00	444.00	752.00
6"	Each	744.00	473.00	956.00
		Gate	Check	Globe
Steel - 2"	Each	$1,012.00	$955.00	$1,270.00
2-1/2"	Each	1,590.00	1,305.00	1,792.00
3"	Each	1,610.00	1,278.00	1,984.00
4"	Each	1,836.00	1,783.00	2,762.00
		Ball	Foot	
Plastic - 1/2"	Each	$27.25	$62.50	
3/4"	Each	32.40	70.40	
1"	Each	38.25	91.30	
1-1/2"	Each	65.30	148.15	
2"	Each	74.70	177.50	

1501.0	BASE MATERIALS AND METHODS, Cont'd...		UNIT	COST
.5	PUMPS			
	Condensate Return - Simplex		Each	$ 2,050.00
	Duplex		Each	5,450.00
	Utility Water Pump -			
	Multi - Two Stage 3" & 4" 75 HP		Each	20,550.00
	Four Stage 3" & 4" 150 HP		Each	38,375.00
	Single - End Suction 1" x 2" 3 HP		Each	5,370.00
	End Suction 2" x 3" 15 HP		Each	6,810.00
	Condenser Water Pump, Pressure - 100 GPM		Each	18,245.00
	300 GPM		Each	24,430.00
	1200 GPM		Each	55,575.00
	2000 GPM		Each	64,200.00
	Submersible Pump 2"		Each	750.00
	Pedestal Pump		Each	230.00
.6	VIBRATION ISOLATION 5" long		Each	383.00
	6" long		Each	745.00
.7	METERS AND GAGES			
	Disc Type - 3/4"		Each	195.00
	1"		Each	237.00
	2"		Each	665.00
	Compound Type - 3"		Each	2,330.00
	4"		Each	3,640.00
.8	TANKS			
	Fuel Storage - Steel - 1,000 Gallons		Each	2,228.00
	2,000		Each	3,180.00
	5,000		Each	7,235.00
	10,000		Each	10,380.00
	Fuel Storage - Fiberglass - 2,000 Gallons		Each	3,670.00
	5,000		Each	6,375.00
	10,000		Each	10,700.00
	Hot Water Storage - 80 Gallons		Each	440.00
	140		Each	680.00
	200		Each	925.00
	400		Each	1,470.00
	600		Each	2,220.00
	Liquid Expansion - 30 Gallons		Each	390.00
	60		Each	630.00
	100		Each	860.00

1502.0 MECHANICAL INSULATION

.1	INSULATION FOR PIPING	Unit	3/8" Foam	1" Wall Fiberglass	2" Wall Fiberglass
	Interior - Pipe 1/2"	LnFt	4.00	4.85	6.90
	3/4"	LnFt	4.10	5.15	7.35
	1"	LnFt	4.45	4.30	7.45
	1-1/4"	LnFt	4.70	5.85	7.66
	1-1/2"	LnFt	5.00	6.40	8.14
	2"	LnFt	5.45	6.65	9.05
	2-1/2"	LnFt	5.95	7.05	9.80
	3"	LnFt	6.40	7.60	11.45
	6"	LnFt	9.15	9.75	15.75
	8"	LnFt	11.20	14.50	17.40
	Exterior - with Aluminum Jacket - Add 2.00/ LnFt				

.2	INSULATION FOR DUCT WORK	Unit	1"	1-1/2"	2"
	Rigid with Vapor Barrier	SqFt	2.55	3.58	4.05
	Blanket	SqFt	5.30	3.95	3.25
.3	INSULATION FOR BOILERS				
	Fiberglass - 2"	SqFt	-	-	12.25
	Calcium Silicate - 2" with C.F.	SqFt	-	-	18.50

		UNIT	COST
1503.0	**FIRE PROTECTION EQUIPMENT**		
.1	AUTOMATIC SPRINKLER EQUIPMENT - Wet System	SqFt	2.42
		(or) Head	232.00
	Dry System	SqFt	2.83
		(or) Head	248.00
	Add for Pendant Type Sprinklers	SqFt	.70
	Add for Deluge System	SqFt	2.31
.2	CARBON DIOXIDE EQUIPMENT - Cylinder	Each	1,110.00
	Detector & Nozzle	Each	375.00
.3	STANDPIPE AND FIRE HOSE EQUIPMENT		
	Standpipe - Exposed 6"	Each	708.00
	Concealed 6"	Each	895.00
	Cabinets - 30" x 30" Aluminum	Each	360.00
	Hose and Nozzle - 1 1/2"	LnFt	3.25
	2 1/2"	LnFt	3.90
1504.0	**PLUMBING**		
.1	EQUIPMENT	-	-
.2	PACKAGE WASTE, VENT OR WATER PIPING	Each	530.00
.3	DOMESTIC WATER SOFTENER	Each	988.00
.4	PLUMBING FIXTURES (Drain, Waste and Vent Not Included - See 1504.5)		
	Porcelain Enameled (unless otherwise noted) **with accessories**		
	Bathtub - 5' - Cast Iron - Enameled	Each	1,275.00
	Steel - Enameled	Each	648.00
	Fiberglass	Each	668.00
	5' x 5' - Cast Iron - Enameled	Each	1,670.00
	Bathtub/ Whirlpool - Fiberglass 6'	Each	4,520.00
	Bidet	Each	1,110.00
	Drinking Fountain - Enameled Wall Hung	Each	673.00
	SS Recessed	Each	820.00
	Garbage Disposal - 1/2 Horsepower	Each	184.00
	Lavatories - 19" x 17"- Oval	Each	340.00
	20" x 18" - Rectangular	Each	420.00
	27" x 23" - Oval Pedestal	Each	843.00
	18" - SS Bowl	Each	430.00
	Add for Handicap Lavatory	Each	212.00
	Shower & Tub - Combined - Fiberglass	Each	1,542.00
	Shower/Stall - Fiberglass - 32" x 32"	Each	920.00
	Fiberglass - 36" x 36"	Each	1,220.00
	Sink, Kitchen - 24" x 21" - Single	Each	589.00
	24" x 21" - SS Single	Each	415.00
	33" x 22" - Double	Each	656.00
	32" x 21" - SS Double	Each	492.00
	Sink, Laundry - Enameled	Each	662.00
	Plastic	Each	420.00
	Sink, Service - 24" x 21"	Each	810.00
	Urinals - Wall Hung	Each	725.00
	Stall or Trough 4'	Each	930.00
	Wash Fountain - Circular - Precast Terrazzo	Each	2,350.00
	Semi-circular - Precast Terrazzo	Each	2,315.00
	Water Closets - Floor Mounted - Tank Type	Each	518.00
	One Piece	Each	705.00
	Wall Mounted	Each	726.00
	Add for Colored Fixtures	Each	25%
	Add for Handicap Water Closet	Each	116.00
	See 1106 for Appliances		
.5	RESIDENTIAL PLUMBING		
	Average Domestic Fixture, Rough In and Trim	Each	585.00
	Average Cost of Drain, Waste, and Vent	Each	1,001.00
	Floor Drains - 4"	Each	530.00
.6	POOL EQUIPMENT - See 1318.0	-	-
.7	FOUNTAIN PIPING		

		UNIT	COST
1505.0	**HEAT GENERATION**		
.1	FUEL HANDLING EQUIPMENT		-
.2	ASH REMOVAL SYSTEM - Electric	Each	9,850.00
	Hand	Each	6,520.00
.3	LINED BREECHINGS		-
.4	BOILERS		
	Package Type - 1,000 Lbs per Hour	Each	31,000.00
	Steam & Hot Water - 2,000 Lbs per Hour	Each	38,500.00
	5,000 Lbs per Hour	Each	64,100.00
	10,000 Lbs per Hour	Each	71,700.00
	15,000 Lbs per Hour	Each	98,500.00
	20,000 Lbs per Hour	Each	107,300.00
	25,000 Lbs per Hour	Each	146,400.00
	Cast Iron - 100 MBH	Each	2,820.00
	Hot Water or Steam - 200 MBH	Each	4,900.00
	300 MBH	Each	5,160.00
	600 MBH	Each	10,320.00
	1,000 MBH	Each	17,000.00
	Hot Water Heaters - 20 GPM	Each	725.00
	30 GPM	Each	935.00
	40 GPM	Each	1,050.00
	50 GPM	Each	1,520.00
1506.0	**REFRIGERATION**		
.1	REFRIGERANT COMPRESSORS		-
.2	CONDENSERS - Air Cooled - 10 Ton	Each	16,450.00
	20 Ton	Each	26,100.00
	30 Ton	Each	28,800.00
	40 Ton	Each	34,780.00
	60 Ton	Each	49,150.00
	80 Ton	Each	58,400.00
	Add for Water Cooled	Each	10%
.3	CHILLERS - Hermetic Centrifugal - 100 Ton	Each	63,000.00
	150 Ton	Each	66,000.00
	300 Ton	Each	93,000.00
	Add for Absorption Type	Each	15%
.4	COOLING TOWERS - 100 Ton	Each	8,970.00
	150 Ton	Each	16,500.00
	300 Ton	Each	44,500.00
1507.0	**HEAT TRANSFERS**		
.1	HOT WATER SPECIALTIES		-
.2	CONDENSATE PUMPS AND RECEIVER SETS		
	Outdoor - Air Cooled - 30,000 BTU	Each	2,250.00
	50,000 BTU	Each	3,060.00
	Indoor - 30,000 BTU	Each	1,150.00
	50,000 BTU	Each	1,535.00
.3	HEAT EXCHANGERS - 100 GPM	Each	1,325.00
	200 GPM	Each	1,430.00
	300 GPM	Each	3,160.00
	600 GPM	Each	6,900.00
	1,000 GPM	Each	8,640.00
.4	TERMINAL UNITS		
	Base Boards - Cast Iron Radiant - 7 1/4"	LnFt	27.00
	9 3/4"	LnFt	28.20
	Tube with Cover - 7 1/4" - 3/4"	LnFt	14.70
	7 1/4" - 1"	LnFt	15.90
	Tube with Cover - 9 3/4" - 3/4"	LnFt	18.40
	9 3/4" - 1"	LnFt	22.50
	14" Fin Tube - Steel	LnFt	27.55
	Copper	LnFt	41.60
	Convectors	Each	400.00
	Radiators	SqFt	9.90

		UNIT	COST
1507.0	**HEAT TRANSFERS, Cont'd...**	-	-
.5	COILS	-	-
.6	UNIT HEATERS - 100,000 BTU	Each	850.00
	150,000 BTU	Each	1,160.00
	200,000 BTU	Each	1,340.00
.7	PACKAGED HEATING AND COOLING	-	2,670.00
.8	STEAM SPECIALTIES	-	610.00
1508.0	**AIR HANDLING AND DISTRIBUTION**		
.1	FURNACE - Duct - 100 MBH	Each	1,440.00
	200 MBH	Each	2,160.00
	300 MBH	Each	3,710.00
.2	FANS - 1,000 CFM	Each	160.00
	5,000 CFM	Each	670.00
	10,000 CFM	Each	1,130.00
.3	DUCT WORK - Galvanized - 26 Ga	Lb	3.70
	24 Ga	Lb	3.95
	22 Ga	Lb	4.45
	20 Ga	Lb	4.85
.4	DUCT ACCESSORIES		
	Constant Volume Duct	Each	660.00
	Reheat Constant Volume Duct	Each	810.00
	Diffusers & Registers - Sidewalk	SqFt	33.00
	Ceiling	SqFt	56.74
.5	RESIDENTIAL HEATING AND AIR CONDITIONING		
	Furnace	Each	1,600.00
	Central Air Conditioning	Each	760.00
	Humidifier	Each	375.00
	Air Cleaner	Each	610.00
	Thermostat	Each	158.00
	Attic Fan	Each	370.00
	Ventilating Damper	Each	135.00
	6" Flue	Each	420.00
.6	COMMERCIAL AIR CONDITIONING		
	Average	Ton	2,750.00
	High	Ton	4,320.00
	Low	Ton	1,360.00
1509.0	**SEWAGE DRAINAGE**		
.1	SEWAGE EJECTORS 100 GPM	Each	8,660.00
.2	GREASE INTERCEPTORS - 200 GPM	Each	10,000.00
	300 GPM	Each	18,500.00
.3	LIFT STATIONS - STEEL, CONCRETE OR FIBERGLASS		
	WITH GENERATOR - 100 GPM	Each	84,600.00
	200 GPM	Each	146,800.00
	500 GPM	Each	214,000.00
.4	SEPTIC TANKS AND DRAIN FIELD		
	Concrete Tanks with Excav. - 1,000 Gallons	Each	1,720.00
	2,000	Each	3,770.00
	5,000	Each	7,900.00
	10,000	Each	15,500.00
	Drain Fields	LnFt	5.50
.5	SEWAGE TREATMENT EQUIPMENT - STEEL OR CONCRETE		
	5,000 Gallons	GPD	11.00
	50,000	GPD	4.00
	100,000	GPD	3.80
.6	AERATION EQUIPMENT - STEEL - 1,000 Gallons	Each	20,400.00
	CAPACITY PER DAY 2,000	Each	30,400.00
	5,000	Each	40,900.00
	10,000	Each	49,500.00
.7	SLUDGE DIGESTION		-
1510.0	**CONTROLS AND INSTRUMENTATION** - No cost for items listed on Index		-
1511.0	**TESTING, ADJUSTING AND BALANCING**		

Costs of Electrical Work are priced as total contractors' costs with an overhead and fee of 20% included.

1601.0 BASIC MATERIALS AND METHODS

.1 CONDUITS (Incl Fittings/Supports)

COST

.11 Rigid

	UNIT	1/2"	3/4"	1-1/2"	2"	3"	4"	5"	6"
Galvanized - Rigid	LnFt	6.35	7.90	12.30	16.85	29.20	41.60	63.30	96.00
EMT	LnFt	4.15	5.35	7.17	9.20	16.10	23.10	-	-
PVC	LnFt	3.95	4.15	5.90	7.13	13.80	18.40	-	-
Add for Running Exposed									

.12 Flexible

	UNIT	1/2"	3/4"	1-1/2"	2"	3"	4"	5"	6"
Greenfield	LnFt	3.84	4.33	8.30	10.10	20.00	-	-	-
Sealtite	LnFt	5.60	7.00	14.55	18.55	39.50	49.50	-	-

.13 Ducts

	UNIT	1/2"	3/4"	1-1/2"	2"	3"	4"	5"	6"
Fibre	LnFt	-	-	-	-	4.90	5.25	6.00	6.65
Transite	LnFt	-	-	-	-	5.00	5.80	6.45	7.20

Cost for Conduits includes Labor, Material, Equipment and Fees and Installed in Wood or Steel Construction.

.2 BOXES, FITTINGS AND SUPPORTS (In Above)

.3 WIRE AND CABLE

	UNIT	Copper T.H.W. COST
Wire - 3 - #14 - 600 Volt	LnFt	2.30
3 - #12 - 600 Volt	LnFt	2.80
3 - #10 - 600 Volt	LnFt	4.05
3 - # 8 - 600 Volt	LnFt	4.80
3 - # 4 - 600 Volt	LnFt	7.00
3 - # 2 - 600 Volt	LnFt	9.25
3 - 1/0	LnFt	12.70
3 - 2/0	LnFt	14.90
3 - 3/0	LnFt	16.70
3 - 4/0	LnFt	19.90
3 - 250 - MCM	LnFt	23.30
3 - 300 - MCM	LnFt	26.40
3 - 350 - MCM	LnFt	29.10
3 - 400 - MCM	LnFt	33.80
3 - 500 - MCM	LnFt	36.55

		ARMORED COPPER		NON-METALLIC	
	UNIT	2 Wire	3 Wire	2 Wire	3 Wire
Cable - #14 bx - 600 Volt	LnFt	4.20	4.70	1.95	3.60
#12 bx - 600 Volt	LnFt	4.45	5.05	2.15	3.80
#10 bx - 600 Volt	LnFt	5.25	6.30	2.70	4.05
# 8 bx - 600 Volt	LnFt	-	7.75	-	4.45
# 6 bx - 600 Volt	LnFt	-	8.60	-	5.00
# 4 bx - 600 Volt	LnFt	-	9.90	-	5.90
Add for Work over 10'					10%
Add for Work in Masonry Construction					10%
Add for Work in Concrete Construction					20%

.4 SWITCH GEAR

Metal Clad 5 KV	26,000.00
15 KV	30,000.00
Add for Outdoor Type	4,950.00

1601.0 BASIC MATERIALS AND METHODS, Cont'd...

		UNIT	COST
.5	SWITCHES AND RECEPTACLES		
	Switches		
	Standard Toggle - 1 Pole	Each	79.00
	4 W	Each	140.00
	4 WL	Each	160.00
	Safety - 30 Amp	Each	204.00
	60 Amp	Each	252.00
	100 Amp	Each	402.00
	200 Amp	Each	620.00
	Three-way -	Each	122.00
	Add for Dimmer - 600 Watt	Each	90.00
	Add for Dimmer - 1500 Watt	Each	192.00
	Receptacles		
	Single	Each	80.00
	Duplex - GFI	Each	101.00
	Add for Dedicated - Separate Circuit	Each	170.00
	Add for Dedicated - Ground	Each	22.00
	Add for Dedicated - Fourplex	Each	80.00
	Clock, Lamps, etc.	Each	81.00
	Add for Weatherproof	Each	20.00
	Plates - Stainless Steel	Each	11.00
	Brass	Each	18.00
.6	TRENCH DUCT AND UNDERFLOOR DUCT (Including Fittings)		
	Underfloor Duct - Average		
	Single Cell - 1 1/4" x 3 1/8"	LnFt	20.40
	1 1/2" x 6 1/2"	LnFt	25.60
	Double Cell - 1 1/4" x 3 1/8"	LnFt	29.50
	1 1/2" x 6 1/2"	LnFt	50.50
	Wireway - Cover Type 2 1/2" x 2 1/2" x 1"	Each	21.50
	2 1/2" x 2 1/2" x 2"	Each	29.70
	2 1/2" x 2 1/2" x 3"	Each	35.20
	4" x 4" x 1"	Each	27.20
	4" x 4" x 2"	Each	33.40
	4" x 4" x 3"	Each	43.00
.7	MOTOR WIRING (Including Controls)		
	10 H.P.	Each	4,360.00
	20 H.P.	Each	4,560.00
	30 H.P.	Each	5,100.00
	40 H.P.	Each	5,450.00
	50 H.P.	Each	6,400.00
	100 H.P.	Each	8,350.00
	200 H.P.	Each	12,800.00
.8	MOTOR STARTERS (600 Volt)		
	Magnetic - 10 H.P.	Each	540.00
	Non-Reversing - 20 H.P.	Each	640.00
	30 H.P.	Each	960.00
	40 H.P.	Each	1,130.00
	50 H.P.	Each	1,600.00
	100 H.P.	Each	2,460.00
	200 H.P.	Each	5,000.00
	Add for Reversing Type	Each	80%
	Add for Explosion Proof	Each	40%
	Add for Motor Circuit Protectors	Each	25%
	Add for Fused Switches	Each	10%
	Manual - 1 H.P.	Each	135.00
	3 H.P.	Each	195.00
	7 1/2 H.P.	Each	230.00

1601.0 BASIC MATERIALS AND METHODS, Cont'd...

		UNIT	COST
.9	CABLE TRAY (Aluminum or Galvanized)		
	Ladder or Punched - 6" wide	LnFt	30.60
	12" wide	LnFt	35.00
	18" wide	LnFt	37.10
	24" wide	LnFt	39.70

1602.0 POWER GENERATION

	Emergency Generators (3-Phase, 4-Wire) (120/208 Volt)		
	15 k.w.	Each	14,600.00
	30 k.w.	Each	29,100.00
	50 k.w.	Each	36,200.00
	75 k.w.	Each	39,400.00
	100 k.w.	Each	50,000.00
	300 k.w.	Each	83,800.00

1603.0 HIGH VOLTAGE DISTRIBUTION - Power Companies

1604.0 SERVICE AND DISTRIBUTION

		UNIT	COST
.1	METERING		
.2	GROUNDING (Including Rods and Accessories)		
	1/2" x 10'	Each	108.00
	5/8" x 10'	Each	119.00
	3/4" x 10'	Each	135.00
.3	SERVICE DISCONNECTS - 100 amp	Each	335.00
	200 amp	Each	620.00
	400 amp	Each	1,010.00
	600 amp	Each	1,960.00
.4	DISTRIBUTION SWITCHBOARDS (240 Volt) - 400 amp	Each	3,920.00
	800 amp	Each	3,020.00
	1600 amp	Each	5,750.00
.5	LIGHT AND POWER PANELS (3-Phase, 4-Wire) (120/208 Volt)		
	12 circuit	Each	810.00
	16 circuit	Each	970.00
	20 circuit	Each	1,120.00
	24 circuit	Each	1,340.00
	30 circuit	Each	1,570.00
	36 circuit	Each	1,740.00
	Add for Circuit Breakers	Each	250.00
.6	TRANSFORMERS		
	Current - 400 amp	Each	3,500.00
	600 amp	Each	3,820.00
	800 amp	Each	4,770.00
	1000 amp	Each	4,680.00

Light and Power	UNIT	SINGLE-PHASE 120/ 240 Volt	3-PHASE 120/ 208 Volt
Dry Type - 3 kva	Each	400.00	595.00
5 kva	Each	590.00	850.00
10 kva	Each	810.00	1,100.00
15 kva	Each	1,140.00	1,520.00
30 kva	Each		2,020.00
45 kva	Each		2,580.00
75 kva	Each		2,810.00
Oil Filled - 150 kva	Each	-	6,200.00
300 kva	Each	-	11,800.00
500 kva	Each	-	15,400.00

1605.0 LIGHTING

	UNIT	COST
.1 LIGHT FIXTURES		
Fluorescent		
Surface		
Industrial - 48" - 1 lamp R.S.	Each	118.00
H.O.	Each	147.00
2 lamp R.S.	Each	140.00
H.O.	Each	180.00
4 lamp R.S.	Each	156.00
H.O.	Each	266.00
96" - 1 lamp H.O.	Each	155.00
R.S.	Each	267.00
2 lamp H.O.	Each	133.00
H.O.	Each	280.00
Commercial - 12" x 48" - 2 lamp R.S.	Each	160.00
24" x 24" - 4 lamp R.S.	Each	207.00
24" x 48" - 4 lamp R.S.	Each	280.00
48" x 48" - 4 lamp R.S.	Each	410.00
12" x 48" - 2 lamp R.S.	Each	195.00
Recessed - 24" x 24" - 4 lamp R.S.	Each	210.00
24" x 48" - 4 lamp R.S.	Each	248.00
48" x 48" - 4 lamp R.S.	Each	430.00
Add for Electronic Ballasts	Each	25.50
Incandescent - 100 watt	Each	103.00
200 watt	Each	118.00
300 Watt	Each	136.00
Quartz - 500 watt	Each	185.00
Sodium - Low Pressure - 35 watt	Each	325.00
55 watt	Each	475.00
Explosion Proof		
Fluorescent - 48" - 2 lamp R.S.	Each	1,160.00
Incandescent - 48" - 200 watt	Each	390.00
Mercury Vapor - 48" - 200 watt	Each	730.00
Emergency - Nickel Cadmium Battery	Each	780.00
Lead Battery	Each	400.00
Exit - Standard	Each	170.00
Exit - Low Voltage - Battery	Each	206.00
Porcelain	Each	80.00
.2 LAMPS		
Fluorescent - 48" - 40 watt	Each	6.80
48" - 60 watt	Each	8.75
96" - 75 watt	Each	11.90
Incandescent - 25 to 100 watt	Each	2.50
400 watt	Each	3.90
Metal Halide - 175 watt	Each	73.00
400 watt	Each	78.30
1000 watt	Each	164.00
Sodium - 300 watt	Each	98.00
400 watt	Each	109.00
1000 watt	Each	250.00
Add for Disposal	Each	1.00

	UNIT	COST
1606.0 SPECIAL SYSTEMS		
LIGHTNING PROTECTION		
Ground Rod and Copper Point - 3/4" to 10"	Each	105.00
Ground Clamps - 2"	Each	130.00
Wire - #2	LnFt	1.55
1607.0 COMMUNICATION SYSTEMS		
.1 TELEPHONE EQUIPMENT		
Cabinets 24" x 36"	Each	345.00
36" x 48"	Each	515.00
Lines	Each	310.00
Phones	Each	175.00
Station	Each	660.00
.2 FIRE ALARM EQUIPMENT		
Control Panel 10 zones	Each	1,610.00
20 zones	Each	2,780.00
Annunciator Panel 10 zones	Each	625.00
Station	Each	265.00
Horn	Each	335.00
Heat Detector	Each	200.00
Smoke Detector	Each	220.00
.3 SECURITY SYSTEMS		
Standard Contact	Each	240.00
Audible Alarm	Each	295.00
Photo Electric Sensor - 500' Range	Each	485.00
Monitor Panel - Standard	Each	555.00
High Security	Each	760.00
Vibration Sensor	Each	210.00
Audio Sensor	Each	150.00
Motion Sensor	Each	355.00
.4 CLOCK PROGRAM EQUIPMENT (Control Panel and Clock with Buzzer)		
Master Time Clock 10 rm - average	Each	490.00
20 rm - average	Each	475.00
30 rm - average	Each	450.00
Time Clock and Cards	Each	1,275.00
Add for Electronic and Bells	Each	20%
.5 INTER-COMMUNICATION EQUIPMENT		
Individual Stations	Each	150.00
Board - Master	Each	620.00
.6 SOUND EQUIPMENT		
.61 Public Address System (Control and Speakers)		
3 to 6 Speakers - average each speaker	Each	595.00
7 to 9 Speakers - average each speaker	Each	535.00
10 to 20 Speakers - average each speaker	Each	465.00
Add for Tape / CD	Each	540.00
.62 Nurses & School Call systems (Panel & Stations)		
10 Stations or Rooms - average each room	Each	755.00
20 Stations or Rooms - average each room	Each	695.00
30 Stations or Rooms - average each room	Each	605.00
Add per Light	Each	72.00

	UNIT	COST
1607.0 COMMUNICATIONS SYSTEMS, Cont'd...		
.7 TELEVISION ANTENNA SYSTEMS		
School Systems - 10 outlets	Each	360.00
20 outlets	Each	355.00
30 outlets	Each	330.00
Apartment Houses - 20 outlets	Each	161.00
30 outlets	Each	151.00
50 outlets	Each	144.00
.8 CLOSED CIRCUIT T.V. STATIONS		
Recorder	Each	4,020.00
Camera	Each	1,700.00
Surveillance	Each	2,120.00
.9 DOCTOR'S REGISTER	Each	7,350.00
Add for Recording Register	Each	6,480.00
1608.0 HEATING AND COOLING		
.1 SNOW MELTING EQUIPMENT - 480 volt	SqFt	11.00
.2 ELECTRIC HEATING EQUIPMENT		
Baseboard - 500 watt	LnFt	42.00
750 watt	LnFt	41.00
1000 watt	LnFt	40.00
Cable Heating	SqFt	18.00
Unit Heaters - 1500 watt	Each	240.00
2500 watt	Each	345.00
1609.0 CONTROLS AND INSTRUMENTATION		
.1 LIGHTING CONTROL EQUIPMENT		-
.2 DIMMING EQUIPMENT		-
.3 TEMPERATURE CONTROL EQUIPMENT		-
1610.0 TESTING		-
1611.0 RESIDENTIAL WORK		
100-Amp Service	Each	950.00
200-Amp Service - Single Phase	Each	1,440.00
Three Phase	Each	2,575.00
Air Conditioner	Each	310.00
Dimmer - 600 Watt	Each	62.00
Dishwasher	Each	85.00
Doorbell	Each	62.00
Dryer - Electric	Each	118.00
Dryer or Washer - Gas	Each	85.00
Duplex Receptacle	Each	30.00
Dedicated	Each	79.00
Exhaust Fan - Bath	Each	103.00
Kitchen	Each	108.00
Fixture, Average	Each	104.00
Porcelain	Each	98.00
Furnace	Each	86.00
Garbage Disposal	Each	82.00
Paddle Fan	Each	212.00
Phone - Data Box	Each	48.00
Range Circuit	Each	150.00
Smoke Detectors	Each	68.00
Switches - Single	Each	30.00
3-Way	Each	68.00
Thermostat	Each	52.00
Water Heater - 20 Amp 120 Volt	Each	130.00
Whirlpool	Each	320.00

Average Square Foot Costs
2008

Housing (with Wood Frame)

Square Foot Costs do not include Garages, Land, Furnishings, Equipment, Landscaping, Financing, or Architect's Fee. Total Costs, except General Contractor's Fee, are included in each division. See Page 2 for Metropolitan Cost Variation Modifier. See Division 13 for Metal Buildings, Greenhouses, and Air-Supported Structures.

		Houses - 3 Bedrooms with Basement			Houses - 3 Bedrooms without Basement		
	Division	Low Rent	Tract or Project	Custom	Low Rent	Tract or Project	Custom
1.	General Conditions	$4.55	$4.65	$5.05	$5.90	$6.10	$6.50
2.	Site Work	3.50	4.00	4.30	5.90	6.18	6.40
3.	Concrete	4.05	4.25	4.52	7.34	7.52	8.34
4.	Masonry	5.10	5.30	7.05	7.25	7.56	10.02
5.	Steel	1.52	1.52	1.64	.75	.74	.76
6.	Carpentry	16.20	15.90	17.92	23.75	23.55	25.62
7.	Moisture & Therm. Prot.	4.25	4.25	4.36	5.92	6.13	6.66
8.	Doors, Windows & Glass	8.60	8.30	8.65	10.60	10.90	11.43
9.	Finishes	7.70	8.40	10.25	11.40	11.58	16.40
10.	Specialties	.80	.82	.90	.88	.89	1.18
11.	Equipment (Cabinets)	2.90	2.95	4.47	5.20	5.15	7.76
12.	Furnishings	.60	.60	.65	.92	.92	.92
13.	Special Construction	-	-	-	-	-	-
14.	Conveying	-	-	-	-	-	-
15.	Mechanical: Plumbing	6.50	6.55	7.70	9.62	9.57	11.90
	Heating	4.12	4.27	4.44	5.80	6.12	8.64
	Air Cond.	-	-	-	-	-	-
16.	Electrical	3.75	3.75	4.52	5.58	5.58	6.62
	SUB TOTAL	$74.14	$75.51	$86.42	$106.81	$108.49	$129.15
	CONTRACTOR'S SERVICES	6.62	6.80	7.75	9.60	9.88	12.90
	TOTAL AVERAGE Sq.Ft. Cost	**$80.76**	**$82.31**	**$94.17**	**$116.41**	**$118.37**	**$142.05**

Unfinished Basement, Storage and Utility Areas included in Sq.Ft. Costs:				No Basement Utilities In Finished Area		
Average Cost/ Unit	$161,520	$164,620	$235,425	$139,692	$140,044	$213,075
Average Sq.Ft. Size/Unit (includes basement)	2,000	2,000	2,500	1,200	1,200	1,500
Add Architect's Fee	$ 7,000	$8,000	$17,800	$5,500	$7,000	$16,000

	COST	
	Sq. Ft.	Ea. Unit
Add for Finishing Basement Space For Bedrooms or Amusement Rooms, 12' x 20'	$31.50	$7,560
Add for Single Garage (no Interior Finish), 12' x 20'	$30.00	$7,200
Add for Double Garage (no Interior Finish), 20 x 20'	$31.50	$12,600
Add (or Deduct) for Bedrooms, 12' x 12'	$44.80	$6,450
Add per Bathroom with 2 Fixtures, 6' x 8'	$140.40	$6,720
Add per Bathroom with 3 Fixtures, 8' x 8'	$140.40	$8,985
Add for Fireplace	-	$7,000
Add for Central Air Conditioning	-	$5,800
Add for Drain Tiling	-	$3,160
Add for Well	-	$7,200
Add for Septic System	-	$7,200

Average Square Foot Costs
2008

Apartments, Hotels

Square Foot Costs do not include Land, Furnishings, Equipment, Landscaping and Financing.

		Apartments			Motels & Hotels		
	Division	2 & 3 Story	2 & 3 Story	High Rise	High Rise	1 & 2 Story	High Rise
		(1)a	(1)b	(2)	(3)	(1)b	(2)
1.	General Conditions	$ 4.30	$ 4.55	$ 6.50	$ 6.95	$ 4.70	$ 6.00
2.	Site Work	3.01	2.96	4.27	4.20	6.20	4.80
3.	Concrete	2.38	2.37	22.70	15.32	2.78	23.25
4.	Masonry	1.75	11.10	2.88	2.75	11.05	14.30
5.	Steel	1.44	1.45	2.30	2.40	1.75	2.20
6.	Carpentry and Millwork	17.00	14.26	5.50	5.10	14.28	4.43
7.	Moisture Protection	3.90	4.12	2.10	2.06	3.80	2.10
8.	Doors, Windows and Glass	6.10	6.64	7.55	7.33	7.61	9.08
9.	Finishes	11.73	11.76	12.05	11.35	11.73	16.15
10.	Specialties	.90	.91	.94	.93	1.10	1.12
11.	Equipment	1.84	2.43	1.88	1.84	3.05	3.25
12.	Furnishings	.92	1.00	1.06	1.08	2.15	1.64
13.	Special Construction	-	-	-	-	-	-
14.	Conveying	-	2.60	3.92	4.05	-	4.55
15.	Mechanical:						
	Plumbing	7.70	7.70	7.55	7.42	8.75	11.80
	Heating and Ventilation	6.18	6.68	7.40	7.10	6.42	8.34
	Air Conditioning	2.20	2.20	2.30	2.25	2.72	5.40
	Sprinklers	-	-	2.43	2.15	2.25	2.30
16.	Electrical	8.10	8.05	9.25	9.60	10.80	11.43
	SUB TOTAL	$79.45	$90.78	$102.58	$93.88	$101.14	$132.14
	CONTRACTOR'S SERVICES	7.95	9.08	10.20	9.41	9.93	13.20
	Construction Sq.Ft. Cost	$87.40	$99.86	$112.78	$103.29	$111.07	$145.34
	Add for Architect's Fee	6.12	7.00	7.00	7.27	7.65	10.20
	TOTAL Sq.Ft. Cost	$93.52	$106.86	$119.78	$110.56	$118.72	$155.54
	Average Cost per Unit without Architect's Fee	$88,800	$101,500	$108,700	$88,400	$77,200	$103,000
	Average Cost per Unit with Architect's Fee	$93,900	$106,500	$113,700	$93,400	$82,20	$108,000

Add for Porches – Wood - $12.00 SqFt
Add for Interior Garages - $11.40 SqFt

	Average Sq.Ft. Size per Unit	950	950	900	800	650	650
	Average Sq.Ft. Living Space	750	750	750	600	450	450

---

(1)a Wall Bearing Wood Frame & Wood or Aluminum Facade
(1)b Wall Bearing Masonry & Wood Joists & Brick Facade
(2) Concrete Frame
(3) Post Tensioned Concrete Slabs, Sheer Walls, Window Wall Exteriors, and Drywall Partitions.

APPENDIX

Average Square Foot Costs
2008

Commercial

Square Foot Costs do not include Land, Furnishings, and Financing.

	Division	Remodeling Office Interior	Office 1-Story (1)	Office 2-Story (2)	Office Up To 5-Story (3)	High Rise (City) Above 5-Story (4)	Parking Ramp (3)
1.	General Conditions	$ 2.75	$ 4.45	$ 4.45	6.60	7.90	4.90
2.	Site Work & Demolition	1.77	2.53	2.51	2.46	2.30	1.65
3.	Concrete	-	7.30	11.34	12.50	8.50	27.95
4.	Masonry	-	11.15	10.60	16.00	3.97	1.60
5.	Steel	-	3.37	11.16	3.90	2.75	2.12
6.	Carpentry and Millwork	8.35	3.86	3.60	5.60	6.32	1.27
7.	Moisture Protection	-	7.25	3.62	2.40	3.05	3.37
8.	Doors, Windows and Glass	1.80	7.00	6.94	14.12	26.78	1.45
9.	Finishes & Sheet Rock	12.20	13.17	12.84	14.83	15.33	1.98
10.	Specialties	-	1.80	1.80	1.85	1.85	-
11.	Equipment	-	5.68	5.03	4.15	5.65	-
12.	Furnishings	-	1.18	1.40	1.55	1.68	-
13.	Special Construction	-	-	-	-	-	-
14.	Conveying	-	-	3.25	5.60	6.10	3.10
15.	Mechanical:						
	Plumbing	4.04	6.10	6.55	7.54	7.85	2.64
	Heating and Ventilation	1.90	7.16	7.00	9.05	9.10	-
	Air Conditioning	1.84	7.12	7.33	8.70	8.68	-
	Sprinklers	-	2.26	2.25	2.30	2.32	-
16.	Electrical	7.80	9.57	10.54	11.60	13.60	3.02
	SUB TOTAL	$42.45	$100.95	$112.21	$130.75	$ 133.73	$55.05
	CONTRACTOR'S SERVICES	4.25	8.72	11.20	11.72	11.70	5.41
	Construction Sq.Ft. Cost	$46.70	$109.67	$123.41	$142.47	$145.43	$60.46
	Add for Architect's Fee	4.67	8.25	8.62	10.40	11.64	4.75
	TOTAL Sq.Ft. Costs	$51.37	$117.92	$132.03	$152.87	$157.07	$65.21
	Deduct for Tenant Areas Unfinished	-	-	22.00	25.00	29.00	-
	Per Car Average	-	-	-	-	-	$17,500
	Add: Masonry Enclosed Ramp	-	-	-	-	-	6.70
	Add: Heated Ramp	-	-	-	-	-	6.70
	Add: Sprinklers for Closed Ramps	-	-	-	-	-	2.60
	Deduct for Precast Concrete Ramp	-	-	-	-	-	8.65

(1) Wall Bearing Masonry and Steel Joists and Decks – No Basement
(2) Wall Bearing Masonry and Precast Concrete Decks – No Basement
(3) Concrete Frame
(4) Steel Frame and Window Wall Facade

Average Square Foot Costs
2008

Commercial and Industrial

Square Foot Costs do not include Land, Furnishings, Landscaping, and Financing.
See Division 13 for Metal Buildings

	Division	Store 1-Story (1)	Store 2-Story (2)	Production 1-Story (1)	Warehouse 1-Story (1)	Warehouse and 1-Story Office (1)	Warehouse and 2-Story Office (3)
1.	General Conditions	$ 4.10	$ 4.10	$ 3.95	$ 3.53	$ 3.65	$ 3.32
2.	Site Work & Demolition	2.24	1.75	2.03	1.98	2.35	1.90
3.	Concrete	6.40	12.37	6.50	6.30	6.98	10.70
4.	Masonry	5.55	9.45	7.38	7.40	8.15	4.50
5.	Steel	10.70	5.60	10.70	10.47	11.40	8.60
6.	Carpentry	2.92	2.97	1.90	1.92	2.58	2.24
7.	Moisture Protection	5.10	2.96	5.60	5.40	5.42	2.70
8.	Doors, Windows and Glass	5.90	5.35	4.43	2.40	4.83	4.22
9.	Finishes	6.68	6.28	5.73	2.04	3.57	5.50
10.	Specialties	1.68	1.70	1.30	1.23	1.23	1.23
11.	Equipment	1.60	1.83	1.72	-	.98	1.10
12.	Furnishings	-	-	-	-	-	-
13.	Special Construction	-	-	-	-	-	-
14.	Conveying	-	3.75	-	-	-	-
15.	Mechanical:						
	Plumbing	4.80	4.12	5.03	2.90	3.65	3.40
	Heating and Ventilation	4.64	4.60	3.57	3.68	4.98	5.73
	Air Conditioning	4.80	5.16	3.40	-	1.27	1.15
	Sprinklers	2.26	2.20	2.13	2.20	2.32	2.25
16.	Electrical	8.90	8.48	9.30	5.65	5.83	5.32
	SUB TOTAL	$78.27	$82.67	$74.67	$57.10	$69.19	$63.86
	CONTRACTOR'S SERVICES	7.80	8.20	7.48	5.71	6.93	6.38
	Construction Sq.Ft. Cost	$86.07	$90.87	$82.15	$62.81	$76.12	$70.24
	Add for Architect's Fees	6.00	6.31	5.76	4.40	5.33	4.92
	TOTAL Sq.Ft. Cost	$92.07	$97.18	$87.91	$67.21	$81.45	$75.16

(1) Wall Bearing Masonry and Steel Joists and Decks – Brick Fronts
(2) Wall Bearing Masonry and Precast Concrete Decks – Brick Fronts
(3) Precast Concrete Wall Panels, Steel Joists, and Deck

Average Square Foot Costs
2008

Educational and Religious

Square Foot Costs do not include Land, Furnishings, Landscaping and Financing.

	Division	Elementary School 1-Story (1)	High School 2-Story (1)	Vocational School 3-Story (1)	College Multi-Story (2)	Gym (3)	Dorm 3-Story (1)	Church (3)
1.	General Conditions	$ 7.10	$ 6.90	$ 7.00	$ 6.90	$ 5.60	$ 6.25	6.70
2.	Site Work	4.10	4.30	4.20	4.10	2.05	2.70	3.96
3.	Concrete	6.50	6.90	5.00	23.30	6.90	5.20	6.30
4.	Masonry	13.90	12.60	13.70	14.30	14.20	12.70	28.90
5.	Steel	10.90	12.30	12.90	4.55	13.35	11.60	1.96
6.	Carpentry	4.15	4.10	3.75	2.75	2.33	3.75	7.60
7.	Moisture Protection	5.85	4.00	4.50	4.52	6.20	5.42	6.45
8.	Doors-Windows-Glass	6.75	6.80	7.10	9.00	6.30	5.85	8.24
9.	Finishes	11.80	9.80	11.00	9.65	8.30	11.30	11.95
10.	Specialties	1.90	1.75	1.75	2.15	1.75	1.67	1.30
11.	Equipment	4.85	4.90	7.20	6.25	9.44	5.95	8.62
12.	Furnishings	-	1.02	1.25	1.30	-	1.25	5.10
13.	Special Construction	-	-	-	-	-	-	-
14.	Conveying	-	-	3.55	3.55	-	3.55	-
15.	Mechanical:							
	Plumbing	10.05	9.70	9.75	13.10	6.10	9.00	6.22
	Heating-Ventilation	13.15	12.90	14.60	13.30	8.40	9.20	9.20
	Air Conditioning	-	-	-	-	-	-	7.00
	Sprinklers	2.30	2.30	2.32	2.35	1.20	2.35	
16.	Electrical	14.50	15.10	15.60	15.85	9.90	11.30	9.92
	SUB TOTAL	$117.80	$115.37	$125.17	$136.92	$102.02	$109.04	129.42
	CONTRACTOR'S SERVICES	11.67	13.38	12.40	13.47	10.10	10.72	12.78
	Constr. Sq.Ft. Cost	$129.47	$128.75	$137.57	$150.39	$112.12	$119.76	142.20
	Add Architect's Fees	8.92	8.76	9.54	10.50	7.78	8.25	9.84
	TOTAL Sq.Ft. Cost	$138.39	$135.71	$147.11	$160.89	$119.90	$128.01	$152.04

(1) Wall Bearing Masonry and Steel Joists and Decks
(2) Concrete Frame and Masonry Facade
(3) Masonry Walls and Wood Roof

Average Square Foot Costs
2008

Medical and Institutional

Square Foot Costs do not include Land, Landscaping, Furnishings, and Financing.

		Clinic 1-Story (1)	Doctors Office 1-Story (1)	Hospital 1-Story (1)	Hospital Multi-Story (2)	Nursing Home 1-Story (1)	Housing for Elderly 1-Story (1)
1.	General Conditions	$ 7.50	$ 7.40	$ 9.85	$ 9.95	$ 8.95	$ 8.30
2.	Site Work	2.52	2.47	3.96	4.00	4.15	4.30
3.	Concrete	7.84	7.78	8.18	24.85	8.50	8.53
4.	Masonry	12.80	11.65	21.20	14.82	15.12	11.10
5.	Steel	9.41	9.30	11.45	2.54	2.55	2.12
6.	Carpentry	7.15	7.05	6.25	4.08	4.40	4.15
7.	Moisture Protection	5.60	5.55	6.03	2.50	6.02	5.98
8.	Doors, Windows and Glass	8.52	8.90	11.33	7.51	9.82	7.85
9.	Finishes	11.92	11.05	15.12	14.60	14.66	12.22
10.	Specialties	1.60	1.60	1.73	1.65	1.65	1.62
11.	Equipment	8.64	8.20	2.04	13.00	6.61	2.93
12.	Furnishings	1.30	1.30	1.38	1.43	1.22	2.59
13.	Special Construction	.95	.93	1.90	1.90	.94	.95
14.	Conveying	-	-	-	7.20	-	6.60
15.	Mechanical:						
	Plumbing	12.55	13.52	20.65	20.12	13.70	13.25
	Heating and Ventilation	10.80	9.53	14.06	14.50	7.27	5.85
	Air Conditioning	8.30	8.06	14.40	12.52	8.38	3.15
	Sprinklers	2.32	2.30	2.32	2.34	2.65	2.32
16.	Electrical	16.55	13.50	25.10	23.30	15.22	13.40
	SUB TOTAL	$136.27	$130.09	$176.95	$182.81	$131.81	$117.21
	CONTRACTOR'S SERVICES	13.58	13.12	17.58	18.18	13.08	11.66
	Construction Sq.Ft. Cost	$149.85	$143.21	$194.53	$200.99	$144.89	$128.87
	Add for Architect's Fees	10.43	10.10	13.54	14.00	10.07	8.97
	TOTAL Sq.Ft. Cost	$160.28	$153.31	$208.07	$214.99	$154.96	$137.84

Average Cost to Remodel Approximately 50% Cost of New

---

(1) Wall Bearing Masonry and Steel Joists and Decks
(2) Concrete Frame and Masonry Façade

Average Square Foot Costs
2008

Government and Finance

Square Foot Costs do not include Land, Landscaping, Furnishings, and Financing.

		Bank 1-Story (1)	Bank & Office Bldg High-Rise (3)	Govt. Office Bldg Multi-Story (2)	Post Office 1-Story (1)	Court House 3-Story (2)	Jail and Prison (2)
1.	General Conditions	$ 8.10	$ 9.30	$ 9.30	$ 7.55	$ 9.20	$ 11.25
2.	Site Work	4.85	4.40	3.72	3.70	3.36	4.46
3.	Concrete	10.80	25.70	27.80	11.85	23.70	32.40
4.	Masonry	15.40	10.75	17.95	10.76	11.52	19.57
5.	Steel	5.25	2.35	2.83	4.10	2.45	5.85
6.	Carpentry	4.84	4.38	4.50	3.95	2.78	4.98
7.	Moisture Protection	4.12	4.63	4.90	4.17	5.15	5.85
8.	Doors, Windows and Glass	11.04	25.75	11.28	8.60	8.10	10.60
9.	Finishes	16.10	18.00	19.10	15.90	15.50	13.15
10.	Specialties	1.70	1.70	3.28	1.77	2.90	7.00
11.	Equipment	13.75	9.15	9.05	12.05	11.53	13.45
12.	Furnishings	1.54	1.40	-	2.05	-	-
13.	Special Construction	-	-	-	-	-	-
14.	Conveying	-	2.95	3.70	1.90	2.70	3.65
15.	Mechanical						
	Plumbing	7.70	9.00	8.93	9.55	12.25	21.25
	Heating and Ventilation	6.60	8.18	8.78	6.30	9.37	16.68
	Air Conditioning	5.30	6.02	7.64	7.60	13.38	13.87
	Sprinklers	2.45	2.35	2.30	2.35	2.35	2.35
16.	Electrical	15.40	18.60	19.20	14.70	18.30	28.38
	SUB TOTAL	$134.94	$164.61	$164.26	$128.85	$ 154.54	$214.74
	CONTRACTOR'S SERVICES	13.54	16.47	16.47	12.92	15.47	21.60
	Construction Sq.Ft. Cost	$148.48	$181.08	$180.73	$141.77	$170.01	$236.34
	Add for Architect's Fees	10.42	12.68	12.68	10.36	11.91	16.63
	TOTAL Sq.Ft. Cost	$158.90	$193.76	$193.41	$152.13	$181.92	$252.97

(1) Wall Bearing Masonry and Precast Concrete Decks
(2) Concrete Frame and Masonry Facade
(3) Concrete Frame and Window Wall

U.S. Measurements & Metric Equivalents – (For Construction)

Weights & Measures (U.S. System)

Length	1 Mile = 320 Rods = 1,760 Yards = 5,280 Feet
Area	1 Mile = 640 Acres = 102,400 Sq. Rods = 3,097,600 Sq. Yards
Area	1 Acre = 160 Sq. Rods = 4,840 Sq. Yards = 43,560 Sq. Feet
Volume	1 Cu. Yard = 27 Cu. Feet = .211 Cord
Capacity	1 Gallon = 4 Quarts = 8 Pints = .13337 Cu. Feet
Weight & Mass	1 Ton = 2,000 Pounds = 32,000 Ounces

U.S. to Metric – Area, Length, Volume & Mass Conversion Factors

Quantity	From U.S.	To Metric	Multiply By
Length	mile	km	1.609 344
	yard	m	0.914 4
	foot	m	0.304 8
	inch	mm	25.4
Area	square mile	km^2	2.590 00
	acre	m^2	4 046.87
	square yard	m^2	0.836 127
	square foot	m^2	0.092 903
	square inch	mm^2	645.16
Volume	cubic yard	m^3	0.764 555
	cubic foot	m^3	0.028 316 85
Mass-(Weight)	lb	kg	0.453
Mass-(Length)	plf	kg/m	1.488
Mass-(Square)	psf	kg/m^2	4.882
Mass-(Cube)	pcf	kg/m^3	16.018

Length Conversion Tables from Fractions to Decimals to Millimeters

Fraction	Decimal	Millimeters	Fraction	Decimal	Millimeters
1/16"	.0625	1.588	9/16"	.5625	14.288
1/8"	.125	3.175	5/8"	.625	15.875
3/16"	.1875	4.763	11/16"	.6874	17.463
1/4"	.250	6.350	¾"	.750	19.050
5/16"	.3125	7.938	13/16"	.8125	20.638
3/8"	.375	9.525	7/8"	.875	22.225
7/16"	.437	11.113	15/16"	.9375	23.813
1/2"	.500	12.700	1"	1.000	25.400

Weights – Construction Products

Substance	Wt.Lb. per Cu.Ft.	Substance	Wt.Lb. per Cu.Ft.	Substance	Wt.Lb. per Cu.Ft.
Aluminum	165	Lead	710	Concrete	144
Brass	534	Paper	58	Cement	90
Bronze	509	Glass	156	Clay	100
Copper	556	Granite	165	Sand	100
Iron	450	Limestone	160	Asphalt	81
Steel	490	Brick	140	Wood	40

Computation of Area

Square or Rectangular	=	Length x Width or Height
Triangle	=	Base x ½ Height
Circumference of Circle	=	Diameter x 3.1416
Area of Circle	=	Radius Squared x 3.1416
Cube of a Column or Cylinder	=	Radius Squared x 3.1416 x Depth
Cube of a Solid	=	Length x Width x Depth
Area of Ellipse	=	½ Length x ½ Height x 3.1416

UNITED STATES INFLATION RATES
July 1, 1970 to June 30, 2007
AC&E PUBLISHING CO. INDEX

Start July 1

YEAR	AVERAGE %	LABOR %	MATERIAL %	CUMULATIVE %
1970-71	8	8	5	0
1971-72	11	15	9	11
1972-73	7	5	10	18
1973-74	13	9	17	31
1974-75	13	10	16	44
1975-76	8	7	15	52
1976-77	10	5	15	62
1977-78	10	5	13	72
1978-79	7	6	8	79
1979-81	10	5	13	89
1980-81	10	11	9	99
1981-82	10	11	10	109
1982-83	5	9	3	114
1983-84	4	5	3	118
1984-85	3	3	3	121
1985-86	3	2	3	124
1986-87	3	3	3	127
1987-88	3	3	4	130
1988-89	4	3	4	134
1989-90	3	3	3	137
1990-91	3	3	4	140
1991-92	4	4	4	144
1992-93	4	3	5	148
1993-94	4	3	5	152
1994-95	4	3	6	156
1995-96	4	3	6	160
1996-97	3	3	3	163
1997-98	4	3	4	167
1998-99	3	3	2	170
1999-2000	3	2	3	173
2000-2001	4	4	4	177
2001-2002	3	4	3	180
2002-2003	4	5	3	184
2003-2004	3	5	2	187
2004-2005	8	4	10	195
2005-2006	8	6	9	203
2006-2007	8	4	11	212
2007-2008	3	4	3	215

INDEX